FINANCIAL ANALYSIS
USING CALCULATORS
Time Value of Money

Elbert B. Greynolds, Jr.
Associate Professor of Accounting
Southern Methodist University

Julius S. Aronofsky
Professor and Chairman of
Management Science and Computers
Southern Methodist University

Robert J. Frame
Professor of Finance
Director of the Management Center
Southern Methodist University

McGraw-Hill Book Company

New York   St. Louis   San Francisco   Auckland   Bogotá   Düsseldorf
Johannesburg   London   Madrid   Mexico   Montreal   New Delhi
Panama   Paris   São Paulo   Singapore   Sydney   Tokyo   Toronto

To Ann, Molly, and Jan

FINANCIAL ANALYSIS USING CALCULATORS
Time Value of Money

1 2 3 4 5 6 7 8 9 0   DODO   7 8 3 2 1 0 9

Library of Congress Cataloging in Publication Data

Greynolds, Elbert B.
  Financial analysis using calculators

  Includes index.
    1. Business mathematics—Data processing.
2. Calculating-machines. I. Aronofsky, Julius S.,
joint author. II. Frame, Robert, joint author.
III. Title.
HF 5695.G73   658.1'52'02854   79-14416
ISBN 0-07-024690-4

This book was set in Times Roman by Precision Typographers Inc.
The editor was Charles E. Stewart;
the production supervisor was Donna Piligra.
R. R. Donnelley & Sons Company was printer and binder.

CONTENTS

PREFACE

This book deals with financial analysis—specifically the analysis of investments, mortgages, leases, sinking funds, and other financial arrangements in which the time value of money plays a critical role. Many of the topics of financial analysis covered in this book have been treated in traditional textbooks dealing with the "mathematics of finance." However, this book is different from those traditional texts in several important ways.

First, we have attempted to reorganize and integrate the traditional topics into a form that is suitable for use by practitioners in modern financial applications as well as serious students of finance. Second, by organizing the formulas and methods for solution with the hand-held calculator or computer, we eliminate the need for tables, which are difficult to use and voluminous. (Most existing books devote from 100 to 200 pages to such tables and a detailed description of how to use them.) Finally, this book extends compound interest concepts to applications typically omitted because they are too involved or too complex to solve using traditional methods and tables.

Despite the emphasis on computational methods, we have attempted throughout the book to develop material that is independent of the specific type of calculator used. This task is made difficult by the wide variation in the logic and features of the calculators of different manufacturers. We were able to accomplish the desired result, however, by classifying calculators along two dimensions: level of sophistication and basic design philosophy. Keystroke examples, given for selected calculator models currently available, can easily be translated to another machine of similar level and type, since the same basic logic applies.

Scattered throughout the book are numerous applications. Because the chapters are functional (in the sense that they deal with basic problem solving concepts or approaches) many types of applications (e.g., mortgages, leases, capital budgeting, etc.) are encountered in several places. An applications index is provided in Chapter 1 to assist the reader in locating illustrative material and examples of interest.

Most of the applications in the book can be solved on any type of calculator, but some solutions are practical only on more sophisticated models. The use of available library programs is stressed, and several customized programs, written especially for this book, are provided.

The book can be used in a variety of ways for different purposes. Practicing professionals who desire a thorough grounding in the techniques of financial analysis can work through Chapters 1 to 9 in sequence. However, readers with more modest goals relating to specific types of problems should have no difficulty in using the applications index to trace through only the relevant material. The book contains a large number of drill exercises, with answers provided for half of them.

The book should also find a variety of uses in business school or applied mathematics courses. It could, for example, be used as the principal text in a traditional mathematics of finance course.

Or it could be used with our companion volume, *Programmable Calculators: Business Applications,* Aronofsky, Frame, and Greynolds (McGraw-Hill, 1978), to offer a combined course in mathematics of finance and introductory computer programming. It could also be used as a reference guide or supplement by students in finance, real estate, accounting, or quantitative analysis courses. Many such courses devote a chapter or segment to topics relating to the time value of money, and instructors or students may wish to have supplemental material providing a more thorough understanding of theory and practice.

Finally, the book should provide a basis for conducting short courses or seminars for practitioners. We have found in our own consulting experience that such short courses are definitely needed. Many who work with financial analysis are well versed in the routine application of tables to their problems, but weak when adaptations of problems or underlying assumptions require them to utilize new formulas and computational methods.

We have received assistance and constructive criticism from colleagues and students too numerous to mention. However, we owe special thanks to Mr. Peter L. Bonfield, Dr. Ralph A. Oliva, and Mr. Samuel W. Webster, all of Texas Instruments, and Mr. David Lyons and Mr. Duke Castle of Hewlett-Packard, who provided information, support, and encouragement. Mr. Todd I. Rubenstein, CPA, worked the exercises and verified the answers. Ms. Mary Kesner, Ms. Edith Benham, and members of the Word Processing Department at SMU diligently typed the several versions of the manuscript. Ms. Myra James cheerfully assisted with correspondence and coordination. Our faculty colleagues and the administration of the Cox School of Business at SMU have continued to support the incorporation of programmable calculators into the business curriculum. This support, together with the innovative environment provided by the School, encouraged the development of this book.

Elbert B. Greynolds, Jr.
Julius S. Aronofsky
Robert J. Frame

ONE

INTRODUCTION

1-1 PURPOSE OF THIS BOOK

An important step in becoming a better business manager or financial analyst is to learn to quantify the financial impact of various business decisions. Effective performance of this task demands both speed and accuracy, each of which is improved by the use of hand-held calculators to replace the traditional computational methods and voluminous financial tables. The explosive growth in calculators with enhanced financial capabilities and modest prices puts this improved performance within the reach of practitioners and students alike.

Stated simply, then, the objectives of this book are twofold:

1. To set forth the basic financial concepts involving the time value of money in a form that is useful for applying them to practical business problems.
2. To organize these concepts so that various applications are quickly and easily solved on hand-held calculators of various types and levels of sophistication.

1-1.1 The Central Role of Compound Interest

In most sophisticated financial analysis, the time value of money, or more specifically *compound interest*, plays a central role. Time-value concepts are particularly important in the current economic environment, which is charac-

1

terized by inflation, capital shortage, and high interest rates. In addition, compounding analysis is used increasingly in both theoretical research and practical financial applications. Many modern business calculators have been specifically designed to deal with compounding calculations, facilitating direct solution of even the most complex problems involving annuities and balloon payments.

1-1.2 The Role of the Calculator

This book is specifically oriented to the hand-held calculator or desk-top computer. The tools and techniques described in the following chapters are developed in a manner that facilitates the use of electronic calculators to carry out sometimes complex and cumbersome calculations that are difficult (if not overwhelming) when carried out by hand or using traditional tables.

Thus this book should provide its reader with a better understanding of both financial analysis and the power and usefulness of hand-held calculators. The final few sections of this chapter will describe the evolution of the calculator and classify the types of calculators available for carrying out financial calculations. First, however, we will describe the organization of the remainder of the book and provide a "road map" to the wide variety of financial applications covered.

1-2 ORGANIZATION OF THE BOOK

Chapter 2 provides a thorough discussion of manual calculator operations—using a calculator to perform ordinary arithmetic calculations, from the simple to the most complex. It will also discuss the use of basic function keys that can be applied to financial problems and the use of calculator memory to store and recall data.

Chapter 3 will begin the treatment of financial analysis by examining the basic concepts involved in compound interest calculations—future value, present value, compounding periods, interest rates, and the interrelationship among all of these.

Chapter 4 will introduce the concept of an *annuity,* or series of equal payments, and its many applications—mortgages, loans, leases, sinking funds, savings accounts, and investments analysis. The discussion in this chapter will be restricted to the *simple annuity* case, where payments are level and the compounding periods and payment periods are the same. Both *ordinary annuities* (payments at the end of each period) and *annuities due* (payments at the beginning of each period) are covered.

Chapter 5 extends the annuity concept to the *general annuity* case, where payments are equal but compounding and payment periods may differ. Again, both ordinary annuities and annuities due are covered, and a generalized approach which is useful in a wide range of practical applications is presented.

Chapter 6 deals with *continuous* compounding, which is finding increasing use in both practical applications (such as capital budgeting) and theoretical finance. Annuity concepts are extended from the familiar case, where both payments and compounding are discrete, to the continuous case (involving continuous compounding, continuous payments, or both).

Chapter 7 develops the analysis of *variable* cash flows. The annuity cases described previously are expanded and generalized to the case where cash payments (or receipts) are variable instead of level. A generalized variable-cash-flow model is developed which treats both inflows and outflows, making it extremely useful in analyzing many types of investment situations. So-called *discounted-cash-flow* methods, including net present value and internal rate of return, are also described.

Chapter 8 extends the annuity models of earlier chapters to incorporate *balloon payments*—irregular payments (either single or multiple) which may be imposed on level payment annuity situations. Practical applications discussed in this chapter include many types of loans and mortgages as well as bond pricing and yield calculations.

Chapter 9 covers a variety of advanced applications not discussed elsewhere, including grouped cash flows, graduated mortgage payments, constant increment annuities, ratio annuities (growth and decay models), loans with advanced or skipped payments, add-on interest, and other topics. It should be emphasized, however, that applications are stressed and covered throughout the book, as described in the following section.

1-3 APPLICATIONS

Because of the practical, user orientation of this book, we have chosen to illustrate the various concepts, formulas, and techniques with practical applications taken from a business or financial situation. For this reason, applications will be spread throughout the book. To assist the reader in locating explanatory or illustrative material concerning a particular application of interest, we have prepared Table 1-1, which will identify appropriate chapter and example references for important applications. This table should serve as a kind of road map to the reader who is seeking solutions to specific financial analysis problems.

The table shows a classification of the majority of the examples covered in the book, grouped into the following general application categories:

1. Mortgages and loans.
2. Savings accounts and sinking funds.
3. General investment.
4. Leases.
5. Capital budgeting.
6. Bonds.

Table 1-1 Selected applications index

Assume that the number of compounding periods, c, equals the number of payment periods, f, or $c = f$, and that discrete compounding is used unless otherwise indicated.

	Example	Comments
I. Mortgage and loans		
A. Solve for present value or current price	8-1	Balloon at end of term
	8-9	Multiple balloons
	9-10	Variable payments
	3-8	Promissory note
	6-6	Promissory note, continuous compounding
B. Solve for future value	3-1	Simple interest
	3-2	Simple interest
C. Solve for payment	4-4	Regular mortgage
	5-4	$c \neq f$ (compounding not equal to payment period)
	5-7	$c \neq f$, Canadian mortgage
	8-3	Balloon, end of term
	8-6	Balloon, other
	9-1a	Deferred payments
	9-1b	Long odd-day interest
	9-1c	Short odd-day interest
	9-3	Constant-increment payments
	9-6	Skipped payments
	9-8	Yearly balloon
	9-12	Graduated payment mortgage (Section 245)
	9-13	Using effective annual interest rate (European method)
	9-7	Constant-principal payments
	9-9	Add-on interest
D. Solve for number of payment periods and amount of first payment	4-6	
	4-14	Beginning-of-period payments
	5-4	$c \neq f$
	8-4	Balloon, end of term
	8-8	Balloon, other
E. Solve for the interest rate	8-5	Balloon, end of term
	9-11	Variable-rate mortgage
	9-14	Interest is annual effective rate (European method)
F. Remaining balance to pay off mortgage or loan	8-7	Balloon
	9-15	Regular mortgage
	9-16	Unequal payments
	9-7	Constant-principal payments
	9-9	Add-on interest
G. Accumulated interest and principal	9-15	Regular mortgage
	9-16	Unequal payments
	9-7	Constant-principal payments
	9-9	Rule of 78
H. Convert yearly payment to monthly payment	5-8	

Table 1-1 Selected applications index *(continued)*

Assume that the number of compounding periods, c, equals the number of payment periods, f, or $c = f$, and that discrete compounding is used unless otherwise indicated.

	Example	Comments
II. Savings accounts and sinking funds		
A. Solve for future value	3-5	Compound interest
	3-6	Compound interest
	6-1	Continuous compounding
	6-2	Continuous compounding
	6-3	Continuous compounding
	6-4	Continuous compounding
	4-9	Beginning-of-period payments
	7-7	Beginning-of-period payments, variable cash flow
	5-1	$c \neq f$, end-of-period payments
	5-2	$c \neq f$, end-of-period payments
	7-8	End-of-period payments, variable cash flow, $c \neq f$
B. Solve for payment	4-12	Beginning-of-period payments
	4-3	End-of-period payments
	6-14	End-of-period payments and continuous compounding
C. Solve for n and final payment	4-5	End-of-period payments
	4-13	Beginning-of-period payments
	6-11	Continuous compounding
	6-15	Continuous compounding
D. Solve for interest rate	6-10	Continuous compounding
	6-19	Continuous compounding
	7-15	Variable-cash-flow beginning-of-period payments
III. General investments		
A. Solve for future value	3-3	Simple interest
	3-7	Compound interest
	4-1	End-of-period payments
	5-3	$c \neq f$
	6-12	Continuous compounding
	6-17	Continuous payments and compounding
	6-18	Discrete payments and continuous compounding
IV. Leases		
A. Solve for present value (PV_d)	4-10	
	5-5	$c \neq f$
	7-6	Variable cash flow
B. Solve for payment	4-11	
	8-10	Residual value
	9-5	Advance payments and residual value
C. Solve for interest rate	4-16	
	5-6	$c \neq f$
	7-14	Variable cash flow
	8-11	Residual value

Table 1-1 Selected applications index *(continued)*

Assume that the number of compounding periods, c, equals the number of payment periods, f, or $c = f$, and that discrete compounding is used unless otherwise indicated.

	Example	Comments
V. Capital budgeting		
A. Solve for present value	7-10	Variable cash flow, continuous payments, and compounding
	8-12	Salvage value
	9-2	Payments increase
B. Solve for internal rate of return	4-8	
	6-16	Continuous compounding
	7-12	Variable cash flow
	7-17	Continuous variable cash flow and continuous compounding
	8-12	Salvage value
VI. Bonds		
A. Solve for price	8-13	Sold on interest date
	8-14	Sold between interest dates
B. Solve for yield	8-13	Sold on interest date
	8-15	Sold between interest dates

A further classification of the examples involves the unknown value to be determined: present value (or current price), future value, required payment, number of payments, interest rate (or yield), and so on.†

Note that many types of applications are spread throughout several chapters. Each chapter deals with a basic problem-solving approach, and a reader desiring a thorough grounding in financial analysis should work through the chapters in sequence. This application index provides a means to trace through only that material that is particularly relevant to a given application.

A large number of exercises (half with solutions) are also given to provide the reader with practice in making the transition from concepts and formulas to practical results. The most effective way to master financial analysis is by actually working through a number of the examples given. In time, this experience will help the user develop a "feel" for compound interest calculations.

As indicated earlier, the hand-held calculator is assumed as the computational device in this process. The remainder of this chapter will explore its evolution and role in financial analysis in some detail.

---

†Because of the intricacies of the tax laws involved in various financial transactions, we have made no attempt to deal with the tax aspects of the applications covered. Therefore, income tax effects are ignored or, in some examples, *after-tax* cash flows are assumed. While income taxes can certainly influence the results of a particular problem, the basic methods of analysis presented here are valid for any set of assumptions regarding taxes.

1-4 EVOLUTION OF THE CALCULATOR

The term *calculator* is generally used to identify the wide-ranging class of devices that have emerged or descended from the simple and inexpensive "four-function" calculator (designed only to add, subtract, multiply, and divide). A bewildering array of calculators is now available, ranging from the simplest four-function calculator to sophisticated programmable models that possess all the characteristics of personal computers.

To provide a workable classification among the array of calculators available in the marketplace, we have classified them with respect to two dimensions:

1. Three *levels* of sophistication—the simpler *manual* calculators; so-called business calculators, possessing special *financial function keys*; and *programmables*.
2. The two basic *design philosophies* that have been adopted by various calculator manufacturers.

We'll first describe the *levels* of sophistication in more detail.

1-5 LEVELS OF CALCULATORS

1-5.1 Level I—Manual

Level I calculators represent the modest, less sophisticated calculators—both in price and performance. Of course, they must contain the four simple functions of add, subtract, multiply, and divide. Generally, however, a few more functional features are needed to solve the financial problems presented in this book in an effective manner. The most important features are (1) the capability of storing intermediate results in data registers, and (2) special function keys to perform the operations of y^x, ln x, and e^x. (The meaning and use of these special features will be explained in Chap. 2.) Fortunately, there are several Level I calculators which contain these minimum desired features available in the marketplace at a modest price. Every application presented in this book can be solved with such a Level I calculator, although for some of the examples, considerable additional expenditure of effort is required to manually manipulate the data entry and all the function-key executions. As you will see, there can be a considerable conservation of manual effort in using the Level II or III calculators described below.

1-5.2 Level II—Financial Function Keys

Level II calculators, often called *business* calculators, have specialized function keys for financial calculations dealing with such subjects as discounting or compounding cash flows, annuity payments, and rates of return. Naturally, these *business* or *financial* calculators also have the capability to perform the manual calculations available with Level I calculators. In addition, many of the more recent financial calculator products also have limited programming capability. Thus Level II calculators provide several interesting user options, such as:

Manual calculations only, as described above for Level I calculators.
Financial function keys only.
Manual calculations combined with the use of financial function keys.
User-created programs combined with the above.

Although the programming capability is an important feature of the newer Level II calculators, it will not be utilized in our discussions of them, where we will concentrate entirely on the financial function keys. As you will see, Level II calculators can solve many business and financial problems with the same or greater efficiency than can the more advanced programmables.

1-5.3 Level III—Programmables

Level III calculators represent the general-purpose pocket programmables. The programmables are sufficiently powerful to deal with a wide range of business and financial calculations. With a programmable, the user has a choice of routinely using a library program written by others, or creating an original, custom-designed program. The primary emphasis in this book will be on effectively using library programs written by others. However, the next section will provide a brief overview of programming concepts and the use of programs to extend the range and power of calculators in solving financial problems.

1-6 THE POWER IN PROGRAMMING

All the applications covered in this book can be solved or analyzed without writing programs. However, programs can significantly enhance the usefulness of a Level II or III calculator in financial applications, and some programs will be presented in later chapters.

Of course, if a financial problem can be solved manually, it can be programmed (and vice versa). There are two possible reasons for writing a program for a financial problem that could be solved manually:

1. *Convenience in solving a repetitive problem:* you do not have to enter all the necessary keystrokes each time the problem is to be solved. The same program can be used repeatedly with different data.
2. *Speed:* the individual steps involved in problem solution can be performed much faster when the program is stored in your calculator.

Programs can also be used to augment the use of financial function keys, add on to library programs, and solve applications not covered by even the widest range of financial keys and library routines available. Even if a calculator has the financial function keys or library programs that will solve a particular problem of interest, programming some of the manual keystrokes required in solution may be desirable. If a particular problem type is to be solved repeatedly, it may become quite tedious to manually calculate the right units for the data and then store the data elements in the right registers. Some of these manual keystrokes are good candidates for a program.

But how is a program actually written or used? It is actually entered into the *memory* of the calculator, where it is retained to be used, perhaps repetitively, as described in the following sections.

1-6.1 Program Memory

A program memory is a basic element of all programmable calculators. To illustrate the concept of program memory, suppose that you are able to specify a problem you want to solve in terms of all the keystrokes necessary for manual solution. You could then proceed in two phases, as follows. In phase 1 you enter essentially the same required keystrokes (or program steps) into program memory. This *program entry* is performed with the calculator in what is called the *learn* mode; the calculator is, in effect, "learning" your program.

In phase 2, you manipulate your calculator in what is called the *run,* or *manual,* mode to start executing your program. It will examine each key sequence in program memory, performing the calculations step by step to give the same results as if you had manually pressed each key in sequence. But the calculator executes these program steps at electronic speed, giving rise to one of the advantages of programming mentioned previously. Even though you may have spent a considerable amount of time composing the program and entering it into memory, the execution time in phase 2 may be but a fraction of a second. Remember also that once your program is in memory, it can be used again and again with different data values.

1-6.2 Saving a Program

Generally, a program entered into calculator memory by pressing keys on the keyboard will be erased from memory when the power is turned off. If the program is to be used more than once, it can be saved, perhaps by recording it on a magnetic card. Then, when it is needed, the card containing the program can be read into the calculator memory and the program can be reused. (If a given calculator does not have the magnetic-card feature, the program steps must be listed and reentered manually from the keyboard, provided there is no "continuous memory."†)

---

†"Continuous memory" is a feature contained in some of the newer calculators. Once the program is entered into such a memory, it will stay there, ready for use, until it is cleared or overwritten. Even if the calculator is switched off, the continuous memory will still retain the program for relatively long time periods (weeks and even months).

1-6.3 Learning to Program

Learning to write simple programs to enhance the capabilities and efficiency of a Level II or III calculator is not a difficult task. While it is beyond the scope of this book, such knowledge can be gained from manuals supplied by the manufacturers of various calculators or from a self-instructional programming book (see, for example, J. S. Aronofsky, R. J. Frame, and E. B. Greynolds, *Programmable Calculators: Business Applications,* McGraw-Hill Book Company, New York, 1978).

1-7 CLASSIFICATION OF CALCULATORS BY MANUFACTURER

As mentioned earlier, calculators can also be classified according to their underlying design philosophy. Although there are several calculator manufacturers, each having numerous models, it is possible to classify them into only two groups, each of which is represented by a leading manufacturer. Therefore, we will describe in summary form the products of only these two companies: Texas Instruments and Hewlett-Packard. These two companies currently have a significant share of the available market, a steady stream of new products entering the marketplace, a commitment to continue developing a range of software to support the hardware products, and a product line that covers all three levels of calculators described earlier.

Calculators represented by the Texas Instruments (TI) family will be referred to as *Type A* calculators, because they use an *algebraic* system of operation (described in detail in Chap. 2). Calculators represented by the Hewlett-Packard (HP) family will be classed as *Type R,* because they employ *"reverse-Polish notation"* (also described in Chap. 2).

Users of other manufacturers' calculators should be able to relate their calculator to a comparable product from one of these two manufacturers. For example, a calculator with keys such as **( )** and **=** is related to the TI family of calculators (Type A); a calculator with an **Enter** or perhaps a ↑ key probably uses the reverse-Polish system adopted by HP (Type R).

In the remainder of this section we will provide a brief overview of the line of calculators produced by TI and HP that can be classified into Level I, II, and III calculators. As you might expect, these product lines are evolving over time in a very dynamic fashion, with new models being announced on a regular basis and older models being discontinued from production.

1-7.1 The TI Family of Products

1-7.1.1 Level I: TI-30, TI-50, and TI-55. The TI-30, TI-50, and TI-55 are identified as the Level I calculators of that family. From Table 1-2, they are seen to have the necessary features and are available at a modest price. These calculators can still be used for solving all the problems presented in this book

Table 1-2 Comparisons of Features of TI Calculators

Level I: TI-30, TI-50, and TI-55

	TI-30	TI-50	TI-55
Maximum number of digits displayed	8	8	8
Data memories	1	2	10
Nested parentheses	Yes	Yes	Yes
Function keys: e^x, $\ln x$, and y^x	Yes	Yes	Yes
Statistical function keys	No	Yes	Yes

Level II: MBA, Business Analyst-II

	MBA	Business Analyst-II
Maximum number of digits displayed	10	8
Maximum number of data registers	12	1
Maximum number of program steps	32	none
Set of financial keys	Yes	Yes
Rate of return for variable cash flow	Yes	No
Statistical function keys	Yes	Yes

Level III: TI-57, TI-58, TI-59, and SR-60 without extensions

	TI-57	TI-58	TI-59	SR-60
Maximum number of digits displayed	10	10	10	10
Maximum number of data registers	8	60	100	100
Maximum number of program steps	50	480	980	1920
Magnetic cards	No	No	Yes	Yes
Printing, numeric and alphanumeric	No	Yes	Yes	Yes
Label addressing	Yes	Yes	Yes	Yes
Conditional branching	Yes	Yes	Yes	Yes
Loops, **Dsz**	Yes	Yes	Yes	Yes
Subroutines	Yes	Yes	Yes	Yes
Solid-state modules	No	Yes	Yes	No

(except that examples involving trial-and-error calculations will prove to be quite tedious on a Level I calculator.) In Chap. 2 the basic concepts involved in making manual calculations will be reviewed in detail.

1-7.1.2 Level II: MBA and Business Analyst. Table 1-2 lists the MBA and Business Analyst-II as the Level II calculators in the TI family. To qualify for this level, these calculators have specialized function keys for financial analysis, which are relatively easy to learn to use. Detailed keystrokes showing how to use these financial function keys will appear at the end of Chaps. 3 to 9, after some of the fundamental concepts in the mathematics of finance have been introduced.

The MBA, which also has programming capability (but a relatively small memory), will be used for illustrative purposes in the following chapters.

Many Level II (and Level III) calculators are also equipped with special keys to handle statistical calculations commonly encountered in financial problems as well as other application areas where data collection and analysis are involved. However, use of these statistical keys will not be covered in this book.

1-7.1.3 Level III: The TI-57, TI-58, TI-59, and SR-60. The TI-57, TI-58, TI-59, and SR-60 are the Level III calculators of the TI family. These programmable calculators can actually function as a complete computer system, greatly increasing their range of possible business applications. Innovations in the design and features of such programmables are certain to appear in the marketplace with increasing frequency.

The most striking feature of the TI-58 and TI-59 is the use of removable solid-state modules for the storage and execution of library programs, many of which deal with financial applications. Remember that Level III programmables generally do not have dedicated financial function keys as do the Level II calculators. Instead, the library programs are initiated by "user-defined label keys," as explained at the end of Chap. 7.

The SR-60, which is identified in Table 1-2 as a *desk-top* calculator, has most of the features available in the other programmables: program memory, data registers, alphanumeric display, printing, magnetic cards, and so on. In addition, the logic is very similar to that used in the TI-58 and TI-59. Because of this similarity, the SR-60 is not specifically included in the examples at the end of Chaps. 3 to 9.

The TI-57, also listed as a Level III calculator in Table 1-2, has fewer program steps and memories than the other Level III calculators and is similar in logic and use.

1-7.2 The Hewlett-Packard Family of Products

1-7.2.1 Level I: HP 31E and HP 32E. The models HP 31E and 32E are listed in Table 1-3 as the Level I calculators in the Hewlett-Packard family. Even

Table 1-3 Comparisons of features of HP calculators

Level I: HP-31E or HP-32E	HP-31E	HP-32E
Maximum number of digits displayed	10	10
Maximum number of addressable data registers	4	15
Function keys: e^x, ln x, and y^x	Yes	Yes
Statistical function keys	No	Yes
Financial function keys	No	No

Level II: HP-37E, HP-38E, and HP-92	HP-37E	HP-38E	HP-92
Maximum number of digits displayed	10	10	10
Maximum number of data registers	16	25	20
Maximum number of program steps	None	100	None
Set of financial keys	Yes	Yes	Yes
Rate of return for variable cash flow	No	Yes	Yes
Statistical function keys	Yes	Yes	Yes

Level III: HP-67 and HP-97	HP-19C	HP-29C	HP-33E	HP-67	HP-97
Maximum number of digits displayed	10	10	10	10	10
Maximum number of data registers	30	30	8	26	26
Maximum number of program steps	98	98	49	224	224
Magnetic cards	No	No	No	Yes	Yes
Printing, numeric	Yes	No	No	No	Yes
Label addressing	No	No	No	Yes	Yes
Conditional branching	Yes	Yes	Yes	Yes	Yes
Loops	Yes	Yes	Yes	Yes	Yes
Subroutines	Yes	Yes	Yes	Yes	Yes

though these Level I calculators have neither financial function keys nor programming steps, they can still be used for solving all the problems presented
in this book. In Chap. 2 the basic concepts in making the manual calculations
using the reverse-Polish notation system employed by HP will be explained
in detail.

1-7.2.2 Level II: HP-37E, HP-38E, and HP-92. As shown in Table 1-3, the HP-
37E, HP-38E, and HP-92 are designated as Level II calculators. To qualify
in this level category, these calculators have specialized function keys for
financial analysis. Illustrations of the use of these financial keys appear at the
end of Chaps. 3 to 9.

Note in the table that the HP-37E has a set of financial function keys but
no programming capabilities. The HP-38E was selected for the keystroke examples because it has a more complete set of financial function keys. Thus the
HP-38E is used in all the examples at the end of subsequent chapters to illustrate Level II solutions for the HP family. However, only its financial function
keys (without programming) will be used in these examples.

The HP-92 Investor is a desk-top printing calculator with an extraordi-
narily complete set of financial and accounting function keys, including customized keys for a wide range of calculations dealing with bonds and depreciation calculations. However, it has no programming capability and is thus
classified as a Level II calculator.

The HP Level II calculators are equipped to handle certain statistical
calculations, including data collection and analysis, but this use will not be
covered in this book.

1-7.2.3 Level III: HP-33E, HP-19C, HP-29C, HP-67, and HP-97. Five models
are identified as HP Level III calculators, usable in programming situations.
The HP-67 or HP-97 is used in later chapters to illustrate Level III calculations, because they have the ability to read and write magnetic cards. The HP-
97 is a desk-top sized calculator with printing capabilities. Program logic and
the magnetic cards are interchangeable between the 67 and 97.

These Level III calculators can actually function as a complete computer
system, greatly increasing the range of possible business applications. Reliance
is placed upon library programs rather than financial function keys. Hence
there is a considerable advantage in using any programmable calculator that
can store the library programs on magnetic cards. Otherwise, the user must
manually keystroke the library program into memory before making a financial
calculation. The problem can be partially overcome by the HP-19C and HP-
29C, which have a "continuous memory," which allows the library program
to be keystroked manually into the continuous memory and retained there for
a reasonably long period, even after the off/on switch has been turned off.
(The 19C also has a built-in printer.)

1-8 KEYSTROKE EXAMPLES

Representative examples have been selected from each chapter to show the actual calculator keystrokes required for solution. These keystroke examples are given at the end of each chapter and are illustrative of a wide range of calculator types and price ranges. Generally, two calculator model numbers are indicated with each keystroke example. While the first model number listed is the one actually used for solution, the alternate model number could also have been used, with only minor differences in storing and recalling data. Furthermore, while these keystroke examples identify only certain specific calculators currently on the market, these calculators have been chosen to be representative of different levels and types, so that the reader can readily adapt them to specific calculators not illustrated in this book.

1-9 A NOTE ON CALCULATOR ACCURACY

In providing the basic approach and equations necessary to solve the many types of financial applications treated in this book, we have made no attempt to either evaluate or correct for numerical inaccuracies that may exist among various makes and models of calculators. Although a reader may obtain slightly different results from those given, in most instances these discrepancies should be small. Answers using the approaches presented should be sufficiently accurate for most practical purposes, regardless of the machine used.

CHAPTER

TWO

MANUAL CALCULATIONS

IN THIS CHAPTER

This chapter deals with the use of a calculator to perform ordinary arithmetic calculations—a useful first step and building block for more sophisticated financial applications. It will also demonstrate:

1. How to handle complex arithmetic operations involving multiple calculations and parentheses.
2. The use of basic function keys that can be applied to financial problems.
3. How to store and recall data in calculator memory.

● ● ● ● ●

This chapter is divided into two main sections, each of which deals with one of the two *types* of calculators. The first section covers Type A calculators, which make use of the *algebraic* system of operation. The second section covers Type R calculators, which use *reverse Polish notation* (RPN).

You will need to read and master only one of these sections, since each contains a complete description of arithmetic calculations, the use of basic financial function keys, and memory operations.

2A MANUAL CALCULATIONS USING TYPE A CALCULATORS

Understanding how basic arithmetic operations are performed on Type A (algebraic) calculators will provide a necessary foundation for the financial applications covered in later chapters. The material in this section is generally applicable to all makes and models of Type A calculators. Although some keys and operations described may not be available on particular models, you should be able to follow the basic discussion, regardless of what calculator you are using. Keystroke examples, which are given for the Texas Instruments family of level I, II, and III calculators, are easily translated to the models of other manufacturers.

2A-1 ARITHMETIC OPERATIONS

A useful first step in learning to use a calculator in financial applications is to apply it to performing ordinary arithmetic calculations. We'll begin with a straightforward addition problem.

Example 2A-1: A simple example of addition Let's begin with a simple addition problem:

$$3 + 5 = ?$$

In the algebraic notation system used by Type A calculators, you simply key in the expression, from left to right, exactly as it appears above. That is, you actually use the four successive *keystrokes* **3 + 5 =** to obtain the desired answer. In this book, we'll show keystroke sequences in vertical fashion, accompanied by the numerical values appearing in the calculator's *display* window as a result of the indicated keystroke sequences. Thus the keystroke-display sequence for our simple addition problem is

Keystroke	Display
3	3
+	3.
5	5
=	8.

Note that the correct answer, 8, is shown in the display window at the conclusion of the required keystroke sequence.

Example 2A-2: Using decimal fractions Since Example 2A-1 involved integers (whole numbers with no decimal fraction), you did not need to bother with entering decimal points. Note, however, that the calculator automatically supplies the correct decimal point (step 2 in the sequence above) as soon as an arithmetic operation key **+** is pressed. The answer, of course, also contains a correctly positioned decimal point.

Suppose you wish to solve an addition problem involving decimal fractions:

$$23.47 + 14 = ?$$

You simply key in the numbers from left to right, also keying in the decimal point at the appropriate time—exactly where it appears in the sequence. The keystroke sequence would be

Keystroke	Display	Keystroke	Display
2	2	+	23.47
3	23	1	1
.	23.	4	14
4	23.4	=	37.47
7	23.47		

As before, the correct answer (with the decimal point correctly positioned) appears in the display window at the conclusion of the appropriate keystroke sequence.

2A-1.1 Floating Decimal Point

Note how the decimal point "floats," or moves in the display as necessary to maintain its correct position. This is handled automatically by the calculator, so that you can key numbers of varying degrees of accuracy into the same problem. In Example 2A-2, a decimal number (23.47) and an integer (14) were simply keyed in as they appear. The calculator maintained the proper position for the decimal. As you'll see, this is a considerable convenience to the user in more complicated problems. Later, you'll also learn how to display an answer to any desired degree of accuracy, e.g., rounding to the nearest whole number.

2A-1.2 Combined Keystroke Format

In more complex problems, the vertical display of *single* keystrokes required to enter numerical values becomes lengthy and cumbersome. Therefore, in the remainder of this book, we will often show the keystrokes needed to enter numbers in a *combined* keystroke format, as follows:

Keystrokes (combined)	Display
23.47	23.47
+	23.47
14	14
=	37.47

Example 2A-3: Subtraction Subtraction is performed using the − key in the same manner as addition. If you want the answer to

$$5.15 - 8.732 = ?$$

simply key in the problem exactly as it reads from left to right.

Keystrokes (combined)	Display
5.15	5.15
−	5.15
8.732	8.732
=	−3.582

Note that the negative answer is indicated by a minus sign preceding the numbers in the display window.

Example 2A-4: Entering a negative number (the change-sign key) Negative numbers are entered just like positive numbers, except that the change-sign key **+/−** is keyed in *after* the numerical entry as the final step. For example, to solve the problem

$$-88 + 25 = ?$$

you could use the keystroke sequence

Keystroke (single)	Display
8	8
8	88
+/−	−88
+	−88.
2	2
5	25
=	−63.

Example 2A-5: Chained operations (addition and subtraction) To see how your calculator handles a series of additions and subtractions, consider the example

$$3.1 + 4.7 - 8 + 13.16 = ?$$

Note how subtotals are accumulated in the display as a result of the keystroke sequence for this problem:

Keystrokes (combined)	Display
3.1	3.1
+	3.1
4.7	4.7
−	7.8 ← ①
8	8
+	−0.2 ← ②
13.16	13.16
=	12.96

Observe that at points ① and ② the display contains a subtotal of the operations performed to that point:

$$\textbf{3.1 + 4.7 −} \qquad \text{displays} \quad 7.8 \quad ①$$
$$\textbf{3.1 + 4.7 − 8 +} \qquad \text{displays} \quad −0.2 \quad ②$$

The final result is obtained by keying the **=**, which completes all pending operations and clears the calculator for the next operation.

Example 2A-6: Multiplication Multiplication, like the operations of addition and subtraction, is performed by simply keying in the problem as it appears. If you wish to compute

$$2 \times 5 = \,?$$

use

Keystroke	Display
2	2
×	2.
5	5
=	10.

The correct answer appears in the display.

Example 2A-7: Chained multiplication A problem like

$$2 \times 5 \times 6 \times 9 = \,?$$

can be solved by keying it in as it appears:

Keystroke	Display
2	2
×	2.
5	5
×	10. ← ①
6	6
×	60. ← ②
9	9
=	540.

Note again that at ① and ② the display contains the accumulated result of previous operations:

$$\textbf{2 × 5 ×} \qquad \text{displays 10.} \leftarrow ①$$
$$\textbf{2 × 5 × 6 ×} \qquad \text{displays 60.} \leftarrow ②$$

The same result could have been obtained by using the equals sign to obtain the intermediate results. You could have formulated the problem this way:

$$2 \times 5 = 10.$$
$$10 \times 6 = 60.$$
$$60 \times 9 = 540.$$

Of course, since

2 × 5 = displays 10.

there would be no need to reenter the number 10 in order to multiply by 6: it is already in the display. (The operation key × instructs the calculator to multiply the contents of the display by the number keyed in following the ×.) You could have used

Keystroke	Display	Keystroke	Display
2	2	**6**	6
×	2.	**=**	60.
5	5	**×**	60.
=	10.	**9**	9
×	10.	**=**	540.

Notice, however, that the intermediate use of the = key was unnecessary. The final result was the same, and no additional information was provided; intermediate results were available in the display without using the =.

Example 2A-8: Division A division problem can be expressed in a variety of ways:

$$14/2 \quad = ?$$
$$14 \div 2 = ?$$
$$2\overline{)14} \quad = ?$$
$$\tfrac{14}{2} \quad = ?$$

Of course, each of these ways of writing the problem means exactly the same thing.

Such problems are solved on most calculators by using the ÷ key:

Keystroke	Display
14	14
÷	14.
2	2
=	7.

Example 2A-9: Chained multiplication and division Problems involving successive multiplications and divisions, such as

$$\frac{3 \times 6}{9}$$

can be solved without intermediate ='s as follows:

Keystroke	Display
3	3
×	3.
6	6
÷	18. ← ①
9	9
=	2.

Note the intermediate result

3 × 6 ÷   displays 18. at ①

Example 2A-10: Chain calculations involving mixed arithmetic operations You have learned that it is possible to solve a problem involving a chain of arithmetic operations by simply keying it in as written. Up to this point, the chain-type problems considered have involved only combinations of (1) addition and subtraction *or* (2) multiplication and division. What happens when we key in a problem involving a mixture of both addition and subtraction operations and multiplication and division operations?

Consider the problem

$$12 + 6 \times 3 = ?$$

If we key this problem in exactly as shown, the result will be

Keystroke	Display
12	12
+	12.
6	6
×	6. ← ①
3	3
=	30.

You should observe that at ① the display does *not* show the intermediate result of performing the operation **12 + 6**. The reason for this is that a chain of *mixed* operations will *not* necessarily be performed in the order written.

Instead, the operations are performed according to what is called the *algebraic hierarchy*. (For Type A calculators without this algebraic hierarchy, an answer of 54 would be obtained.)

2A-1.3 Algebraic Hierarchy

Lacking specific instructions to the contrary (to be covered below) many Type A calculators will perform a series of mixed arithmetic operations according to a well-accepted mathematical convention called the algebraic hierarchy. The order of calculation prescribed by this convention is as follows:

Multiplication and division are performed before *addition and subtraction.*

Thus, in Example 2A-10,

$$12 + 6 \times 3 = ?$$

keying the problem as written resulted in the multiplication $6 \times 3 = 18$ being performed *first*. Only then is the addition operation performed, giving $12 + 18 = 30$.

Example 2A-11: The use of parentheses You have probably noticed that in Example 2A-10 the result would have been different if the addition had been performed first, since $12 + 6 = 18$ and $18 \times 3 = 54$. Changing the order of operations gives a result of 54, rather than the answer of 30 obtained according to the priorities of the algebraic hierarchy. If you had intended the addition to be performed first (giving the answer of 54), how could you have overcome the priorities by which your calculator operates? It can easily be done *by using parentheses*. For example, you could reformulate the problem as

$$(12 + 6) \times 3 = ?$$

Now, key in the problem just as it is written, including the parentheses. This will give

Keystroke	Display	Keystroke	Display
(	0.	)	18.
12	12	×	18.
+	12.	3	3
6	6	=	54.

Note that the parentheses cause the calculator to evaluate the quantity $12 + 6$. Whenever an expression is set off by parentheses a Type A calculator will evaluate that expression and then use the value obtained in any larger expression of which it is a part. Thus, you can control the order of operations by using parentheses. It is a good idea to use parentheses to avoid incorrect problem formulation.

Example 2A-12: Nested parentheses You can also use parentheses within other parentheses (nests) to specify the order in which operations are completed. The sequencing is again specified by the rules of the algebraic hierarchy: an expression will be evaluated from the innermost set of parentheses outward. To evaluate the expression

$$((7 \times 9) + 3) \div 6 = ?$$

you would again key it in exactly as it is written, with the following result:

Keystroke	Display	Keystroke	Display
(	0.	+	63.
(	0.	3	3
7	7	)	66.
×	7.	÷	66.
9	9	6	6
)	63.	=	11.

Note that each time a closing parenthesis) is keystroked, an expression is evaluated (without the use of the = key).

Example 2A-13: More practice To review your understanding of arithmetic operations and the use of parentheses, consider the following example:

$$3 + (-5 \times (2 + 4))/(7 - 4) = ?$$

Keystroking this expression exactly as it appears will provide the correct results. Remember, however, that entering the negative **5** following the first parenthesis) should be accomplished by keying **5** *first* and then the +/− key. An attempt to follow an opening parenthesis (with a minus sign − may result in a flashing display (error condition).

A proper keystroke sequence is

Keystroke	Display	Keystroke	Display	Keystroke	Display
3	3	2	2	(	−30.
+	3.	+	2.	7	7
(	3.	4	4	−	7.
5	5	)	6.	4	4
+/−	−5	)	−30.	)	3.
×	−5.	÷	−30.	=	−7.
(	−5.				

An additional level of parentheses could have been included in the formulation of the problem without changing the result provided by the algebraic hierarchy:

$$3 + ((-5 \times (2 + 4))/(7 - 4))$$

The end result of keystroking this expression would be the same, but the additional set of parentheses makes it clear that the division is to be performed before the final addition (the sequence of operations provided by the algebraic hierarchy without more explicit instructions).

A good rule to remember is

When in doubt, use parentheses!

2A-1.4 Clearing Operations CLR and CE

The clear key **CLR** clears the calculator of all pending operations. It causes a zero to appear in the display. It's a good idea to begin any new arithmetic operation by pressing the **CLR** key. You may have noticed, however, that the = key also *completes* all operations you have keyed in, thereby clearing the calculator for a new set of operations.

The clear-entry key **CE** enables you to correct any error you might have made in entering a number, *without* affecting any results that you've already calculated as well as any operations you have pending. For example, if you're solving

$$2.2 + 6.8 + 4.5 = ?$$

but hit the wrong key in entering the last number, say you enter 4.2 instead of 4.5, you can press **CE** and simply enter 4.5 again, without having to start back at the beginning of the whole sequence.

2A-2 FUNCTION KEYS

This section describes the use of various basic *function* keys that may be available on your calculator. (Description of other keys used in programming, will not be discussed in this book.) We'll begin with a brief discussion of the *dual-function keys*.

2A-2.1 The Shift Key 2nd

You may note that many of the keys on your calculator actually have more than one function. The function printed on each key is called the *first function*, which you can use by simply pressing the key (as described below). Many keys also have a second function printed immediately above the key; it can be used by keystroking the **2nd** key *followed* by the given function key. Thus the calculator keyboard operates somewhat like a typewriter with its shift key that makes more symbols available than there are keys on the keyboard (a difference, of course, is that on the calculator you press the shift **2nd** key first but do *not* hold it down while pressing the function key). Throughout the rest of this book, for simplicity, we generally omit the **2nd** key in describing keystroke sequences. Just remember to use it as you would a typewriter shift when it is required.

2A-2.2 The Inverse Key INV

Another dual-function key, the inverse key **INV**, also provides additional functions without requiring additional keys. The **INV** key preceding certain function keys reverses the function. Such uses of **INV** will be discussed later as they arise. Use of the **INV** key before a function which has no reverse function, or inverse, will simply be ignored by the calculator.

2A-2.3 Basic Function Keys

There are a variety of other function keys available on different Type A calculators which act immediately and directly on the number contained in the display.

x^2 This key calculates the *square* of the number in the display; i.e., it causes the number in the display to be multiplied times itself. To find the square of 13, key in 13 followed by the x^2 key:

Keystroke	Display	
13	13	
x^2	169.	*ans.*

$\sqrt{x}$ This key finds the *square root* of the displayed number (where the answer multiplied by itself would equal the originally displayed number). To obtain the square root of 625:

Keystroke	Display	
625	625	
$\sqrt{x}$	25.	*ans.*

1/x   The *reciprocal* key divides the displayed number into 1.

log   This key obtains the *logarithm* (to the base 10) of the display value. Logarithms are used in several financial applications which are described in detail later in the book. Basically, logarithms are *powers* required to obtain a given number. To illustrate, the logarithm of 100 (to a base of 10) is equal to 2, since $10^2 = 100$.

In   This key obtains the *natural* logarithm (useful in various mathematical and financial applications) of the display number. For natural logarithms, the base is e ($e = 2.718281828$).

|x| The *absolute-value* key makes the sign of the displayed number positive (a change in sign if it was negative to begin with, no change if it was positive). (Note that this key requires the shift or **2nd** key preceding it.)

Int   The *integer* key deletes everything to the right of the decimal point in a displayed number, leaving only the integer value. (Note that this key also requires a **2nd** key preceding it.) The key sequence **INV Int** *deletes* the integer portion (to the left of the decimal point), leaving only the fractional or decimal part of the number in the display.

2A-2.4 An Advanced Function Key y^x

The y^x key has particular significance for financial applications. This powerful key allows you to find the roots and powers of any positive number. It is therefore a generalized version of the x^2 and $\sqrt{x}$ keys (for powers and roots other than 2). We class it as an advanced function key because it is really a function of *two* variables rather than one. The y is the number to be raised to a power, and x is the power.

First, let's see how you could use this key to compute 13^2 (this is the same computation made earlier with the x^2 key). Using the y^x key, note that $y = 13$ and $x = 2$; then proceed with a four-step process:

Step	Keystroke	Display
1. Key in the value of y (in this case 13)	**13**	13
2. Press the y^x key	y^x	13.
3. Key in value of x (in this case 2)	**2**	2
4. Press the = key	=	169.

Of course, you already know that this result could have been obtained with the x^2 key, but suppose you wanted to compute $(13)^3$, that is, $13 \times 13 \times 13$. Using the y^x key,

Keystroke	Display
13	13
y^x	13.
3	3
=	2197.

Now, use your calculator to prove that

$$(2)^{18} = 262,144$$

The y^x can also be used to obtain the roots of a number. By use of the $\sqrt{x}$ key we already found the answer for $\sqrt{625}$. Since, in general, $\sqrt[n]{y} = y^{1/n}$,

$$\sqrt{625} = (625)^{1/2}$$

and the same answer can be obtained using y^x in the following keystroke:

Keystroke	Display
625	625
y^x	625.
(	625.
1	1
÷	1.
2	2
)	0.5
=	25.

Example 2A-14: Compound interest: an important application of y^x An important application of the y^x key that will recur frequently in later chapters of this book as well as actual practice is in computing *compound interest*. Suppose, for example, that you decided to set aside $100 for 20 years, invested in a savings account at 6% annual interest. What will the balance in your account be if it is undisturbed for 20 years?

You know that at the end of 1 year you would have

Principal (initial payment)	$100
Interest ($100 × .06)	6
Balance (future value)	$106

Note that this could be obtained by taking $100(1.06) = $106.

In the second year, you would earn interest not only on your initial investment of $100 but on the previously accumulated interest as well:

Beginning balance	$106
Interest ($106 × .06)	6.36
Ending balance (future value)	$112.36

You could also compute the balance in your account at the end of the second year by taking $106(1.06) = $112.36. Since the $106 was obtained as ($100)(1.06), this second year balance is really

$$(\$100)(1.06)(1.06) \quad \text{or} \quad (\$100)(1.06)^2$$

In fact, this represents a general approach to finding the future value of any sum of money invested at a specified interest rate for a specified time period.

$$FV = P(1 + i)^n$$

where FV = future value

P = initial investment, or principal

i = interest rate (per time period)

n = number of time periods

Your third-year balance would be

$$FV = \$100\ (1 + .06)^3$$
$$= \$100 \times (1.06)^3$$
$$= \$119.10 \quad \text{rounded to nearest cent}$$

You can now compute the value at the end of 20 years:

Keystroke	Display	Keystroke	Display
100	100	**)**	1.06
×	100.	**y^x**	1.06
(	100.	**20**	20
1.06	1.06	**=**	320.7135472

The answer (rounded) is that the account would contain $320.71 at the end of 20 years.

2A-2.5 Mathematical Function Keys

There are a number of mathematical function keys on the various Type A calculators, such as **sin, cos, tan, Deg, Rad,** which have little usefulness in business applications. We will have no reason to refer to them in this book, but they are explained in detail in the respective user's manuals.

2A-3 DISPLAY CONTROL

2A-3.1 Fix-Decimal Control: The Fix Key

This key allows you to fix the accuracy you want to have displayed in your calculations. The **Fix** key, followed by any number 0 through 8, establishes the number of digits to the right of the decimal point that will appear in your display. Actual accuracy of the calculations is not affected (they are far more accurate than necessary for most business purposes). Rounding takes place only in the displayed answer. For example, the sequence **Fix 2** will cause an answer like 147.8852224 to appear as

147.89   (note the rounding)

Fix 1 will change this answer to 147.9; **Fix 0** will cause 148. to be displayed.

2A-3.2 Clearing the Fix

You can clear the fix, returning to the usual 10-digit display, either by using the sequence **Fix 9** or by using the inverse key **INV Fix**.† Of course, the display fix will also be cleared by switching the calculator off and then back on (which clears everything).

2A-4 MEMORY OPERATIONS

2A-4.1 Memory Registers

One or more multipurpose data memory registers, which we call simply *data registers,* may be available in your calculator. They provide an opportunity for you to store numbers you need to recall and use later. You will be able to store and recall data without affecting operations in progress.

2A-4.2 The Store Key STO

Pressing the **STO** key simply instructs the calculator to *store* the number contained in the display in a location you specify. Thus the store key must always be followed by a specific data memory location (unless the calculator has a single memory). For example, the keystroke sequence **STO 05** causes the displayed number to be stored in data register 05. Because many Type A calculators have more than 10 data registers, two-digit representation of the register number (05 rather than simply 5) is required (or at least is desirable to avoid confusion).‡ In this book, we'll use the following notation to describe this storing operation:

$$D \rightarrow R_{05}$$

where D represents the display number, the arrow indicates the storing operation, and R_{05} denotes data memory location number 05.

Whenever you store a number in a memory register, any number previously stored there is automatically erased and replaced by the displayed number.

2A-4.3 The Recall Key RCL

Pressing the recall key, followed by a data-register number, causes the number contained in that particular data register to be recalled from memory and shown in the display. The recall operation does *not* alter the contents of the given data register, which may be recalled and used as many times as needed in a

---

†Since the **Fix** key requires a shift **2nd**, the actual keystroke sequence is **INV 2nd Fix**.

‡On calculators such as the MBA, TI-57, and SR-56, which have fewer memory registers, the memory commands are followed by a single digit specifying location, for example, **STO 5**. Calculators such as the BA and BA-II with one memory use only **STO** or **RCL**.

given calculation. Only a store operation or clearing operation (discussed below) will alter the contents of a data register.

2A-4.4 The Exchange Key **Exc**

This key (which requires a preceding shift **2nd** key) followed by the number of a data register n simply exchanges, or swaps, the number in the designated data register with the number in the display. That is, the display value is stored in n, and the replaced value in register n is displayed.

2A-4.5 Clearing Data Registers

You can clear (or *zero*) any specific data register by entering a zero into the display and storing it in the appropriate data register. For example, to clear data register 05, the following steps are used:

0 STO 0 5

We show this in our notation as

$$0 \rightarrow R_n$$

where n represents the data-register number. You can also clear all data registers by using the clear memory key **CMs**.†

Example 2A-15: Using data registers in calculations The use of data registers and the **STO** and **RCL** keys discussed above can best be understood by working through an example. Suppose you want to calculate

$$\frac{3 + 5 \times 2}{\frac{12}{6} + 3} = ?$$

You learned in a previous section how to evaluate this type of expression by using parentheses. (For practice, you may want to work it out that way.) Alternatively, we could solve the problem in the following steps:

Step 1: Calculate $3 + 5 \times 2$ and store the result in data register 05. In our notation

$$3 + 5 \times 2 \rightarrow R_{05}$$

Step 2: Calculate $\frac{12}{6} + 3$ and store the result in data register 06:

$$\frac{12}{6} + 3 \rightarrow R_{06}$$

Step 3: Recall the contents of R_{05} and divide by the contents of R_{06}:

$$\frac{R_{05}}{R_{06}} = ?$$

---

†The TI-57, which does not have a **CMs** key, uses the key sequence **INV, C.t.** to clear all memories. The BA-II uses **Mode** to clear memory.

Step 4: Store the result in R_{07}:

$$\frac{R_{05}}{R_{06}} = \frac{3 + 5 \times 2}{\frac{12}{6} + 3} \rightarrow R_{07}$$

The keystroke sequence to accomplish these steps is as follows:

Step	Keystroke	Display	Step	Keystroke	Display	Step	Keystroke	Display
1	**3**	3	2	**12**	12	3	**RCL**	5.
	+	3.		**÷**	12.		**05**	13.
	5	5		**6**	6		**÷**	13.
	×	5.		**+**	2.		**RCL**	13.
	2	2.		**3**	3		**06**	5.
	=	13.		**=**	5.		**=**	2.6
	STO	13.		**STO**	5.	4	**STO**	2.6
	05	13.		**06**	5.		**07**	2.6

The result, 2.6, is now stored in data register 07. Note how the keystrokes **RCL 06** were equivalent to keying in a numerical value (in this case 5).

2A-5 OTHER MEMORY OPERATIONS

2A-5.1 Adding to a Data Register: The Sum Key SUM

This key, followed by a data-register number, instructs the calculator to add the number in display to the contents of the specified data register, storing the result in that same data register (thereby erasing its previous contents). The display number remains unchanged by the **SUM** operation.

   Example 2A-16: This operation allows you to accumulate the sum of a series of arithmetic computations in a data register. You could use this key to evaluate

$$(2 \times 4) + (7 \times 6) + (8 \times 2) = ?$$

A keystroke sequence using the **SUM** key would be:

Keystroke	Display	Keystroke	Display	Keystroke	Display
CLR	0	**01**	8.	**8**	8
CMs	0.	**7**	7	**×**	8.
2	2	**×**	7.	**2**	2
×	2.	**6**	6	**=**	16.
4	4	**=**	42.	**SUM**	16.
=	8.	**SUM**	42.	**01**	16.
SUM	8.	**01**	42	**RCL**	16.
				01	66.

Note that the final result can be observed in the display only by recalling the contents of data register 01, where the sum is being accumulated. Remember that the *results* of the **SUM** operation do *not* show up in the display.

2A-5.2 Multiplying a Data Register: The Product Key **Prd**

The product key, followed by a data-register number, instructs the calculator to *multiply* the number in the display times the contents of the specified data register, replacing the previous contents of that register with the result of the multiplication. Use of the **Prd** key is thus quite similar to the **SUM** key in that the contents of a data register are altered while the display is left unchanged.

2A-5.3 Subtraction and Division to a Data Register

You may be wondering at this point why there are no special keys on your calculator similar to **SUM** and **Prd** for the other arithmetic operations, subtraction and division. These operations are available through the use of the **INV** key, which, as you learned earlier, simply reverses the function of certain keys on the calculator. For example, the keystroke sequence **INV SUM *n*** instructs the calculator to *subtract* the display number from the contents of data register number *n*. Similarly, a **INV Prd *n*** key sequence divides the contents of memory register *n* by the display number.

2R MANUAL CALCULATIONS USING TYPE R CALCULATORS

Understanding how basic arithmetic operations are performed on Type R (reverse Polish notation) calculators will provide a necessary foundation for the financial applications covered in later chapters. The material in this section is generally applicable to all makes and models of Type R calculators. Although some keys and operations described may not be available on particular models, you should be able to follow the basic discussion, regardless of what calculator you are using. Keystroke examples, which are given for the Hewlett-Packard family of calculators, are easily translated to the models of other manufacturers.

2R-1 ARITHMETIC OPERATIONS

Example 2R-1: A simple example of addition Let's begin with a simple addition problem:

$$3 + 5 = ?$$

In the RPN logic system (used by the HP family of calculators), the addition of two numbers is performed by placing both of the numbers in the calculator before performing the operation of addition. The two numbers to be added are separated using the **ENTER↑** key. Thus, place the two numbers in the calculator and perform addition:

1. Key in the first number.
2. Press **ENTER↑** to separate the number from the second.
3. Key in the second number.
4. Press the **+** key to perform addition.

Now, to solve Example 2R-1,

$$3 + 5 = ?$$

the following keystrokes are required:

Keystroke	Display
3	3.
ENTER↑	3.00
5	5.
+	8.00

Note that the correct answer, 8.00, is shown in the display window at the conclusion of the required keystroke sequence.

Example 2R-2: Using decimal fractions Since Example 2R-1 involved integers (whole numbers with no decimal fraction), you did not need to bother with entering decimal points. Note, however, that the calculator automatically supplies a decimal point as soon as a numeric key is pressed. The answer, of course, also contains a correctly positioned decimal point.

Suppose you wish to solve an addition problem involving decimal fractions:

$$23.47 + 14 = ?$$

You simply key in the numbers from left to right, separating them with the **ENTER↑** key. The keystroke sequence would be

Keystroke	Display	Keystroke	Display
2	2.	**ENTER↑**	23.47
3	23.	**1**	1.
.	23.	**4**	14.
4	23.4	**+**	37.47
7	23.47		

As before, the correct answer (with the decimal point correctly positioned) appears in the display window at the conclusion of the appropriate keystroke sequence.

2R-1.1 Floating Decimal Point

Note how the decimal point "floats," or moves in the display as necessary to maintain its correct position. This is handled automatically by the calculator, so that you can key numbers of varying degrees of accuracy into the same problem. In Example 2R-2 a decimal number (23.47) and an integer (14) were simply keyed in as they appear. The calculator maintained the proper position for the decimal. As you'll see, this is a considerable convenience to the user in more complicated problems. Later, you'll also learn how to display an answer to any desired degree of accuracy, e.g., rounding to the nearest whole number.

2R-1.2 Combined Keystroke Format

In more complex problems, the vertical display of *single* keystrokes required to enter numerical values becomes lengthy and cumbersome. Therefore, in the remainder of this book, we will often show the keystrokes needed to enter numbers in a *combined* keystroke format, as follows:

Keystrokes (combined)	Display
23.47	23.47
ENTER↑	23.47
14	14.
+	37.47

Example 2R-3: Subtraction Subtraction is performed using the − key in the same manner as addition. If you want the answer to

$$5.15 - 8.732 = ?$$

simply key in the problem exactly as before, except for the final keystroke.

Keystrokes (combined)	Display
5.15	5.15
ENTER↑	5.15
8.732	8.732
−	−3.58

Note that the negative answer in the display is −3.58, whereas the correct answer with all decimal places shown should be −3.582. The calculator was designed to perform this way, rounding the answer to two decimal places. With an HP calculator, the display is set to show only two decimal places, although you will learn later how to change the display to show up to nine decimal places if you so choose.

Example 2R-4: Entering a negative number (the change-sign key) Negative numbers are entered just like positive numbers, except that the change-sign key **CHS** is keyed in *after* the numerical entry as the final step. For example, to solve the problem

$$-88 + 25 = ?$$

you could use the keystroke sequence

Keystroke (single)	Display
8	8.
8	88.
CHS	−88.
ENTER↑	−88.00
2	2.
5	25.
+	−63.00

Example 2R-5: Chained operations (addition and subtraction) To see how your calculator handles a series of additions and subtractions, consider the example

$$3.1 + 4.7 - 8 + 13.16 = ?$$

It is necessary to use the **ENTER↑** key only once, after the first entry. After that, it is simply a matter of keying in the data in order, as shown, indicating the arithmetic operation desired and observing the subtotals. That is,

Keystrokes (combined)	Display
3.1	3.1
ENTER↑	3.10
4.7	4.7
+	7.80 ← ①
8	8.
−	−0.20 ← ②
13.16	13.16
+	12.96

Observe that at points ① and ② the display contains a subtotal of the operations performed to that point:

$$\textbf{3.1 + 4.7 -}\qquad \text{displays}\quad 7.80\quad ①$$

$$\textbf{3.1 + 4.7 - 8 +}\qquad \text{displays} -0.20\quad ②$$

The final result is obtained by keying the **+**, which completes the last partial sum.

Example 2R-6: Multiplication   Multiplication, like the operations of addition and subtraction, is performed by simply keying in the numbers followed by the arithmetic operation. If you wish to compute

$$2 \times 5 = \text{?}$$

use

Keystroke	Display
2	2.
ENTER↑	2.00
5	5.
×	10.00

The correct answer appears in the display.

Example 2R-7: Chained multiplication   A problem like

$$2 \times 5 \times 6 \times 9 = \text{?}$$

can be solved by keying it in as follows:

Keystroke	Display
2	2.
ENTER↑	2.00
5	5.
×	10.00 ← ①
6	6.
×	60.00 ← ②
9	9.
×	540.00

Note again that at ① and ② the display contains the accumulated result of previous operations:

$$\textbf{2 × 5 ×} = 10\qquad\qquad ← ①$$

$$\textbf{2 × 5 × 6 ×} = 60\qquad ← ②$$

Example 2R-8: Division A division problem can be expressed in a variety of ways:

$$14/2 \quad = \, ?$$
$$14 \div 2 = \, ?$$
$$2\overline{)14} \quad = \, ?$$
$$\tfrac{14}{2} \quad = \, ?$$

Of course, each of these ways of writing the problem means exactly the same thing.

Such problems are solved on most calculators by using the ÷ key:

Keystroke	Display
14	14.
ENTER↑	14.00
2	2.
÷	7.00

Example 2R-9: Chained multiplication and division Problems involving successive multiplications and divisions, such as

$$\frac{3 \times 6}{9}$$

are solved with only one **ENTER↑** keystroke.

Keystroke	Display
3	3.
ENTER↑	3.00
6	6.
×	18.00 ← ①
9	9
÷	2.00

Note the intermediate result

$$\textbf{3} \times \textbf{6} \div = 18 \quad \text{at} \ ①$$

Example 2R-10: Chain calculations involving mixed arithmetic operations You have learned that it is possible to solve a problem involving a chain of arithmetic operations. However, up to this point, the chain-type problems considered have involved only combinations of (1) addition and subtraction *or* (2) multiplication and division. What happens when we key in a problem involving a mixture of both addition and subtraction operations and multiplication and division operations?

Consider the problem

$$12 + 6 \times 3 = ?$$

The correct keystroke sequence depends upon the problem definition. Let's assume that we mean

$$12 + (6 \times 3) = ?$$

If you were working this problem with a pencil and paper, you would first calculate the intermediate result of (6×3) to get 18. Then you would add 12 to 18 to get 30. This is the same order that should be used for keystroking the data.

Keystroke	Display
6	6.
ENTER↑	6.00
3	3.
×	18.00
12	12.
+	30.00

You should observe that a chain of *mixed* operations is *not* necessarily performed in the order written. Keying the problem as shown above resulted in the multiplication $6 \times 3 = 18$ being performed *first*. Only then is the addition operation performed, giving $12 + 18 = 30.$†

Example 2R-11: The use of parentheses You have probably noticed that in Example 2R-10 the result would have been different if the addition had been performed first, since $12 + 6 = 18$ and $18 \times 3 = 54$. Changing the order of operations gives a result of 54, rather than the answer of 30. For example, reformulate the problem as

$$(12 + 6) \times 3 = ?$$

To solve this problem with the RPN logic system, you would again start inside the parentheses, entering that data first and performing the arithmetic operation indicated.

---

†It is possible to solve this problem by entering the data as written but reversing the order of arithmetic operations, i.e., **12, ENTER↑, 6, ENTER↑, 3, ×, +**. As expected, the answer is still 30. However, this is not the recommended procedure. Instead, it is recommended that you work through one operation at a time, as shown in the text above.

Example 2R-12: Nested parentheses You will encounter parentheses within other parentheses (nests) to specify the order in which operations are completed. To evaluate the expression

$$((7 \times 9) + 3) \div 6 = ?$$

you would key in the data for the innermost parentheses and perform only one operation at a time. Then go on to the next innermost parentheses, as follows:

Keystroke	Display
7	7
ENTER↑	7.00
9	9.
×	63.00
3	3.
+	66.00
6	6.
÷	11.00

Example 2R-13: More practice To review your understanding of arithmetic operations and the use of parentheses, consider the following example:

$$3 + (-5 \times (2 + 4))/(7 - 4) = ?$$

A proper keystroke sequence would be

Keystroke	Display	Keystroke	Display
2	2.	7	7.
ENTER↑	2.00	ENTER↑	7.00
4	4.	4	4.
+	6.00	−	3.00
5	5.	÷	−10.00
CHS	−5.	3	3.
×	−30.00	+	−7.00

These types of keystroke sequences are possible because the HP family of calculators has an automatic memory stack which stores up to four intermediate results inside the calculator until you need them, then inserts them into the calculation. You need to know the number of intermediate results stored in the 4-level stack. Otherwise, when working through a complicated formula, you could inadvertently **ENTER↑** a new data value into an already fully loaded data memory stack. This could result in the erasing of an intermediate result you were saving for a later calculation.

The best way to avoid such mistakes is to know generally what pending results are in the stack and to keep the pending results in the stack to a minimum by completing each arithmetic operation as soon as possible. Although it is not strictly necessary, you may want to know more about the workings of the stack, which is explained in more detail in the following paragraphs.

2R-1.3 The Automatic Memory Stack

In the HP family almost all the calculators have four registers inside the calculator that are positioned to form the automatic memory stack. These registers are called X, Y, Z, and T registers. They can be visualized as being "stacked," one on top of the other, with X (the display register) on the bottom.

2R-1.3.1 Manipulating the stack. Suppose you turn on the calculator and want to enter the two data values of Example 2R-1, 3 + 5 = ? The keystrokes of Example 2R-1 will be repeated with the stack contents shown.

	Register			
Keystroke	X	Y	Z	T
3	3.	0.00	0.00	0.00
ENTER↑	3.00	3.00	0.00	0.00
5	5.	3.00	0.00	0.00
+	8.00	0.00	0.00	0.00

The explanation of what happened in the stack is as follows:

1. When the slide switch is moved from off to on, all the stack registers are cleared to zero.
2. When 3 is entered into the keyboard, the 3. goes to the X register and is displayed.
3. Pressing the **ENTER↑** key moves the 3 from X to Y and duplicates the 3 in X. (It also moves Y up to Z, Z up to T, and the old value of T is lost.)
4. When 5 is entered into the keyboard, it replaces the 3 in X.
5. Pressing the **+** function key executes the following operations:
   a. The contents of the X register is added to the contents of the Y register and the sum goes into the X register. That is, 8 goes into X.
   b. The Z value moves down to Y, the T value to Z, and T value is duplicated by remaining in T.

2R-1.4 Clearing the Display

When you press the **CLX** key the displayed X register is cleared to zero and no other registers are affected. If you made a mistake while keystroking the last data entry, simply press **CLX** to clear the X register and enter the correct data value. If you want to clear all four registers in the stack, then press **CLX, ENTER↑, ENTER↑,** and **ENTER↑**, although usually it is not necessary to clear the entire stack. Some calculators have a **CL ALL** function which clears and sets to zero the stack registers and all addressable registers.

2R-1.4.1 Automatic "lifts" and "drops". We have already observed that the stack automatically "drops" when a two-number arithmetic operation is completed. To illustrate, suppose the stack values are a, b, c, and d for registers X, Y, Z, and T, respectively. That is:

Stack	Contents
T	d
Z	c
Y	b
X	a

When the **+** key is pressed, the stack "drops," as shown below:

Stack	Contents
T	d
Z	d
Y	c
X	a + b

The same dropping action would occur for the other arithmetic operations: −, ×, or ÷. The contents of T drop to Z, Z to Y, and the contents of X and Y combine to give the result in X.

We can also use this example to illustrate "lifting." Suppose after completing the add operation above, you wish to enter the value e. After keystroking in the value for e, we have

Stack	Contents
T	d
Z	c
Y	a + b
X	e

Notice that the values "lifted" in the stack without pressing the **ENTER↑** key.

2R-2 FUNCTION KEYS

This section describes the use of various basic *function* keys that may be available on your calculator. (Description of other keys used in programming will not be discussed in this book.) We'll begin with a brief discussion of the *dual-function keys*.

2R-2.1 The Gold Key f

Most keys on the keyboard perform two functions. One function is indicated by the symbol on the face of the key, while another function is indicated by the gold symbol written above the key. To select the function printed in gold, press the gold prefix key **f**, then press the function key.† Thus the calculator keyboard operates somewhat like a typewriter with its shift key that makes more symbols available than there are keys on the keyboard (a difference, of course, is that on the calculator you press the shift key first but do *not* hold it down while pressing the function key). Throughout the rest of this book, for simplicity, we generally omit the shift key in describing keystroke sequences. Just remember to use it as you would a typewriter shift when it is required.

2R-2.2 One-Number Function Keys

One-number function keys execute upon the number in the X register only, and the contents of the Y, Z, and T registers are unaffected.

x^2 This key calculates the *square* of the number in the display; i.e., it causes the number in the display to be multiplied times itself. To find the square of 13, key in 13 followed by the x^2 key:

Keystroke	Display	
13	13.	
x^2	169.00	*ans*

$\sqrt{x}$ This key finds the *square root* of the displayed number (where the answer multiplied by itself would equal the originally displayed number). To obtain the square root of 625:

---

†Some calculators in the HP family have triple function keys. They have a function symbol on the face, a gold symbol above the face, and a blue symbol below the face. So there is a blue prefix key **g** that functions the same as the gold **f** key.

Keystroke	Display
625	625.
$\sqrt{x}$	25.00 *ans*

1/x The *reciprocal* key divides the displayed number into 1.

log This key obtains the *logarithm* (to the base 10) of the display value. Logarithms are used in several financial applications which are described in detail later in the book. Basically, logarithms are *powers* required to obtain a given number. To illustrate, the logarithm of 100 (to a base of 10) is equal to 2, since $10^2 = 100$.

ln This key obtains the natural logarithm (useful in various mathematical and financial applications) of the display numbers. For natural logarithms, the base is e ($e = 2.718281828459$).

|x| The *absolute-value* key makes the sign of the displayed number positive (a change in sign if it was negative to begin with, no change if it was positive).

INT The *integer* key deletes everything to the right of the decimal point in a displayed number, leaving only the integer value.†

2R-2.3 An Advanced Function Key y^x

The powerful y^x key allows you to find the roots and powers of any positive number. It is therefore a generalized version of the x^2 and $\sqrt{x}$ keys (for powers and roots other than 2). We class it as an advanced function key because it is really a function of *two* variables rather than one. The y is the number to be raised to a power, and x is the power.

First, let's see how you could use this key to compute 13^2 (this is the same computation made earlier with the x^2 key). Using the y^x key, note that $y = 13$ and $x = 2$; then proceed with a four-step process:

Step	Keystroke	Display
1. Key in the value of y (in this case 13)	**13**	13.
2. Press **ENTER↑**	**ENTER↑**	13.00
3. Key in value of x (in this case 2)	**2**	2.
4. Press the y^x key	y^x	169.00

†On some models, such as the HP-38E, **INT** stands for interest; thus the key has a different meaning and use.

Of course, you already know this result could have been obtained with the x^2 key, but suppose you wanted to compute $(13)^3$, that is, $13 \times 13 \times 13$. Using the y^x key,

Keystroke	Display
13	13.
ENTER↑	13.00
3	3.
y^x	2197.00

Now, use your calculator to prove that

$$(2)^{18} = 262,144.00$$

The y^x can also be used to obtain the roots of a number. By use of the $\sqrt{x}$ key we already found the answer for $\sqrt{625}$. Since, in general, $\sqrt[n]{y} = y^{1/n}$,

$$\sqrt{625} = (625)^{1/2}$$

and the same answer can be obtained using y^x in the following keystroke:

Keystroke	Display
625	625.
ENTER↑	625.00
1	1.
ENTER↑	1.00
2	2.
÷	0.50
y^x	25.00

Example 2R-14: Compound interest: an important application of y^x An important application of the y^x key that will recur frequently in later chapters of this book as well as actual practice is in computing *compound interest*. Suppose, for example, that you decided to set aside $100 for 20 years, invested in a savings account at 6% annual interest. What will the balance in your account be if it is undisturbed for 20 years?

You know that at the end of 1 year you would have

Principal (initial payment)	$100
Interest ($100 × .06)	6
Balance (future value)	$106

Note that this could be obtained by taking $100(1.06) = $106.

In the second year, you would earn interest not only on your initial investment of $100 but on the previously accumulated interest as well:

Beginning balance	$106
Interest ($106 × .06)	6.36
Ending balance (future value)	$112.36

You could also compute the balance in your account at the end of the second year by taking $106(1.06) = $112.36. Since the $106 was obtained as ($100)(1.06), this second year balance is really

$$(\$100)(1.06)(1.06) \quad \text{or} \quad (\$100)(1.06)^2$$

In fact, this represents a general approach to finding the future value of any sum of money invested at a specified interest rate for a specified time period.

$$FV = P(1 + i)^n$$

where FV = future value
  P = initial investment, or principal
  i = interest rate (per time period)
  n = number of time periods

Your third-year balance would be

$$FV = \$100 (1 + .06)^3$$
$$= \$100 \times (1.06)^3$$
$$= \$119.10 \quad \text{rounded to nearest cent}$$

You can now compute the value at the end of 20 years:

Keystroke	Display
1.06	1.06
ENTER↑	1.06
20	20.
y^x	3.21
100	100.
×	320.71

The answer (rounded) is that the account would contain $320.71 at the end of 20 years.

2R-2.4 Mathematical Function Keys

There are a number of mathematical function keys on the various Type R calculators, such as **SIN, COS, TAN, DEG, RAD**, which have little usefulness in business applications. We will have no reason to refer to them in this book, but they are explained in detail in the respective user's manuals.

2R-3 DISPLAY CONTROL

2R-3.1 Fix-Decimal Control: The DSP Key†

This key allows you to fix the accuracy you want to have displayed in your calculations. The **DSP** key, followed by any number 0 through 9, establishes the number of digits to the right of the decimal point that will appear in your display. Actual accuracy of the calculations is not affected (they are far more accurate than necessary for most business purposes). Rounding takes place only in the displayed answer. For example, the sequence **DSP 2** will cause an answer like 147.8852224 to appear as

$$147.89 \qquad \text{(note the rounding)}$$

DSP 1 will change this answer to 147.9; **DSP 0** will cause 148. to be displayed. (You should try this on your calculator.)

2R-4 MEMORY OPERATIONS

2R-4.1 Memory Registers

A number of multipurpose data memory registers, which we call simply *data registers,* are available in your calculator. They provide an opportunity for you to store numbers you need to recall and use later. You will be able to store and recall data for use in subsequent operations.

2R-4.2 The Store Key STO

Pressing the **STO** key simply instructs the calculator to *store* the number contained in the display in a location you specify. Thus the store key must always be followed by a specific data memory location. For example, the keystroke sequence **STO 5** causes the displayed number to be stored in data register 5. In this book, we'll use the following notation to describe this storing operation:

$$X \rightarrow R_5$$

where X represents the display number in the X register, the arrow indicates the storing operation, and R_5 denotes data memory location number 5.

†Some HP calculators, such as the HP-37E use the gold **f** key in place of **DSP**.

Whenever you store a number in a memory register, any number previously stored there is automatically erased and replaced by the displayed number.

2R-4.3 The Recall Key **RCL**

Pressing the recall key, followed by a data-register number, causes the number contained in that particular data register to be recalled from memory and shown in the display. The recall operation does *not* alter the contents of the given data register, which may be recalled and used as many times as needed in a given calculation. Only a store operation or clearing operation (discussed below) will alter the contents of a data register.

2R-4.4 Clearing Data Registers

You can clear (or *zero*) any specific data register by entering a zero into the display and storing it in the appropriate data register. For example, to clear data register 5, the following steps are used:

$$\textbf{0 STO 5}$$

We show this in our notation as

$$0 \rightarrow R_n$$

where n represents the data-register number. You can also clear all data registers by using the clear key appropriate for your calculator.

Example 2R-15: Using data registers in calculations The use of data registers and the **STO** and **RCL** keys discussed above can best be understood by working through an example. Suppose you want to calculate

$$\frac{3 + (5 \times 2)}{\frac{12}{6} + 3} = ?$$

You learned in a previous section how to evaluate this type of expression by working through the problem step by step. (For practice, you may want to work it out that way.) Alternatively, we could solve the problem in the following steps:

Step 1: Calculate $3 + (5 \times 2)$ and store the result in data register 5. In our notation

$$3 + (5 \times 2) \rightarrow R_5$$

Step 2: Calculate $\frac{12}{6} + 3$ and store the result in data register 6:

$$\frac{12}{6} + 3 \rightarrow R_6$$

Step 3: Recall the contents of R_5 and divide by the contents of R_6:

$$\frac{R_5}{R_6} = ?$$

Step 4: Store the result in R_7:

$$\frac{R_5}{R_6} = \frac{3 + (5 \times 2)}{\frac{12}{6} + 3} \rightarrow R_7$$

The keystroke sequence to accomplish these steps is as follows:

Keystroke	Display	Keystroke	Display	Keystroke	Display
5	5.	**12**	12.	**RCL**	5.00
ENTER↑	5.00	**ENTER↑**	12.00	**5**	13.00
2	2.	**6**	6.	**RCL**	13.00
×	10.00	**÷**	2.00	**6**	5.00
3	3.	**3**	3.	**÷**	2.60
+	13.00	**+**	5.00	**STO**	2.60
STO	13.00	**STO**	5.00	**7**	2.60
5	13.00	**6**	5.00		

The result, 2.60, is now stored in data register 7. Note how the keystrokes **RCL 6** were equivalent to keying in a numerical value (in this case 5.00).

2R-5 OTHER MEMORY OPERATIONS

The final example in this section deals with cumulative multiplication, which represents an interesting and useful operation with an RPN logic system.

Example 2R-16 Suppose you wish to accumulate the sum of a series of arithmetic computations in a data register:

$$(2 \times 4) + (7 \times 6) + (8 \times 2) = ?$$

The keystroke operations become

Keystroke	Display	Keystroke	Display
2	2.	**×**	42.00
ENTER↑	2.00	**+**	50.00
4	4.	**8**	8.
×	8.00	**ENTER↑**	8.00
7	7.	**2**	2.
ENTER↑	7.00	**×**	16.00
6	6.	**+**	66.00

The keystrokes shown above accumulate the total in the X register. An alternative approach, illustrating the function of summing the intermediate totals into data register 1, is shown below;

Keystroke	Display	Keystroke	Display
2	2.	X	42.00
ENTER↑	2.00	STO + 1	42.00
4	4.	8	8.
×	8.00	ENTER↑	8.00
STO 1	8.00	2	2.
7	7.	X	16.00
ENTER↑	7.00	STO + 1	16.00
6	6.	RCL 1	66.00

In order to sum the contents of the X register into data register 1, the command sequence is **STO + 1**. The general command, **STO + N, STO − N, STO × N,** or **STO ÷ N,** allows summing, subtracting, multiplying, and dividing the contents of a data register by the X register (display value) and stores the results in data register **N**.

EXERCISES

2-1 Solve:

$$500 \times .085 \times \tfrac{1}{4} = ?$$

  answer: **10.625**

2-2 Determine

$$1500 \times (1 + (.0975/3)) = ?$$

2-3 Solve:

$$\left(\frac{((3 + 5) \times (4 - 3))}{(5 + 2)} \right) \times \left(\frac{1}{6} \right) \div \left(\frac{(7 - 3)}{((4 + 6) \times (8 - 2))} \right) = ?$$

  answer: **2.8571429**

2-4 Solve:

$$10 \times (((-7.5 \div .3) + (6.3 - 1.2))/((-5 + 3.1)/(-.3))) \div ((4.2 + 7.5)/(-5 + 2.2)) = ?$$

2-5 Solve:

$$5 \times ((5^2 \times \tfrac{1}{4}) \div \sqrt{16^4})^{-.2} = ?$$

  answer: **10.506111**

2-6 Store the values below in the registers indicated

5	4	16	.2
R_{01}	R_{02}	R_{03}	R_{04}

and solve:

$$R_{01} \times \left(\left(\left(\left(R_{01}^2 \times \frac{1}{R_{02}} \right) \div \sqrt{R_{03}} \right)^{R_{02}} \right)^{-R_{04}} \right) = ?$$

2-7 Solve the following expression using the parenthesis and function keys indicated:

$$\left((5.2^{-2} \times \tfrac{1}{17})^{.4} \times \sqrt{17.25} \right)^{1/3} = ?$$

answer: **.709802**

2-8 Use your calculators to extend the following line items on an invoice; i.e., for every line item extend by multiplying sales price × number of units sold. Sum the total (price × units) to data register 7.

Sales price, $	11.50	12.78	8.42	15.95	6.95	19.49
Units sold	1250	968	2865	1422	3556	4253

2-9 Solve:

$$1500 \times \left(1 + \frac{.06}{2} \right)^{15 \times 2} = ?$$

answer: **3640.8937**

2-10 Solve:

$$\frac{\ln(84{,}175/22{,}150)}{\ln(1 + .0813314)} = ?$$

CHAPTER
THREE

BASIC CONCEPTS IN COMPOUND INTEREST

IN THIS CHAPTER

This chapter will present the basic concepts involved in compound interest calculations. It will define and explain the concepts of:

1. Compound amounts and future value.
2. Discount amounts and present value.
3. Equivalency relationships among payments on different dates and different rates of interest.

You will be able to solve a variety of financial problems involving interest and compounding. You can determine the value of any of the following four variables where the other three are known:

1. Future amount or value.
2. Present amount or value.
3. Time involved (number of compounding periods).
4. Interest rate.

●   ●   ●   ●   ●

You'll recall that the primary objective of this book is to redevelop the body of knowledge often called mathematics of finance, simplified by the use of handheld calculators to perform the tedious and sometimes complex calculations. This chapter deals with the fundamental concepts involved in interest calculations and the *time value* of money. We will assume no prior knowledge of these concepts or the problem-solving methods associated with them, and will begin with some very basic concepts involving *interest*.

3-1 INTEREST

Interest has been defined as the amount paid for the use of borrowed money. One might consider interest as a "rental" charge paid for the use of borrowed money, analogous to the rental charge that would be paid for the use of equipment, buildings, or other resources. If you borrow money, it is necessary to pay interest; if you have money, you can get interest for it. Money is therefore said to have a *time value*. A dollar now is worth more than a dollar expected at some future time because of the interest earnings it could generate in the meantime.

More broadly speaking, interest may be thought of as the return available from the productive investment of capital. While we will have occasion to deal with this concept of return on investment later in this book, it is perhaps more straightforward to explain interest calculations and concepts in situations where money is actually borrowed or loaned. Consider the following example:

Example 3-1 Mr. B (the Borrower) obtains $500 from Mr. L (the Lender), signing a formal note which states that at the end of 12 months Mr. B will pay to Mr. L the $500 he borrowed—the *principal* of the loan—and, in addition an *interest* payment of $47.50. The total *amount due* at the end of the time period is the principal plus interest: $500 + $47.50 = $547.50.

3-1.1 Calculating the Interest Rate

The *rate* of interest earned or charged is the ratio of the amount of interest earned in a stated time period to the principal. In Example 3-1 the interest earned or charged is $47.50, the principal amount borrowed is $500, and the interest rate is the ratio $47.50/500 = .095 or 9.5% per annum. (Since the time period involved is 1 year, this interest rate is an annual rate.)

3-2 GENERAL RELATIONSHIPS

Since we are now dealing with four different quantities (amount due, principal, interest rate, and time), it is worthwhile to introduce the following symbols to represent them.

Let P = principal
r = interest rate
t = time period
I = interest charged in dollars for the loan of the principal P
S = amount due at the end of the time period

Now the relationships discussed above can be expressed in symbolic form. The *interest charged* is

$$I = P \cdot r \cdot t \tag{3-1}$$

At the end of the time period both the principal and the interest charges must be paid. That is,

$$S = P + I \tag{3-2}$$

You should pay particular attention to the units used in the equations above. The time period, t, is in units of years and, unless specifically stated otherwise, the time period for the interest rate r is 1 year. The r is conventionally stated as an *annual* rate of interest, expressed either as a percentage or the equivalent decimal fraction, regardless of the time period involved. In Example 3-1 the interest rate in the percentage form is 9.5% and in the equivalent decimal fraction form is .095. While the percentage form is usually used in business conversations and written loan documents, the *decimal fractional form must be used in all computations.*

Example 3-2 Find the interest charged and the amount due if $500 is loaned for 3 months at 8.5%.

Since it is not stated otherwise, you should assume that the interest of 8.5% is an annual rate of interest. The interest charged is

$$I = P{\cdot}r{\cdot}t = P \times 0.085 \times \tfrac{1}{4}$$

$$= 500 \times .085 \times \tfrac{1}{4}$$

$$= \$10.625$$

or (rounding) $10.63. The amount due is

$$S = P + I = 500 + 10.63 = \$510.63$$

It is often useful to express the amount due, S, in a form that depends directly on the interest rate, r. This is accomplished by eliminating I from Eqs. (3-1) and (3-2) to get

$$S = P(1 + r{\cdot}t) \tag{3-3}$$

A further modification will prove to be even more useful later when we get to more complex situations. Let $1/c$ represent the elapsed time for which funds were borrowed, expressed in units of years. (Recall that in Example 3-2 the elapsed time was three months or $\tfrac{1}{4}$ year.) Then

$$i_c = r\frac{1}{c} = \frac{r}{c} \tag{3-4}$$

where i_c represents the interest rate charged for the actual elapsed period. Since

$$i_c = r \times t = r \times \frac{1}{c} \tag{3-5}$$

Equation (3-3) can be rewritten as

$$S = P(1 + i_c) \tag{3-6}$$

This is a fundamental relationship that will be used frequently in future chapters.

Some further explanation can be given for the elapsed time, $1/c$, and its reciprocal, c. If a loan at the specified rate is renewed every time it comes due, then the number of renewals and the number of times interest charges are computed are expressed by c. That is,

$\dfrac{1}{c}$ = elapsed time for basing a single interest charge, expressed in units of years

c = number of interest charge calculations per year

Example 3-3 If $1500 is invested for 4 months at an annual interest rate of 9.75%, what will be the total amount due (the *future value* of the investment)?

$$\frac{1}{c} = \tfrac{4}{12} = \tfrac{1}{3} \text{ of a year}$$

$$c = 3 \text{ times per year}$$

$$i_c = \frac{r}{c} = \frac{.0975}{3}$$

The amount due or the future value is:

$$S = \text{FV} = P(1 + i_c) = 1500 \left(1 + \frac{.0975}{3} \right)$$

$$= \$1548.75$$

Note this use of the term *future value* to express the total amount of money returned to the investor four months in the future.

Example 3-4 How much do you need to invest today if you want to have returned to you in 9 months a total amount of $4075, where the annual interest rate is 7.5%? (Notice that in this example it is the principal, P, which is unknown.)

$$\text{FV} = 4075$$

$$\frac{1}{c} = \tfrac{9}{12} = \tfrac{3}{4} \text{ year}$$

$$i_c = .075 \times \tfrac{3}{4}$$

$$4075 = P(1 + .075 \times \tfrac{3}{4})$$

$$= P \times 1.05625$$

Solving for P:

$$P = \frac{4075}{1.05625} = \$3857.99$$

3-3 COMPOUND AMOUNT

In many situations, the interest charge is made or computed periodically, while a loan remains outstanding. Let's consider a savings account as an example. At stated time intervals the interest is computed and added to the principal. Then this new sum is used to compute interest for the following time period. The process is repeated for subsequent time periods with a new sum of principal and accumulated interest. At the termination of the loan or investment transaction the final accumulated sum is called the *compound amount*. The difference between the compound amount and the original principal is called the *compound interest*. The elapsed time or time period between two consecutive interest computations is called the *interest period* or compound period.

Example 3-5 Suppose you deposit $100 in a savings account where interest is compounded annually at 7%. What will be the balance in the account at the end of first, second, third, and fourth years?

The solution to this problem can be expressed in tabular form.†

End of year	Yearly interest	Cumulative interest	End-of-year balance
0	$ —	$ —	$100
1	7.00	7.00	107.00
2	7.49	14.49	114.49
3	8.0143	22.5043	122.5043
4	8.575301	31.079601	131.079601

†Although it would be reasonable to round to the nearest cent, all decimal places are shown for illustrative purposes.

The following relationships may be observed in the results above:

Balance at end of year 1 = $100 \times (1 + .07) = 100(1 + .07)^1$

Balance at end of year 2 = $100 \times (1 + .07)(1 + .07) = 100(1 + .07)^2$

Balance at end of year 3 = $100 \times (1 + .07)(1 + .07)(1 + .07) = 100(1 + .07)^3$

Balance at end of year 4 = $100 \times (1 + .07)(1 + .07)(1 + .07)(1 + .07)$

$$= 100(1 + .07)^4$$

We can now generalize the expression to find the balance at the end of year n.

$$\text{Balance at EOY } n = 100 \times (1 + .07)^n$$

This leads to the following generalized formula for compounding:

$$FV = PV(1 + i_c)^n \qquad (3\text{-}7)$$

where PV = original principal amount or the *present value*
FV = compound amount of PV, or the future value at a specified later date
n = number of periods where compound interest is calculated
i_c = interest rate for the time period when compound interest calculations are made

Equation (3-7) is known as the fundamental formula for compound interest. Virtually every formula or result obtained in the remainder of the book is based upon this equation.

Notice that the n represents the number of *compounding periods,* not the *number of years*. In Example 3-4 the problem stated that interest should be compounded *annually,* so in that case n is counted in yearly increments and $i_c = .07$ is still the annual interest rate.

Remember, however, that even in cases where there are multiple (or fractional) compounding calculations per year, it is still conventional to reference an *annual* interest, such as the *yearly nominal rate*.

If

$$r = \text{nominal annual interest rate}$$

$$c = \text{number of compounding periods per year}$$

then

$$i_c = \frac{r}{c}$$

as already indicated in Eq. (3-5).

Example 3-6 Use the same information as in Example 3-5, but compound *quarterly* instead of annually and find the balance at the end of 4 years. Here

$$r = .07 \qquad i_c = \frac{.07}{4} = .0175$$

$$PV = \$100 \qquad n = 4 \times 4 = 16$$

$$FV = PV(1 + i_c)^n = 100(1 + .0175)^{16}$$

$$= \$131.9929351$$

As to be expected, the future value at the end of 4 years has increased slightly when compounding is done quarterly instead of annually.

Example 3-7 How much will $1500 accumulate to in 15 years at an annual nominal rate of 6%, compounded semiannually?

Here

$$n = 15 \times 2 = 30$$

$$PV = \$1500$$

$$i_c = \frac{.06}{2} = .03$$

and

$$FV = 1500 \left(1 + \frac{.06}{2} \right)^{15 \times 2} = 1500(1 + .03)^{30} = \$3640.893707$$

3-4 DISCOUNT AMOUNT

Quite often it is necessary to decide how much should be invested now so that we will have a specified compounded amount to use at a known later date. The amount we wish to know is called the *present value,* PV.

Thus, if a future value, FV, will be made available to us n years from now and if compounding takes place annually, then the present value, PV, can be determined from the following form of the generalized equation for compounding, Eq. (3-7):

$$PV = \frac{FV}{(1 + i_c)^n} = FV(1 + i_c)^{-n} \tag{3-8}$$

This equation is obtained from Eq. (3-7) by simply rearranging the terms to solve for PV.† Remember that, as before, i_c represents the interest rate for the compounding period and n represents the number of discounting periods that reduce the future value back to the present value.

Example 3-8 Find the present value of a promissory note which pays $12,000 on a date which is due 5 years from now. Money is assumed to have a time value of 9% per year, compounded annually. Then

$$PV = \$12,000 \times (1 + .09)^{-5} = \$7799.176636$$

Example 3-9 Suppose $25,000 will be made available in 2 years. What is its value today if money is worth 8.75% per year, compounded monthly?

---

† Recall that from the basic mathematical laws of exponents, $x^{-n} = 1/x^n$, so that

$$\frac{1}{(1 + 1_c)^n} = \frac{1}{1/(1 + i_c)^{-n}} = (1 + i_c)^{-n}$$

$$FV = \$25,000$$

$$i_c = \frac{.0875}{12} = .007291667$$

$$n = 2 \times 12 = 24$$

$$PV = 25,000 \times (1 + .007291667)^{-24} = \$20,999.7546$$

3-5 EQUIVALENT RELATIONSHIPS

From the preceding examples it is apparent that there is a relationship between present value, PV, and future value, FV, in a particular financial situation. They are, of course, linked by Eq. (3-7),

$$FV = PV(1 + i_c)^n$$

If an investor is indifferent as to whether to accept the present amount (PV) now, or alternatively to wait n compounding periods at an interest earning rate i_c to receive FV, then it is reasonable to say that the two alternatives are *equivalent*.

3-5.1 Equivalent-Value Diagram

The concept of changing the value of money, based on compounding or discounting, can be expressed graphically by means of a *time diagram*. Suppose a sum of money, V_0, is due at a stated time, t_0. Then there is an equivalent value, V_n, due at a later date, t_n, provided that the value has been compounded accordingly. Likewise, there is an equivalent value, V_{-n} due at an earlier date, t_{-n}. Thus compounding or discounting a value V_0 can be viewed as transferring or shifting on a time diagram, as shown in Time Diagram 3-1. In such situations the forward value V_n is equivalent to V_0, which is, in turn, equivalent to the backward value, V_{-n}.

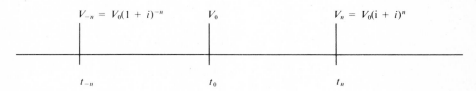

Time Diagram 3-1

Example 3-10 Suppose a payment of $2000 is due at the end of 2 years and another payment of $2500 is due at the end of 5 years. Determine the value of both amounts under the following conditions:

(a) Both amounts are paid now.
(b) Both rates are paid at end of 2 years.
(c) Both amounts are paid at end of 5 years.
(d) The time value of money is 8.75% compounded annually.

	(a) Present	(b) End of 2 years	(c) End of 5 years
First amount	$2000(1.0875)^{-2}$	2000×1	$2000(1.0875)^3$
Second amount	$2500(1.0875)^{-5}$	$2500(1.0875)^{-3}$	2500×1

Results of the indicated computations are:

	Present	End of 2 years	End of 5 years
First amount	$1691.108	$2000	$2572.277
Second amount	1643.591	1943.803	2500
Totals	$3334.699	$3943.803	$5072.277

These totals are equivalent values, as shown in Time Diagram 3-10. This type of time diagram will prove to be invaluable in Chap. 4.

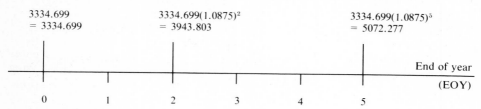

Time Diagram 3-10

3-5.2 Payments on Different Dates

If two separate amounts of money are due on different dates and they must be compared, it is desirable to replace one or both of them with their respective equivalent values on a given date so comparisons can be made. Consider the following example of this type of problem.

Example 3-11 Suppose you owe $1500 which is due in 2 years and $4000 which is due in 5 years on two separate notes (promises to pay). You reach an agreement with the creditor to whom the money is owed that you will pay off both notes 1 year from now, by stipulating that you will pay the equivalent amounts at an annual interest rate of 6%, compounded quarterly.

Amount to be paid on first note $= 1500(1 + .06/4)^{-1 \times 4}$ $= \$1413.2763$

Amount to be paid on second note $= 4000(1 + .06/4)^{-4 \times 4}$ $= \underline{3152.1242}$

Total amount paid 1 year from now $\underline{\$4565.4005}$

Notice that your equivalent payment in 1 year is substantially less than the total face amount of the two notes ($5500) due at their maturity.

3-5.3 Equivalent Rates

In many of the examples presented in this chapter, the interest rate is stated as a nominal annual interest rate even though actual calculations are made at the interest rate, i_c, that is effective for a particular compounding period. You'll recall that

$$r = \text{nominal annual interest rate}$$

$$c = \text{number of compounding periods for year}$$

$$i_c = \frac{r}{c}$$

It is important to distinguish between the *nominal* annual interest rate and the *effective* annual interest rate.

The *nominal annual rate, r*, which is usually the stated interest rate in a borrowing/lending situaton, is described by the relationship $r = i_c \times c$.

The *effective annual rate, i_e*, is really the true rate of interest earnings, determined from allowing interest to accumulate for 1 year when it is compounded c times per year at the compound rate of i_c.

To find the effective annual rate, we can simply equate the following equivalent amounts; compound $1 once at effective annual rate i_e, and compound $1 for c times at rate i_c. That is,

$$(1 + i_e)^1 = (1 + i_c)^c \tag{3-9}$$

or, rearranging,

$$i_e = (1 + i_c)^c - 1 \tag{3-10}$$

Example 3-12 What is the effective annual rate corresponding to the nominal annual rate of 8.75%, compounded quarterly?

$$1 + i_e = \left(1 + \frac{.0875}{4} \right)^4$$

$$i_e = (1.021875)^4 - 1 = .090413193$$

or

$$i_e = 9.0413\%$$

3-6 THE FOUR UNKNOWNS: FV, PV, i, and n

From the preceding examples you have seen that it is possible to replace an interest rate with an equivalent rate having different compounding periods. Likewise, amounts can be transformed to a different amount on a different due date, so that equivalency is preserved.

It may be necessary to solve for any of the four variables FV, PV, i, or n in an equivalency relationship. We can solve for any one of these four variables provided the other three are known. Since four separate formulas are required, each one will be developed (or restated) separately. The computational approaches to be used in solving these formulas on hand-held calculators will be covered in Sec. 3-7.

3-6.1 Solve for FV or PV

We have already developed the basic relationship for FV in Eq. (3-7):

$$FV = PV(1 + i_c)^n$$

Likewise, the formula for PV was given in Eq. (3-8):

$$PV = FV(1 + i_c)^{-n}$$

3-6.2 Solve for Interest Rate, i_c

Here we want to solve for i_c where FV, PV, and n are known. Let's reexamine Eq. (3-7):

$$FV = PV(1 + i_c)^n$$

Fortunately, this formula can be rearranged to explicitly solve for i_c:

$$i_c = \left(\frac{FV}{PV}\right)^{1/n} - 1 \qquad (3\text{-}11)$$

Consider an example.

Example 3-13 Solve for the nominal annual interest rate, compounded quarterly, at which \$22,150 will accumulate to \$42,180 in 8 years.

$$PV = \$22{,}150 \qquad FV = \$42{,}180$$

$$n = 8 \times 4 = 32 \qquad c = 4$$

$$i_c = \left(\frac{FV}{PV}\right)^{1/n} - 1 = \left(\frac{42{,}180}{22{,}150}\right)^{1/32} - 1$$

$$= .02033234$$

$$r = c \cdot i_c = .08133$$

$$= 8.133\%$$

3-6.3 Solve for the Number of Compounding Periods, *n*

The final formula required is to solve for *n* when i_c, PV, and FV are given. While we will not show the derivation here, it is again possible to obtain an explicit formula:

$$n = \frac{\ln(\text{FV}/\text{PV})}{\ln(1 + i_c)} \tag{3-12}$$

It is a relatively simple matter to solve for *n* using a calculator that has a logarithmic function key (called ln or log).† Calculations with the three classes of calculators are given in the following section.

Example 3-14 In Example 3-13, how long will it take for the FV to accumulate to $84,175 if the PV remains at $22,150 and the interest rate is still the 8.133% nominal annual interest compounded quarterly?

$$\text{PV} = \$22,150 \qquad \text{FV} = \$84,175$$

$$i_c = \frac{.08133}{4} = .0203325$$

$$n = \frac{\ln(\text{FV}/\text{PV})}{\ln(1 + i_c)} = \frac{\ln(3.800225734)}{\ln(1.0203325)}$$

$$= 66.3266935$$

$$\text{Elapsed time} = \frac{n}{4} = 16.58 \text{ years}$$

3-7 HAND-HELD CALCULATORS

An important purpose of this book is to cover the use of hand-held calculators in solving compounding and discounting problems. We have now developed sufficient material in this chapter to turn our attention strictly to the computational techniques. As we shall see, calculation methods for the types of problems covered have changed drastically *owing to the advent of hand-held calculators*. One important difference to note is the complete liberation from mathematical tables. With a hand-held calculator the analyst no longer needs tables of compound interest, discount factors, powers, or logarithms. It is unnecessary to learn how to interpolate between table entries or work through a table in reverse to solve the type of problems discussed in this chapter. Hand-held calculators can be used to achieve the same results with much less effort and more accuracy.

---

†Either an **ln** or **log** key can be used in this computation, as long as it is applied consistently.

You'll recall from Chapter 1 that our calculator discussions will consider three levels of calculators:

Level I.   Covers the inexpensive calculator that has no programming capabilities but does have at least a y^x function key, an **ln** (or **log**) key and at least one memory. This level of calculator is perfectly adequate for all the problems in this chapter, even though as we shall see, the other calculators do have some advantages.

Level II.   Covers the calculators with financial function keys but with limited programming features. While we won't use the programming features in this chapter, you'll see that the financial function keys will serve a very useful purpose.

Level III.   Covers the more expensive programmable calculators where programs can be recorded on a small magnetic card and reused later. One of the attractive features of these programmables is the library programs (already prewritten) that are very relevant for more advanced problems.

The remainder of this section is organized as follows:

1. Selected examples presented throughout the chapter will be restated or revised as necessary, and the actual keystrokes for hand-held calculations will be detailed.
2. Examples of solutions using both Type A (algebraic) and Type R (RPN) calculators will be presented where appropriate.

3-7.1 Level I Keystrokes

Keystrokes for Example 3-7 (solve for FV). We will indicate all the keystrokes required in solving Example 3-7 on both a Type A (TI) Level I calculator and on a comparable Type R (HP) model. In either case no memory storage is required. In this example all the keystrokes are listed on a separate line.† In later examples they will be combined where appropriate into natural groupings. Let's begin with the basic formula involved:

$$FV = 1500 \times \left(1 + \frac{.06}{2}\right)^{15 \times 2}$$

†No serious attempt will be made in these illustrations to solve a problem in the minimum number of steps. We will use more keystrokes wherever it provides more clarity for the reader.

Type A, Level I keystrokes for Example 3-7

TI-30/50 keystrokes	Display	Comments
C	0.	Clear
1	1.	
+	1.	
.06	0.06	r
÷	0.06	
2	2.	c
=	1.03	
y^x	1.03	
(	1.03	
15	15.	
×	15.	
2	2.	
)	30.	n
×	2.4272625	
1500	1500.	PV
=	3640.8937	FV

Type R, Level I keystrokes for Example 3-7

HP-31E/32E keystrokes	Display	Comments
ALL	0.0000	Clear
.06	0.06	r
ENTER↑	0.0600	
2	2.	c
÷	0.0300	
1	1.	
+	1.0300	
15	15.	
ENTER↑	15.0000	
2	2.	
×	30.0000	n
y^x	2.4273	
1500	1,500.	PV
×	3,640.8937	FV

Keystrokes for Example 3-11. Here, we'll repeat Example 3-11, a discounting problem, to solve for PV, indicating all the necessary keystrokes for the Level I calculators. The formulas are:

$$\text{Amount paid on both notes} = 1500\left(1 + \frac{.06}{4}\right)^{-1\times4} + 4000\left(1 + \frac{.06}{4}\right)^{-4\times4}$$

$$= 1500(1.015)^{-4} + 4000(1.015)^{-16}$$

Type A, Level I keystrokes for Example 3-11

TI-30/50 keystrokes	Display	Comments
C	0.	
1	1.	
+	1.	
.06	0.06	r
÷	0.06	
4	4.	
=	1.015	$1 + i_c$
STO	1.015	
1500	1500.	FV_1
×	1500.	
RCL	1.015	
y^x	1.015	
(	1.015	
1	1.	
+/−	−1.	
×	−1.	
4	4.	
)	−4.	
+	1413.2763	PV_1
4000	4000.	FV_2
×	4000.	
RCL	1.015	
y^x	1.015	
(	1.015	
4	4.	
+/−	−4.	
×	−4.	
4	4.	
)	−16.	
=	4565.4006	$PV_1 + PV_2$

Type R, Level I keystrokes for Example 3-11

HP-31E/32E keystrokes	Display	Comments
ALL	0.0000	Clear
.06	0.06	r
ENTER↑	0.0600	
4	4.	
÷	0.0150	
1	1.	
+	1.0150	
STO 1	1.0150	$1 + i_c$
1	1.	
CHS	−1.	
ENTER↑	−1.0000	
4	4.	
×	−4.0000	
yˣ	0.9422	
1500	1,500.	FV_1
×	1,413.2763	
STO 2	1,413.2763	PV_1
RCL 1	1.0150	
4	4.	
CHS	−4.	
ENTER↑	−4.0000	
4	4.	
×	−16.0000	
yˣ	0.7880	
4000	4,000.	FV_2
×	3,152.1242	PV_2
RCL 2	1,413.2763	PV_1
+	4,565.4005	$PV_1 + PV_2$

Keystrokes for Example 3-13. We'll repeat Example 3-13 showing all the keystrokes for the Level I calculator. The required formula,

$$i_c = \left(\frac{42,180}{22,150} \right)^{1/32} - 1$$

does not require any more sophistication than the use of function keys **yˣ** and at least one memory. However, most inexpensive calculators that have an **yˣ** function key will also have the reciprocal function key, **1/x**. Although not needed, the **1/x** key is used in the solution below.

Type A, Level I keystrokes for Example 3-13

TI-30/50 keystrokes	Display	Comments
C	0.	Clear
42180	42180.	FV
÷	42180.	
22150	22150.	PV
=	1.9042889	
y^x	1.9042889	
32	32.	n
1/x	0.03125	
−	1.0203323	
1	1.	
=	.02033234	i_c

Type R, Level I keystrokes for Example 3-13

HP-31E/32E keystrokes	Display	Comments
ALL	0.0000	Clear
42180	42,180.	FV
ENTER↑	42,180.00	
22150	22,150.	PV
÷	1.9043	
32	32.	n
1/x	0.0313	
y^x	1.0203	
1	1.	
−	0.0203	i_c

Keystrokes for Example 3-14. Now, let's repeat Example (3-14) indicating all the keystrokes. This example requires a logarithm function key—either the **ln** key (logarithm to the base e) or the **log** key (logarithm to the base 10). However, the user must be consistent in whichever logarithm key is selected. That is, use either the formula

$$n = \frac{\ln(FV/PV)}{\ln(1 + i_c)}$$

or

$$n = \frac{\log(FV/PV)}{\log(1 + i_c)}$$

Either one will work. Let's use

$$n = \frac{\ln(84,175/22,150)}{\ln(1 + .08133/4)}$$

Type A, Level I keystrokes for Example 3-14

TI-30/50 keystrokes	Display	Comments
C	0.	Clear
84175	84175	FV
÷	84175	
22150	22150	PV
=	3.8002257	
ln *x*	1.3350605	
÷	1.3350605	
(	1.3350605	
1	1.	
+	1.	
.08133	0.08133	
÷	0.08133	
4	4.	
)	1.0203325	$1 + i_c$
ln *x*	.02012855	
=	66.326694	n

Type R, Level I keystrokes for Example 3-14

HP-31E/32E keystrokes	Display	Comments
ALL	0.0000	Clear
84175	84,175.	FV
ENTER↑	84,175.0000	
22150	22,150.	PV
÷	3.8002	
ln	1.3351	
.08133	0.08133	
ENTER↑	0.0813	
4	4.	
÷	0.0203	
1	1.	
+	1.0203	$1 + i_c$
ln	0.0201	
÷	66.3267	n

3-7.2 Level II Calculators

As you will recall, the Level II calculators have quite a number of financial function keys, but they have little or no programming capability. The financial function keys are uniquely designed to simplify the compounding/discounting calculations and this is our first opportunity to demonstrate their power.

The financial keys of interest are identified as follows: **n, %i, PV**, and **FV**. Regardless of whether we are using a Type A or Type R financial calculator, the financial function keys serve essentially the same purpose. For either type the computational process is simple. We first merely enter the known data and press the appropriate function key.

Next,

1. For the TI-MBA, indicate the unknown to be solved for by pressing the compute key, **CPT**, and then the appropriate financial function key.
2. For the HP 37E or 38E, simply press the appropriate financial function key for the unknown value.

Keystrokes for Example 3-7. Resolve Example 3-7 by using a Level II unit with financial function keys. The data are

$$PV = \$1500 \qquad i_c = \frac{6\%}{2} \qquad n = 15 \times 2$$

Solving for any of the other three unknowns will involve the same type of process. To illustrate, let's work out other examples.

Type A, Level II keystrokes for Example 3-7

TI-MBA/BA-II keystrokes	Display	Comments
CA	0	Clear
1500	1500	PV
PV	1500.	
6	6	$r\%$
÷	6.	
2	2	
=	3.	$i_c\%$
%i	3.	
2	2	
×	2.	
15	15	
=	30.	n
n	30.	
CPT	30.	
FV	3640.893709	FV

Type R, Level II keystrokes for Example 3-7

HP-37E/38E keystrokes	Display	Comments
FIN	0.00	Clear
1500	1,500.	PV
PV	1,500.00	
6	6.	$r\%$
ENTER↑	6.00	
2	2.	
÷	3.00	$i_c\%$
i	3.00	
2	2.	
ENTER↑	2.00	
15	15.	
×	30.00	n
n	30.00	
FV	− 3,640.89	FV

Don't turn off your calculator. Suppose you want to change the number of compounding periods in Example 3-7 from 30 to 40 compounding periods and re-solve for FV. Simply enter **40, n,** and compute **FV.**

Keystrokes for Example 3-14. Repeat Example 3-14 to illustrate the function keys rather than the formulas with logarithms.

$$FV = \$84,175 \qquad PV = \$22,150 \qquad i_c = \frac{8.133\%}{4}$$

Type A, Level II keystrokes for Example 3-14

TI-MBA/BA-II keystrokes	Display	Comments
CA	0	
84175	84175	FV
FV	84175.	
22150	22150	PV
PV	22150.	
8.133	8.133	$r\%$
÷	8.133	
4	4	
=	2.03325	$i\%$
%i	2.03325	
CPT	2.03325	
n	66.32669341	n

Type R, Level II keystrokes for Example 3-14

HP-37E/38E keystrokes	Display	Comments
FIN	0.00	Clear
84175	84,175	FV
FV	84,175.00	
22150	22,150.	
CHS	−22,150.	PV
PV	−22,150.00	
8.133	8.133	$r\%$
ENTER↑	8.13	
4	4.	
÷	2.03	$i\%$
i	2.03	
n	66.33	n

3-7.3 Level III Keystrokes

Programmable calculators have a striking advantage over nonprogrammables, especially the ones that use magnetic cards or the newer solid-state module programs, or both. Even if a user has no programming skills, it is still practical to utilize the external routines or the so-called "library" programs. This is especially so since the major manufacturers, TI and HP, have developed many effective library programs.

These programs are called *external routines* because they are stored *outside* the calculator in machine-readable form rather than within the internal circuitry (as is the case with Level II calculators). These external routines are stored on magnetic cards, which can be written (recorded) as well as read, or on solid-state read-only modules. In either form, the external routine, or program, can literally be stored on the shelf until needed, at which point it is inserted into the calculator.

Significance of solid-state modules. Although library programs on magnetic cards are very important, one of the most exciting advances in the state of the art in programmable technology is the introduction of solid-state modules on the TI-58 and TI-59. The sole purpose of the solid-state module is to provide a better operational method of storing and using library programs. Their use will be explained in later chapters.

The virtues of financial library programs cannot be adequately demonstrated on the relatively simple applications of compounding and discounting introduced in this chapter. While there are some library programs aimed at the types of problems of this chapter, the keystrokes are very similar to the ones described for the Level II calculator. We'll provide only one example here to demonstrate solving for FV when using a solid-state module and library program.

Keystrokes for Example 3-7. We'll repeat Example 3-7 on the TI-59, using the library program on the removable solid-state module called the *Master Library*. The particular program of interest is called ML-18 COMPOUND INTEREST. Again the data are FV = 1500, i_c = 6%/2, n = 2 × 15. We use the same data with the magnetic card library program SD-05A for the HP-97. Commentaries are provided to explain the keystrokes.

Type A, Level III keystrokes for Example 3-7

TI-58/59 keystrokes	Display	Comments
Pgm 18	0.	Call ML-18
E'	0.00	
1500	1500	PV
C	1500.00	
6	6	$r\%$
÷	6.00	
2	2	
=	3.00	$i_c\%$
B	3.00	
15	15	
×	15.00	
2	2	
=	30.00	n
A	30.00	
0	0	
D	3640.89	FV

Type R, Level III keystrokes for Example 3-7

HP-97/67 keystrokes	Display	Comments
		Program SD-05A
fA	0.00	Start function
1500	1500.	PV
STO D	1500.00	
6	6.	
ENTER↑	12.	
2		
÷	3.00	$i_c\%$
STO B	3.00	
15	15.	
ENTER↑	15.00	
2	2.	
×	30.00	n
STO A	30.00	
E	3640.89	FV

EXERCISES

3-1 Find the amount due at the end of $10\frac{1}{4}$ years if $1000 is invested at the annual rate of 5% compounded monthly.

3-2 Repeat Exercise 3-1 using the following data:

Amount invested, $	Annual interest rate, %	Number of compounding periods/year	Duration time for investment, years
(a) 2000	8.5	2	4
(b) 1000	9.25	4	4
(c) 875	12.75	12	14
(d) 750	14.0	360	2

answers: (a) **$2790.22**; (c) **$5165.76**

3-3 Discount the future values given below under the following conditions:

Present value, $	Future value, $	Interest rate, % per compounding period	Number of compounding periods
(a) ?	3,500	2	14
(b) ?	4,200	4	10
(c) ?	6,431.25	0.65	20
(d) ?	150,231	.5	25

answers: (a) **$2652.56**; (c) **$5649.63**

3-4 What is the effective annual rate corresponding to the following nominal annual rates and compounding periods?

Effective annual rate, %	Nominal annual rate, %	Number of compounding periods/year
(a) ?	9	2
(b) ?	10	4
(c) ?	8	12
(d) ?	12	2

answers: (a) **9.2%**; (c) **8.3%**

3-5 Solve for the nominal annual interest rate r under the following conditions:

Nominal annual rate, %	Present value, $	Future value, $	Number of compounding periods/year	Number of years
(a) ?	22,200	41,000	4	7
(b) ?	10,100	15,000	2	3
(c) ?	450	780	12	1.5
(d) ?	18,000	22,000	12	2.25
(e) ?	750	1,100	2	4.5

(*Hint:* See Example 3-13.)
answers: (*a*) **8.86%**; (*c*) **37.24%**

3-6 How long will it take for the future value, FV, to accumulate to $84,175 for the PV and interest rates given below:

Present value, $	Nominal annual interest rate, %	Number of compounding periods/year
(a) 2000	9.25	4
(b) 3500	11.5	2
(c) 4200	12	1
(d) 6000	8.5	12

answers: (*a*) n = **163.58**, (*c*) n = **26.45**

3-7 Which alternative would you prefer and why?
 (*a*) Accept $1500 now from Mr. A in order to deposit it in a Certificate of Deposit (CD), which pays 7% per year, compounded monthly, for a time period of 4 years. Or, instead, wait 4 years and accept $2000 as Mr. A's payment.
 (*b*) Compare $1500 now, or $2500 5 years from now when the other alternative is the same $1500 CD at the same 7%, compounded monthly, for 5 years.

3-8 If $1000 is invested now, $1500 2 years from now, and $1600 4 years from now, all at the nominal annual rate of 9.75% compounded monthly, what will be the total amount 10 years from now?

3-9 Find the FV when:
 (*a*) PV = $1000, i_c = 2%, n = 12
 (*b*) PV = $2000, i_c = 3%, n = 6
 (*c*) PV = $3000, i_c = .28%, n = 9.7
 (*d*) PV = $4000, i_c = 8%, n = 6.4
 answers: (*a*) **$1268.24**; (*c*) **$3082.48**

3-10 Find the PV when:

    (*a*) FV = \$6000, *r* = 8%, *c* = 2, *n* = 8

    (*b*) FV = \$5000, *r* = 9%, *c* = 4, *n* = 16

    (*c*) FV = \$4000, *r* = 10%, *c* = 12, *n* = 36

    (*d*) FV = \$3000, *r* = 11%, *c* = 1, *n* = 10

    answers: (*a*) **\$4384.14**; (*c*) **\$2966.96**

FOUR

SIMPLE ANNUITIES

IN THIS CHAPTER

In this chapter you will learn the time value of money concepts necessary to compute unknown values for mortgages, loans, leases, sinking funds, savings accounts, and capital budgeting analysis. The applications in this chapter assume equal compounding and payment periods as well as level or equal payments. Applications where the payment intervals do not coincide with the compounding periods will be treated in Chapter 5. Balloon payment applications are discussed in Chapter 8.

● ● ● ● ●

In Chapter 3 you learned to make compound interest calculations where a single amount was paid or received. We will now examine the situation in which a series of equal payments occur—one each period for a given number of periods. Such series of payments are called *annuities*. A *simple annuity* is one in which the interest compounding period is the same as the payment period—for example, where payments are made each month and interest is compounded monthly. In simple annuities it is assumed that the compounding takes place at the end of each period.

Simple annuities may be classified into two types, depending upon whether the payment is assumed to be made at the beginning or the end of the period. The classification is as follows:

1. Simple ordinary annuity—payment at end of period.
2. Simple annuity due—payment at beginning of period.

Both types of annuities will be discussed in this chapter.

Four basic variables are involved in a simple annuity situation:

1. n—number of periods.
2. $\%i$—interest rate per compounding period.
3. PMT—payment per period.
4. FV or PV—future value or present value of the annuity.

In this chapter we will show you how to solve for each of the four basic variables when the others are known. Each section demonstrates the approach necessary for a Level I calculator with y^x and **ln x** keys and one or two memories. Level II and III calculators have special function keys or programs to solve for the four variables. With these calculators you need only to concentrate on the proper identification of the annuity situation so that the proper key or program is selected. Representative keystroke solutions for annuity problems are shown at the end of the chapter. We'll begin with a discussion of simple ordinary annuities.

SIMPLE ORDINARY ANNUITIES

4-1 ORDINARY ANNUITIES—FV

In Chapter 3 you used the compound interest formula $FV = PV(1 + i_c)^n$ for the future value of a single payment. Let's expand this relationship to the case in which a series of equal payments are made at the end of several equal periods—a simple ordinary annuity. Consider the following example.

Example 4-1 If you invest $100 at the end of each year for 3 years to earn interest compounded at an annual rate of 10%, how much will you have on deposit at the end of the third year?

Time Diagram 4-1 shows the timing of the payments. Note that the $100 invested at the end of the first period is compounded only two times. The second payment is compounded once and the third payment is not compounded at all.

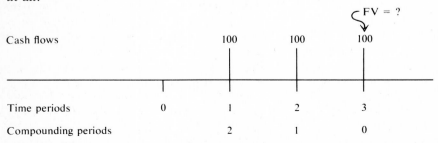

Time Diagram 4-1

Table 4-1

Year	Compounding periods	Interest factor		Payment		FV
1	2	$(1.1)^2$	×	$100	=	$121
2	1	$(1.1)^1$	×	100	=	110
3	0	$(1.1)^0$	×	100	=	100
		Sum of factors = 3.31				
				Sum of specific future values =		$331

The future value of this simple ordinary annuity can be determined by computing the future values for each of the individual payments and then simply summing them. This procedure is illustrated in Table 4-1. As shown in the table, $100 invested at the end of each of 3 years at 10% will compound to a total of $331.

Of course, this computational procedure is valid whether the payments are equal or unequal. But for the equal payments involved in a simple ordinary annuity; the future value may be calculated more easily by use of the following
Payment for Ordinary Annuity, PV Given

> Simple Ordinary Annuity—Future Value

$$FV = PMT \frac{(1 + i_c)^n - 1}{i_c} \tag{4-1}$$

where T = elapsed time for the annuity, years
f = number of payments per year
$n = T \times f$ = number of payments
FV = amount at the end of n periods
PMT = constant cash payment each period
i_c = compound interest rate per compounding period

Let's use the formula to solve Example 4-1:

$$FV = \$100 \times \frac{(1.1)^3 - 1}{.1}$$

$$= \$100 \times 3.31$$

$$= \$331$$

A calculator with a y^x key will provide a solution to this complex formula in a few easy keystrokes. In addition, many calculators now have this type of

†Derivation of this formula, which is relatively straightforward, is given in Appendix 4A at the end of this chapter.

annuity calculation preprogrammed, so that once the relevant values have been entered the solution is obtained by merely pressing the appropriate key.

The annuity relationship shown in Eq. 4-1 can be expressed with some different notation. The last part of the expression is often called the *sinking fund factor*, denoted by the symbols $S(n,i_c)$:

$$S(n,i_c) = \frac{(1 + i_c)^n - 1}{i_c} \tag{4-2}$$

You can think of this factor as the FV of a $1 payment made at the end of each period for n periods at i_c interest per period. Note that in Example 4-1,

$$S(n,i_c) = \frac{(1.1)^3 - 1}{.1} = 3.31$$

which is the same as the sum of the compound interest factors, $[(1.1)^2 + (1.1)^1 + (1.1)^0]$, as shown in Table 4-1.

Using this new notation, the FV of an ordinary annuity can be expressed as

$$FV = PMT \times S(n,i_c) \tag{4-3}$$

We will use this more convenient notation often, because it avoids repeating the same symbols over and over.

4-2 SIMPLE ORDINARY ANNUITIES—PV

In Sec. 4-1 we determined the future value of a simple ordinary annuity. To determine its *present value*, we can apply the basic compound interest formula from Chapter 3:

$$PV = \frac{FV}{(1 + i_c)^n} \tag{3-8}$$

Consider an example similar to 4-1, except that the present value of the annuity is required.

Example 4-2 What is the present value of $100 received at the end of each year for 3 years, if the payments are discounted at an annual rate of 10%?

Time Diagram 4-2 shows the timing of the payments and compounding periods involved. Note that the third payment is discounted three periods, the second two periods, and the first one period.

The PV computation involves three compounding periods, as contrasted to the two compounding periods when solving for FV, because in the FV case the last payment, made at the *end* of the period, was not compounded. Present value is computed at the *beginning* of period 1, so that the payment made at the end of period 1 (as well as all following payments) must be discounted. PV

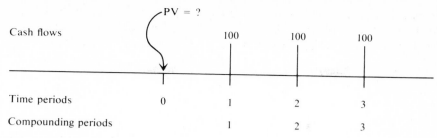

Time Diagram 4-2

therefore involves one extra compounding period when compared to the FV case. You should now appreciate the value of time diagrams in this type of problem. Mistakes are all too easily made without them.

Table 4-2 shows the solution to Example 4-2 using the compound interest formula. As before, the same results can be more easily determined using a formula:

> Simple Ordinary Annuity—Present Value

$$PV = PMT \times \frac{1 - (1 + i_c)^{-n}}{i_c} \qquad (4\text{-}4)$$

where PV = present value at beginning of period 1
  PMT = payment made at the end of each period
  n = number of periods
  i_c = interest rate per compounding period

The answer using the formula is

$$PV = 100 \times \frac{1 - (1.1)^{-3}}{.1}$$

$$= 100 \times 2.486851991$$

$$= \$248.6851991$$

Table 4-2

Year	Discounting periods	Discount factor		Payment		PV
1	1	$1/(1.1)^1$	×	$100	=	$ 90.90909091
2	2	$1/(1.1)^2$	×	100	=	82.6446281
3	3	$1/(1.1)^3$	×	100	=	75.13148009
		Sum of factors = 2.486851991				
			Sum of specific present values		=	$248.6851991

This is exactly the same answer we found using the compound interest formula one year at a time. Again, you should note that the sum of the individual discount factors $[1/(1.1)^{+1} + 1/(1.1)^{+2} + 1/(1.1)^{+3}]$ is equal to the value of

$$A(n,i_c) = \frac{1 - (1 + i_c)^{-n}}{i_c}$$

This latter term can be called the *present-value factor, $A(n,i_c)$*, which represents the present value of \$1 received at the end of each period for n periods discounted at $i_c\%$ per period. The annuity formula for ordinary annuities—PV can be shown as

$$PV = PMT \times A(n,i_c) \qquad (4\text{-}5)$$

The terms $S(n,i_c)$ and $A(n,i_c)$ will be frequently used later in computations relating to other types of annuities.

4-3 EQUIVALENCY OF PV AND FV AMOUNTS IN ORDINARY ANNUITIES

The concept of equivalency introduced in Chapter 3 applies as well to annuities. This can be demonstrated in terms of Examples 4-1 and 4-2 involving simple ordinary annuities.

Time Diagram 4-3a shows both present value as well as the future value of the annuity, as determined in Examples 4-1 and 4-2. The equivalency concept provides that the value of money at any one point of time can be shifted to another point by using the compound interest relationship:

$$FV = PV(1 + i_c)^n \qquad (3\text{-}7)$$

In our example,

$$FV = \$248.6851991 \times (1.1)^3$$

$$= \$331$$

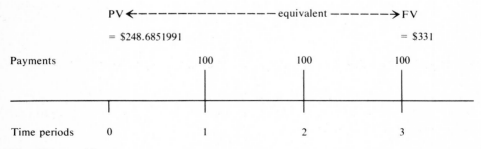

Time Diagram 4-3a

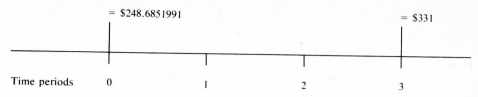

Time Diagram 4-3b

Alternatively, we could calculate

$$PV = \$331 \times (1.1)^{-3}$$

$$= \$248.6851991$$

We can now develop Time Diagram 4-3b, which omits the individual payments but shows the same FV–PV relationship. If either PV or FV of an ordinary annuity is known, the other value can be calculated using the equivalency relationship. In other words, if you know FV you know PV, and vice versa. Note that if

$$FV = PMT \times S(n,i_c)$$

we can also say that

$$PV = (1 + i_c)^{-n} \times PMT \times S(n,i_c)$$

Conversely, if

$$PV = PMT \times A(n,i_c)$$

then we can state

$$FV = (1 + i)^{n} \times PMT \times A(n,i_c)$$

By setting the preceding relationships for FV equal to each other we can determine the equivalency relationship between the factors $S(n,i_c)$ and $A(n,i_c)$:

$$PMT \times S(n,i_c) = (1 + i_c)^{n} \times PMT \times A(n,i_c)$$

Dividing both sides of the equation by PMT gives

$$S(n,i_c) = (1 + i_c)^{n} \times A(n,i_c) \tag{4-6}$$

We will use this relationship in later sections for various annuity calculations.

4-4 SOLVING FOR PMT WITH ORDINARY ANNUITIES

Using the ordinary annuity formulas developed in Secs. 4-1 and 4-2, we can easily solve for the payment (PMT) required. For example, the ordinary annuity–future value formula

$$FV = PMT \times S(n,i_c)$$

can be solved for payment to give

Payment for Ordinary Annuity, FV Given

$$PMT = \frac{FV}{S(n,i_c)} \qquad (4\text{-}7a)$$

Or, using the computational formula for $S(n,i_c)$:

$$PMT = FV \times \frac{i_c}{(1 + i_c)^n - 1} \qquad (4\text{-}7b)$$

The same procedure can be used for ordinary annuities, **PV** given:

Payment for Ordinary Annuity, PV Given

$$PMT = \frac{PV}{A(n,i_c)} \qquad (4\text{-}8a)$$

or

$$PMT = PV \times \frac{i_c}{1 - (1 + i_c)^{-n}} \qquad (4\text{-}8b)$$

Examples 4-3 and 4-4 will demonstrate the use of these formulas.

Example 4-3 A company is establishing a sinking fund to provide for the eventual retirement of a debt issue to accumulate $150,000.† They want to accumulate $150,000 by the end of 5 years. How much must be deposited at the end of each quarter into a savings account that pays 8% per year compounded quarterly?

Since the annual rate is 8% and there are four compounding and payment periods each year,

$$r = .08$$

$$i_c = \frac{r}{c} = \frac{.08}{4} = .02$$

$$n = T \times f$$

$$= 5 \times 4 = 20$$

---

†The term "sinking fund" is commonly used to describe ordinary annuity—FV cases. However, the reader should be aware that situations vary in actual practice and not assume that all sinking funds have payments at the end of each period. The timing of payments and compounding periods should always be checked.

So

$$PMT = \$150,000 \times \frac{1}{S(20,.02)}$$

$$= \$150,000 \times \frac{.02}{(1.02)^{20} - 1}$$

$$= \$150,000 \times .0411567181$$

$$= \$6173.507719$$

The company must deposit \$6173.51 at the end of each quarter to accumulate \$150,000 at the end of the 20th quarter.

Now, let's examine a mortgage loan application.

Example 4-4 Suppose you want to obtain a \$50,000 mortgage on a home you wish to purchase. For a 30-year, 9% mortgage, how much will your monthly payment (of interest plus principal) be?

$$r = .09$$

$$c = 12$$

$$i_c = \frac{.09}{12} = .0075$$

$$n = T \times f$$

$$= 30 \times 12 = 360$$

$$PMT = \$50,000 \times \frac{1}{A(360,.0075)}$$

$$= \$50,000 \times \frac{.0075}{1 - (1.0075)^{-360}}$$

$$= \$50,000 \times .0080462262$$

$$= \$402.3113085$$

Your monthly payment is \$402.31.

Now, suppose you could afford a monthly interest plus principal payment of \$300. How large a mortgage could you obtain? From formula (4-4):

$$PV = PMT \times \frac{1 - (1 + i_c)^{-n}}{i_c}$$

$$= \$300 \times \frac{1 - (1 + .0075)^{-360}}{.0075} = \$300 \times 124.2818657 = \$37,284.56$$

The examples above illustrate how easy it is to solve complex formulas using a calculator rather than tables.

4-5 ORDINARY ANNUITIES—FV, SOLVING FOR *n* AND FINAL PAYMENT

When the number of compounding periods, n, is unknown, the solution becomes a bit more complex. The formula to solve for n with ordinary annuities—FV, shown below, requires the use of logarithms, but the availability of a **ln x** key or **log** key makes calculator solution straightforward. The formulas shown here use the natural log (ln), but log to the base 10 (log) works just as well and can be substituted. Either the **ln** key or the **log** key can be used to obtain the solution.

> Solve for *n*—Ordinary Annuity—FV

$$n = \frac{\ln\left(FV \times \dfrac{i_c}{PMT} + 1\right)}{\ln(1 + i_c)} \qquad (4\text{-}9)$$

Now let's examine an example that requires solving for n in a sinking fund situation.

Example 4-5 A company deposits $10,000 at the end of each month in a savings account paying 6% annually, compounded monthly, in order to accumulate $200,000. (See Time Diagram 4-5.) How many payments are required?

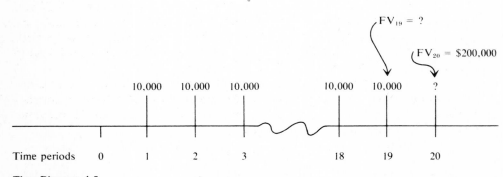

Time Diagram 4-5

Using the ordinary annuity—FV solve-for-n formula, we obtain

$$r = 6\% = .06$$

$$c = 12$$

$$f = 12$$

$$FV = \$200,000$$

$$PMT = \$10,000$$

$$i_c = \frac{.06}{12} = .005$$

$$n = \frac{\ln\left(200,000 \times \dfrac{.005}{10,000} + 1\right)}{\ln(1.005)}$$

$$= \frac{\ln(1.1)}{\ln(1.005)} = \frac{.0953101798}{.0049875415} = 19.10965144$$

Something more than 19 regular payments is required. After 19 regular payments of \$10,000, the future value (FV_{19}) has not built up to the required \$200,000. (Note the FV_{19} = ? on Time Diagram 4-5.) To calculate the future value at the end of the 19th period, we simply apply the ordinary annuity—FV formula:

$$FV_{19} = 10,000 \times S(n,i_c) = 10,000 \times S(19,.005)$$

$$= \$198,797.17$$

The future value, after 19 level payments of \$10,000, is only \$198,797.17 instead of \$200,000; it is short by \$1202.83. Since payments are made only at the end of periods, the short fall must be made up by (1) making an additional (presumably smaller) payment at the end of period 20, or (2) making a larger than usual payment at the end of period 19. These two options will be considered in turn.

Option 1 After 19 level payments of \$10,000, a future value of \$198,797.17 had been accumulated. By the end of the 20th period (when the smaller final payment is made) this FV will have compounded forward one additional period, to an amount $FV_{19}(1 + i_c)$. This amount can then be subtracted from the desired FV (sinking fund) to determine the final payment.

To formalize this procedure for computing the final payment, some additional notation will be useful. We will use the notation $M.X$ to indicate fractional periods when solving for the number of payments. From the previous example the 19.109 would be shown as

$$19.109 = M.X$$

where M = 19 and X = .109, the fractional period.

You should note that even if your calculator has special routines or keys to solve for n, i_c, PMT, PV, and FV, the final payment will not be automatically determined. It must be computed using the procedure above for calculators with or without financial function keys. This procedure can be summarized as follows:

1. Calculate n (the amount $M.X$) as shown previously.
2. Calculate the future value at the end of period M.
3. Compound the future value at the end of period M forward one period.
4. Subtract the amount computed in step 3 from the desired FV at the end of the last period.

Let's apply this procedure to our previous example. Because step 1 was previously performed, the solution below starts with step 2.

Step 2:

$$\text{Future value end of period } 19 = \$10,000 \times S(19,.005)$$

$$= \$10,000 \times \frac{(1.005)^{19} - 1}{.005}$$

$$FV_{19} = \$198,797.1685$$

Step 3: Compound FV_{19} forward to period 20.

$$FV_{19}(1 + i) = 198,797.1685 \times (1.005)$$

$$= \$199,791.1543$$

Step 4: Compute final payment.

$$\text{Final payment} = \$200,000 - \$199,791.1543$$

$$= \$208.8456575$$

The final payment is $208.85. While calculators with special function keys can perform this calculation very quickly, even a regular calculator with y^x and **ln x** keys can solve it in a few keystrokes.

The procedure can also be summarized in a formula as follows:

> Final Payment—Ordinary Annuity—FV

$$\text{Amount of final payment} = FV - [PMT \times S(M,i_c)] \times (1 + i_c) \qquad (4\text{-}10)$$

where FV = desired future value at end of period n
  PMT = regular periodic payments
  i_c = interest rate per compounding period
  n = number of payments
  M = last period for full payment

Option 2 This option involved simply increasing the amount of the 19th payment so that the full $200,000 sinking fund required is available at the end of the 19th period. Actually, this amount is already known; we simply increase the last payment of $10,000 by the short fall $200,000 − $198,791.17 = $1202.83. The company would make 18 equal payments of $10,000 each followed by a 19th and final payment of $11,202.83.

4-6 ORDINARY ANNUITIES—PV, SOLVING FOR *n* AND FINAL PAYMENT

Formulas may also be developed to solve for the number of payments and the final payment for the ordinary annuity—PV situation. The formula for the number of payments is

---

Number of Payments—Ordinary Annuity—PV

$$n = \frac{-\ln\left(1 - PV \times \dfrac{i_c}{PMT}\right)}{\ln(1 + i_c)} \qquad (4\text{-}11)$$

Example 4-6 and its solution illustrate the use of the formula and the procedure required to determine the amount of the final payment.

Example 4-6 A company is planning to borrow $750,000 to be repaid in monthly payments of $15,000 at an annual interest rate of 9%, compounded monthly. How many regular monthly payments must be made, and what is the amount of the final payment at the end of the last month?

$$PV = \$750,000$$

$$PMT = \$15,000$$

$$r = 9\%$$

$$c = 12$$

$$f = 12$$

$$i_c = \frac{.09}{12} = .0075$$

$$n = \frac{-\ln\left(1 - \$750,000 \times \dfrac{.0075}{15,000}\right)}{\ln(1.0075)}$$

$$= 62.90185972$$

Again, the answer provides for a fractional period and a resulting partial payment. Of course, if the PV, PMT, and $i_c\%$ are given, the number of periods rarely will be an exact integer. To determine the final payment (which is less than the regular $15,000 monthly payment) in this ordinary annuity—PV situation, we follow the same basic procedure as for the FV case. Time Diagram 4-6 shows the basic cash flow situation. The diagram shows that only the final payment, to be made at the end of period 63, is unknown. The PV for 62 periods (PV_{62}) is indicated with ?, because the difference between it and the present value of $750,000 is the amount of the debt remaining unpaid after the 62 payments. This amount is then compounded forward to the end of the 63rd period to determine the final payment amount. To summarize, solving for the final payment requires the following steps:

Step 1: Determine the fractional number of payments $M.X$.

Step 2: Compute the PV of M payments.

Step 3: Subtract the PV of M payments from the original PV amount to determine the present value of the last payment.

Step 4: Compound the present value of the final payment forward $M + 1$ periods to determine the last payment amount.

The computation of the final payment for Example 4-6 is shown below beginning with step 2 because step 1 was previously performed.

$$M.X = 62.9018$$

$$M = 62$$

$$M + 1 = 63$$

Step 2: **PV of M payments**

$$PV_{62} = 15,000(A(62,.0075))$$

$$= 15,000 \times \frac{1 - (1.0075)^{-62}}{.0075}$$

$$= \$741,548.1682$$

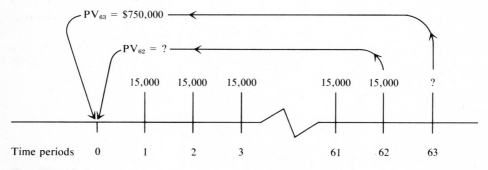

Time Diagram 4-6

Step 3: PV of last payment

$$\text{PV last payment} = 750{,}000 - 741{,}548.1682$$

$$= \$8451.831792$$

Step 4: Final payment

$$\text{Final payment} = 8451.831792(1.0075)^{63}$$

$$= \$13{,}532.85094$$

The final payment is \$13,532.85 to be made at the end of period 63. This procedure can be condensed into the formula shown below:

> Final Payment—Ordinary Annuity—PV

$$\text{Final payment} = [\text{PV} - \text{PMT} \times A(M,i_c)] \times (1 + i_c)^{M+1} \qquad (4\text{-}12)$$

Note that by using this general procedure, loan schedules can be easily prepared for situations where the loan amount, payment, and interest rate are specified without resorting to tables or elaborate schedules. The examples at the end of the chapter show this procedure for calculators having financial keys.

4-7 SOLVING FOR i_c—ORDINARY ANNUITIES—FV

Solving for the interest rate, i_c, as the unknown in a simple annuity situation, is fundamentally different from solving for the other variables. Whereas the basic annuity equation can be rearranged and solved for each of the three variables FV, PMT, and n, it is not possible to explicitly solve this equation in terms of i_c. Therefore, i_c can only be determined by *trial and error*.

The procedure used is an *iteration* routine, in which repeated trials are made until the desired level of accuracy is achieved. If extreme accuracy is not needed, the time (or the number of key strokes) required to solve for i_c is not excessive. If a good initial "guess" is made for the value of i_c, time and keystroke requirements are further minimized.

Formulas are given below for (1) the initial guess that should be used as a starting point, and (2) the increment that should be deducted from the previous estimate of i_c to obtain the new, revised estimate.

Again and again, a revised increment should be determined from the last estimate of i_c to obtain an improved estimate. The key formulas given below, Eqs. (4-14a) and (4-14b), are explained in more detail in Appendix 6B.

The starting point is an initial guess for i_c†:

$$i_0 = \frac{\text{FV}}{\text{PMT} \times n^2} - \frac{\text{PMT}}{\text{FV}} \qquad (4\text{-}13)$$

†The formula for initial guess is taken from *Texas Instruments Slide Rule Calculator, SR-56: Applications Library,* Dallas, Texas, 1976, p. 96.

(Note that the subscript c on i has been omitted. So i_0 simply means the zeroth estimate of i_c.)

The increment to subtract from the intermediate estimate i_k is

$$\Delta i_k = \frac{(1 + i_k)^n - 1 - \dfrac{FV \times i_k}{PMT}}{n(1 + i_k)^{n-1} + \dfrac{1 - (1 + i_k)^n}{i_k}} \tag{4-14a}$$

and the improved estimate i_{k+1} is obtained from

$$i_{k+1} = i_k - \Delta i_k \tag{4-14b}$$

So the iterative process involves repeated use of Eqs. (4-14a) and (4-14b) with the expectation that each revised estimate will come closer and closer to the desired answer for i_c.

This approach allows you to get a quick estimate and in many cases a very accurate answer in three or four iterations of Eq. (4-14b). Because most calculators with **y^x** and **ln** or **log** keys have one or more memories, the intermediate calculations can be stored in memory for further calculations, thus saving considerable effort. We will use the notation R_1, R_2, R_3, and so on, to indicate a value stored in memory. For example, the notation $(R_1)^4$ means: recall the value in memory 1 and raise it to the fourth power, using the **y^x** key. The solution to the example below will show the abbreviated memory notation as well as the actual values in the formulas.

Example 4-7 Suppose you have been offered an investment opportunity in which you invest $1200 at the end of each year for 10 years. At the end of this time you receive a sum of $17,800. What is the rate of return (interest rate) in this situation?

The first step is to compute the initial guess for i_c, which is then used in the formula for the adjustment, Δi_c. This $-\Delta i_c$ is added to the original i_c and the procedure repeated for a new Δi_c. The value of Δi_c at each step indicates the accuracy of the answer; the smaller Δi_c, the more accurate the answer.

Step 1: Initial approximation for i_c:

$$i_0 = \frac{\$17,800}{\$1200(10)(10)} - \frac{\$1200}{\$17,800} \qquad \text{from Eq. (4-13)}$$

$$= .080917603$$

If your calculator has memories, store this result in memory 1, (R_1).

Step 2: Solve for Δi:

$$\Delta i_0 = \frac{(1.080917603)^{10} - 1 - \dfrac{17,800}{1200}(.080917603)}{10(1.080917603)^9 + \dfrac{1 - (1.080917603)^{10}}{.080917603}} \qquad \text{from Eq. (4-14)}$$

Before solving the formula, note that most of the numbers are 1.080917603 or .080917603, which are $1 + i$ and i, respectively. If your calculator has two memories, then $(1 + i)$ can be stored in memory 2 (remember that i is in memory 1), reducing the formula to the form below:

$$\Delta i_0 = \frac{(R_2)^{10} - 1 - \dfrac{17,800}{1200}(R_1)}{10(R_2)^9 + \dfrac{1 - (R_2)^{10}}{R_1}}$$

Of course, if your calculator has more than two memories, you could also store the value FV/PMT (17,800/1200). Carrying out the calculations, we obtain

$$\Delta i_0 = \frac{-.0229395637}{5.593584052}$$

$$= -.0041010492$$

Step 3: Calculate new i_c (in this case, i_1):

$$i_1 = .080917603 - (-.0041010492)$$

$$= .0850186522$$

The procedure could stop at this point. The first adjustment factor, .0041010492, contains no nonzero digits in the first two places to the right of the decimal, which means that the new answer, .0850186522, is accurate to one and perhaps two decimal places. If that level of accuracy were satisfactory, we could stop after one iteration. Here, for purposes of illustration, we will repeat the process until a more accurate answer is obtained.

Repeating steps 2 and 3 for the second iteration:

$$i_2 = i_{1_2} - \Delta i_2$$

$$= .0850186522 - \frac{(1.0850186522)^{10} - 1 - \dfrac{17,800}{1200}(.0850186522)}{10(1.0850186522)^9 + \dfrac{1 - (1.0850186522)^{10}}{.0850186522}}$$

or, in memory notation,

$$i_2 = R_1 - \frac{(R_2)^{10} - 1 - \dfrac{17,800}{1200}(R_1)}{10(R_2)^9 + \dfrac{1 - (R_2)^{10}}{R_1}}$$

$$= .0850186522 - \frac{.0002621495}{6.005364643}$$

$$= .0850186522 - .0000436526$$

$$= .0849749997$$

The second iteration gives an estimate of i_c which is accurate to approximately four places.

Again repeating steps 2 and 3 for a third iteration:

$$i_3 = .0849749997 - \frac{(1.0849749997)^{10} - 1 - \dfrac{17,800}{1200}(.0849749997)}{10(1.0849749997)^9 + \dfrac{1 - (1.0849749997)^{10}}{.0849749997}}$$

$$= .0849749997 - \frac{.0000000301}{6.000902365}$$

$$= .0849749997 - .000000005$$

$$= .0849749947$$

The third iteration gives an answer to approximately eight places. This would certainly be sufficient accuracy for almost any application, but the fourth iteration is shown below for illustration:

$$i_4 = .0849749947 - \frac{(1.084974995)^{10} - 1 - \dfrac{17,800}{1200}(.0849749947)}{10(1.084974995)^9 + \dfrac{1 - (1.084974995)^{10}}{.0849749947}}$$

$$= .0849749947 - \frac{0}{6.000901852}$$

$$= .0849749947$$

The final answer using this iteration routine is 8.49749947%. Since the Δi_c has become zero, further iterations are not possible. (You may get slightly different answers, depending on the number of digits with which your calculator operates. This example was worked using a calculator which operates with 14 digits.) The next step is to check your answer by computing the future value using the ordinary annuity—FV formula.

Step 4: Check the answer.

$$FV = PMT \frac{(1 + i)^n - 1}{i}$$

$$= 1200 \times \frac{(1.0849749947)^{10} - 1}{.0849749947}$$

$$= \$17,799.9998$$

Rounded to the nearest cent, the FV is

$$FV = 17,800.00$$

The answer is off by .0002 dollar, or accurate to three places. The return on the investment opportunity in Example 4-7 is approximately 8.4975%.

Using the memory keys in the calculations of Δi enables you to calculate an accurate yield more quickly than you could calculate an approximate answer using conventional tables and interpolation techniques. Thus you are freed from tables when a calculator with y^x and **ln x** keys is available (especially if it has two or more memories) or a Level II or III calculator which solves directly for the interest rate.

To test your understanding of this iteration method, you should work the problems at the end of the chapter.

4-8 SOLVING FOR i_c—ORDINARY ANNUITIES—PV

Solving for i_c ordinary annuities—PV uses the same procedure as in Section 4-7 except that the formulas are different. Because the procedures are similar, the solution to Example 4-8 is shown without the intermediate calculations after the first iteration. The formulas are:

Initial approximation of i_c†:

$$i_0 = \frac{PMT}{PV} - \frac{PV}{PMT \times n^2}$$ (4-15)

The increment to be deducted:

$$\Delta i_k = \frac{1 - (1 + i_k)^{-n} - \dfrac{PV}{PMT} \times i_k}{n(1 + i_k)^{-n-1} + \dfrac{(i + i_k)^{-n} - 1}{i_k}}$$ (4-16)

Revised value for i_c:

$$i_{k+1} = i_k - \Delta i_k$$

Example 4-8 A company is evaluating a project which returns $2500 at the end of each month for 60 months. The project requires an $82,000 investment at the beginning of the first period. What is this project's yield?

Step 1: Compute the initial approximation for i.

$$i_0 = \frac{2500}{82,000} - \frac{82,000}{2500(60)(60)}$$

$$= .0304878049 - .0091111111$$

$$= .0213766938$$

†Ibid., p. 82.

Step 2: Compute Δi.

$$\Delta i_1 = \frac{1 - (1.0213766938)^{-60} - \dfrac{82,000}{2500}(.0213766938)}{60(1.0213766938)^{-61} + \dfrac{1.0213766938^{-60} - 1}{.0213766938}}$$

Storing the i and $(1 + i)$ values in memories 1 and 2 gives

$$\Delta i_1 = \frac{1 - R_2^{-60} - \dfrac{82,000}{2500}(R_1)}{60R_2^{-61} + \dfrac{R_2^{-60} - 1}{R_1}}$$

As shown in the previous section, using memories speeds up computations and reduces errors because you don't reenter the new i and $(1 + i)$ values. Furthermore, if your calculator has more than two memories, all the values can be stored and recalled when necessary.

Returning to the example, the Δi is

$$\Delta i_1 = -.0010372397$$

Step 3: Compute the revised i_c.

$$i_1 = .0213766938 - (-.0013072397)$$

$$= .0224139335$$

Repeating steps 2 and 3 for i_2:

$$\Delta i_2 = -.0000197758$$

$$i_2 = .0224139335 - (-.0000197758)$$

$$= .0224337093$$

Solving for i_3:

$$\Delta i_2 = -.000000007$$

$$i_3 = .0224337093 + .000000007$$

$$= .0224337163$$

Solving for i_4:

$$\Delta i_3 = -4 \times 10^{-13}$$

$$i_4 = .0224337163 + 4 \times 10^{-13}$$

$$= .0224337163$$

Iteration 4 gives the final answer; the return per month is 2.24337163%. Now check your answer.

Step 4: Compute PV to verify interest rate.

$$PV = PMT \frac{1 - (1 + i_c)^{-n}}{i}$$

$$= 2500 \frac{1 - (1.0224337163)^{-60}}{.0224337163}$$

$$= \$81,999.99944$$

Our answer is .00056 dollar off the present value of $82,000. Rounding it to two decimal places gives $82,000.00.

Now that we are satisfied with our answer, the annual yield is computed. Because the number of compounding periods per year is equal to 12, the annual rate is

$$\text{Annual rate } r = 12(.0224337163)$$

$$= .2692045956$$

As a percent, the rate of return on the proposed project is 26.92045956%.

Ordinary Annuities—Summary

The preceding sections have discussed ordinary annuities which are identified by two characteristics: (1) the payment occurring at the end of the period, and (2) equal payments. You have learned how to solve for each of the five variables—n, $\%i$, PMT, PV, and FV. Because simple annuities assume that payments made or received occur at the end of each period, payments occur at the same time as compounding. This means that when determining FV, the last payment is not compounded, so there is one more payment period than compounding period. When determining PV, the number of payment periods equals the number of compounding periods.

SIMPLE ANNUITIES DUE

4-9 ANNUITIES DUE—FV_d

As contrasted to ordinary annuities, where payments occur at the end of each period, *annuities due* have payments made or received at the beginning of each period. A *simple* annuity due has the number of compounding periods per year equal to the number of payment periods per year.

As you'll see, an important difference between an ordinary annuity and an annuity due is the number of compounding periods. This is best illustrated by an actual example. Example 4-9 below is identical to Example 4-1 except that we are computing the FV of a simple annuity due instead of an ordinary annuity.

Example 4-9 If you invest $100 at the *beginning* of each year for 3 years compounded at 10%, how much will be on deposit at the end of 3 years?

You could, of course, solve this problem by the straightforward methods of Chapter 3. This computation, carried out in Table 4-3, shows the FV_d of the annuity due, $364.10. However, this result could also be obtained by building on our earlier result. Examine Time Diagram 4-9, which shows the distinction between an annuity due and an ordinary annuity for the same problem. Note that the compounding occurs at the end of each period and three payments are made in both cases, although the timing of the payments and the number of compounding periods are different. For this annuity-due situation, payments are made at the beginning of each period with three compounding periods. The first payment is compounded three times; the second payment is compounded two times, and the third is compounded one time. In the case of the ordinary annuity, the first payment is compounded only two times, the second one time, and the third payment is not compounded at all. Thus, for the FV case the annuity due has one more compounding period. The FV symbol on the diagrams is the future value of the ordinary annuity; FV_d is the future value of the annuity due.

Since the ordinary annuity has two compounding periods and the annuity due has three compounding periods, we can take the FV of an ordinary annuity and compound it forward one period to determine the FV of an annuity due.

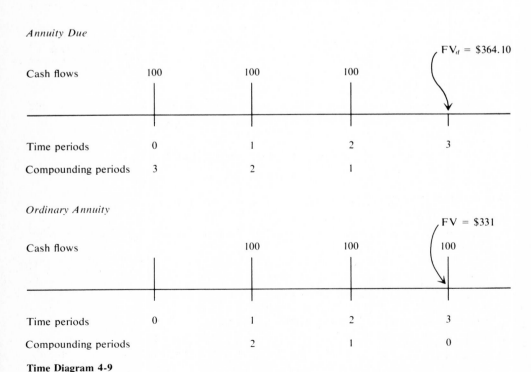

Annuity Due

				FV_d = $364.10
Cash flows	100	100	100	
Time periods	0	1	2	3
Compounding periods	3	2	1	

Ordinary Annuity

				FV = $331
Cash flows		100	100	100
Time periods	0	1	2	3
Compounding periods		2	1	0

Time Diagram 4-9

Table 4-3

Year	Compounding periods	Interest factor		Payment		FV$_d$
1	3	$(1.1)^3$	$\times$	$100	=	$133.1
2	2	$(1.1)^2$	$\times$	100	=	121
3	1	$(1.1)^1$	$\times$	100	=	110
	Sum of factors = 3.641					
			Sum of specific future values		=	$364.10

We'll adopt the symbol FV$_d$ to indicate the future value of an annuity due, leaving the term FV to indicate the future value of an ordinary annuity. Recall that the FV for Example 4-1 is $331. Thus FV$_d$ is obtained by compounding the FV forward by $(1 + i)$:

$$FV_d = FV(1 + i_c)$$

$$= \$331(1.1)$$

$$= \$364.10$$

This is the same result as obtained in Table 4-3.

Remember that the FV of an ordinary annuity is PMT $\times$ $S(n,i)$. So a formula for FV$_d$ can be given as

> FV$_d$ of an Annuity Due

$$FV_d = PMT \times (1 + i_c) \times S(n,i)$$

or

$$FV_d = PMT(1 + i_c)\left[\frac{(1 + i_c)^n - 1}{i_c}\right] \qquad (4\text{-}17)$$

Note that no new terms are involved here except for FV$_d$.

4-10 ANNUITIES DUE—PV$_d$

The present value of an annuity due, PV$_d$, is found using a relationship similar to the one developed in Sec. 4-9.

> PV$_d$ of an Annuity Due

$$PV_d = (1 + i_c)PV$$

$$= (1 + i_c)(PMT)A(n,i_c)$$

$$= (1 + i_c)(PMT)\left[\frac{1 - (1 + i_c)^{-n}}{i_c}\right] \qquad (4\text{-}18)$$

The logic underlying this formula can be explained by referring to Example 4-10, which is the same as Example 4-2 except that payments occur at the beginning of each period.

Example 4-10 If you received $100 at the *beginning* of each year for 3 years, what is the present value assuming that the payments are discounted at an annual rate of 10%?

Time Diagram 4-10 shows the diagram for both an annuity due and an ordinary annuity.

Examination of the two diagrams shows that the difference in PV is again caused by the number of compounding periods, which is different due to the timing of the payments. In fact, if we stopped discounting the ordinary annuity at the end of its first period, the number of payments and compounding periods would be identical to the annuity due situation. Therefore, the PV of an ordinary annuity can be compounded forward one period to convert it to the PV_d of an annuity due. From Example 4-2 we obtained PV = $248.6851991, which times $(1 + i_c)$ compounds to $273.553719.

Annuity Due

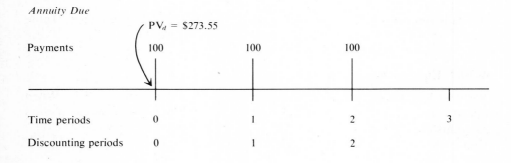

Ordinary Annuity

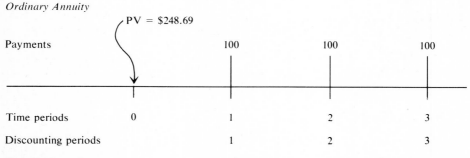

Time Diagram 4-10

Table 4-4

Year	Discounting periods	Discount factor		Payment		PV_d
1	0	$(1/(1.1)^0)$	×	$100	=	$100
2	1	$(1/(1.1)^1)$	×	100	=	90.90909091
3	2	$(1/(1.1)^2)$	×	100	=	82.6446281
	Sum of factors = 2.73553719					
			Sum of specific present values		=	$273.553719

Using the formula, we obtain

$$PV_d = 100 \times (1.1) \times \frac{1 - (1.1)^{-3}}{.1}$$

$$= (1.1)(100)(2.486851991)$$

$$= (1.1)(248.6851991)$$

$$= \$273.553719$$

This answer is also identical to that found by a direct approach, Table 4-4.

4-10.1 Equivalence of PV_d and FV_d

PV_d and FV_d have an equivalent relationship, just as did PV and FV. When one is known, the other can be calculated given i_c and n, using the compound relationship $FV_d = PV_d(1 + i_c)^n$. The logic underlying this equivalent relationship is the same as for ordinary annuities.

4-11 SOLVING FOR THE PAYMENT OF AN ANNUITY DUE

Solving for the payment of an annuity due requires only solving Eqs. (4-17) and (4-18) for PMT. The formulas for the FV_d and PV_d cases are shown below:

> PMT of an Annuity Due—FV_d Case

$$PMT = \frac{FV_d}{(1 + i) \times S(n,i_c)}$$

$$= \frac{FV_d(i_c)}{(1 + i_c) \times [(1 + i_c)^n - 1]} \tag{4-19}$$

PMT of an Annuity Due—PV_d case

$$PMT = \frac{PV_d}{(1 + i_c) \times A(n,i_c)}$$

$$= \frac{PV_d(i_c)}{(1 + i_c)[1 - (1 + i)^{-n}]} \qquad (4\text{-}20)$$

The two formulas are illustrated below.

Example 4-11 The CB Company is considering the purchase of a machine for $85,000. The manufacturer of the machine has also offered to lease the machine under an agreement where the present value of the equal monthly payments discounted at 12% annually, compounded monthly, is $85,000. If the payments are made at the start of each month for the life of the lease, 8 years, what is the amount of each payment?

The total number of payments and compounding periods is $8 \times 12 = 96$. The annual rate of 12% annual is converted to a monthly rate of 1%.

$$c = 12$$

$$n = 8 \times 12 = 96$$

$$i_c = \frac{r}{c}$$

$$= \frac{.12}{12} = .01$$

$$PV_d = \$85,000$$

$$PMT = \frac{\$85,000}{(1.01)A(96,.01)} \qquad \text{from Eq. (4-20)}$$

$$= \frac{85,000(.01)}{(1.01)[1 - (1.01)^{-96}]}$$

$$= \$1367.813387$$

Thus, payments of $1367.81 are necessary under the proposed lease agreement.

Example 4-12 The ABC company wants to accumulate $100,000 in a fund earning 8% annually, but compounded quarterly, over the next 2 years. What payment made at the beginning of each quarter is necessary to accumulate the desired amount?

$$n = 2 \times 4 = 8$$

$$i_c = \frac{r}{c}$$

$$= \frac{.08}{4}$$

$$= .02$$

$$FV_d = \$100,000$$

$$PMT = \frac{\$100,000}{(1.02)\,S(8,.02)} \qquad \text{from Eq. (4-19)}$$

$$= \frac{\$100,000(.02)}{(1.02)[(1.02)^8 - 1]}$$

$$= \$11,422.52933$$

To accumulate the $100,000, then, $11,422.53 must be deposited at the beginning of each quarter.†

4-12 SOLVING FOR THE NUMBER OF PAYMENTS AND THE AMOUNT OF THE FINAL PAYMENT—FV$_d$ CASE

The formula necessary to solve for the number of payments for an annuity due—FV$_d$ case is

> Solve for n—Annuity Due—FV$_d$

$$n = \frac{\ln\left[(1 + i_c) + \dfrac{FV_d}{PMT}(i_c) \right]}{\ln(1 + i_c)} - 1 \qquad (4\text{-}21)$$

The use of this formula often results in a fractional answer such as 5.3 periods, which means five payments of the specified amount and a sixth partial payment made one period after the last regular payment (or added to the last payment). For the annuities due—FV$_d$ case, the partial payment to be made one period later is

$$\text{Final partial payment} = FV_d(1 + i_c)^{-1} - [PMT(1 + i_c)\,S(M,i_c)] \qquad (4\text{-}22)$$

†Note that the payment is rounded to the nearest penny. When a large number of payment periods are involved, this rounding can cause minor differences in the PV or FV. In the example above, the FV$_d$ with payments of $11,422.52 is $99,999.91835 as compared to the FV$_d$ with payments of $11,422.53, which is $100,000.0059, for a difference of .08755. This usually is unimportant but it can explain minor differences in amounts you obtain when checking calculations.

where M is the number of regular payments. The computational formula is

$$\text{Final partial payment} = FV_d(1 + i_c)^{-1} - \left[PMT(1 + i_c)\frac{(1 + i)^M - 1}{i} \right] \quad (4\text{-}23)$$

Example 4-13 illustrates the solution using these formulas.

Example 4-13 A company is planning on depositing $12,000 a quarter until $75,000 is accumulated. How many deposits are necessary at the beginning of each quarter with an annual rate of 6%, and what is the final payment?

Step 1: Solve for the number of payments.

$$PMT = \$12,000$$

$$FV_d = \$75,000$$

$$i_c = \frac{r}{c}$$

$$= \frac{.06}{4}$$

$$= .015$$

$$n = \frac{\ln\left[(1.015) + \frac{\$75,000}{\$12,000}(.015) \right]}{\ln (1.015)} - 1$$

$$= \frac{\ln(1.10875)}{\ln(1.015)} - 1$$

$$= 5.93370552$$

To accumulate $75,000 the company must make 5.93370552 payments of $12,000. But because .93370552 payment cannot be made, six payments will be made. The final payment at the start of the sixth period is:

Step 2: Compute final payment, using Eq. (4-23).

$$M = 5$$

$$i_c = .015$$

$$PMT = \$12,000$$

$$FV_d = \$75,000$$

$$\text{Final payment} = 75,000(1.015)^{-1} - [12,000(1.015)S(5,.015)]$$

$$= 75,000(1.015)^{-1} - \left[12,000(1.015)\frac{(1.015)^5 - 1}{.015} \right]$$

$$= \$11,137.01447$$

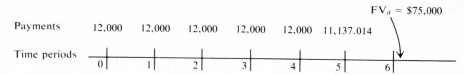

Time Diagram 4-13

A final payment of $11,137.01 at the beginning of the sixth period is necessary to have $75,000 at the end of the sixth period.

Notice the timing of the payments and compounding periods in Time Diagram 4-13. After five payments the future value at the end of period 5 is $62,754.6115, but we want a future value of $75,000 at the end of period 6. We must make a payment at the beginning of period 6 which, added to the FV of $62,754.61115, will compound to $75,000. The payment necessary is the difference between the present value of $75,000 at the beginning of period 6 and the FV_d of the deposits at that time.

FV_d of 75,000 discounted one period

$(1.015)^{-1}(75,000)$ $= \$73,891.62562$

Less FV_d of payments
after five periods   <u>62,754.61115</u>

Partial payment   <u>$\$11,137.01447$†</u>

Proof: Compounding the FV_d at the beginning of period 5 plus the final payment one period further:

$$(62,754.6115 + 11,137.01437)(1.015) = \$75,000.00026$$

4-13 SOLVING FOR THE NUMBER OF PAYMENTS AND THE AMOUNT OF THE FINAL PAYMENT FOR AN ANNUITY DUE—PV_d

The formula to determine the number of payments for an annuity due—PV_d case is

Solving for n—Annuity Due—PV_d

$$n = 1 - \frac{\ln\left[(1 + i_c) - \dfrac{PV_d}{PMT}i_c\right]}{\ln(1 + i_c)} \tag{4-24}$$

†If the final payment amount had been included with the last of the five equal payments (one period earlier), the required amount would have been

$$\$11,137.01437/(1 + i_c) = \$10,972.43$$

Since n is seldom an integer, the final payment must generally be computed as

$$\text{Final partial payment} = (1 + i_c)^M[PV_d - PMT(1 + i)A(M,i_c)] \quad (4\text{-}25)$$

The computational formula is

$$\text{Final partial payment} = PV_d(1 + i_c)^M$$

$$- PMT\left[\frac{(1 + i_c)^{M+1} - (1 + i_c)}{i_c}\right] \quad (4\text{-}26)$$

Example 4-14 demonstrates the use of these formulas.

Example 4-14 A company borrows $150,000 at 8.5% compounded semi-annually with $35,000 semiannual payments. How many payments must be made to repay the loan, and what is the amount of the final payment? Payments are made at the *beginning* of the period.

$$PV_d = \$150,000$$

$$PMT = \$35,000$$

$$c = f = 2$$

$$i_c = \frac{r}{c} = \frac{.085}{2} = .0425$$

$$n = 1 - \frac{\ln\left[1.0425 - \frac{150,000}{35,000}(.0425)\right]}{\ln(1.0425)} \quad \text{from Eq. (4-24)}$$

$$= 4.613686731$$

The loan will require four regular payments of $35,000 and a final payment of a partial amount. Solving for the final payment in Eq. (4-26) and using $M = 4$,

$$\text{Final payment} = 150,000(1.0425)^4 - 35,000\left[\frac{(1.0425)^5 - (1.0425)}{.0425}\right]$$

$$= \$21,651.44$$

Again, you should examine Time Diagram 4-14. PV_d is the loan amount and the present value of five payments. PV_d' ($n = 4$) is the present value of four $35,000 payments. The difference between the two values is the present value of the last payment. Knowing its present value enables us to compute the equivalent value at the beginning of the fifth period. The final payment is equal to

$$(150,000 - 131,669.15)(1 + i_c)^M = 18,330.85(1.0425)^4 = \$21,651.44$$

as calculated above.

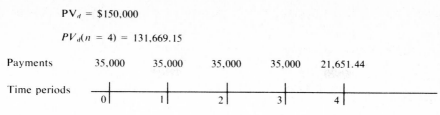

$PV_d = \$150,000$

$PV_d(n = 4) = 131,669.15$

| Payments | 35,000 | 35,000 | 35,000 | 35,000 | 21,651.44 |

| Time periods | | | | | |

0   1   2   3   4

Time Diagram 4-14

4-14 SOLVING FOR i_c—ANNUITY DUE—FV_d

Solving for the unknown interest rate i_c requires the use of the iteration procedure described below. As with ordinary annuities, you should first solve for an initial value and then use an iteration formula to solve for i_c, usually obtaining a satisfactory answer after three or four iterations. (A less accurate answer can usually be found with one or two iterations.)

To determine initial i_c:

$$i_0 = \frac{FV_d}{PMT(n)(n)} - \frac{PMT}{FV_d} \tag{4-27}$$

To determine Δi_k for the kth iteration:

$$\Delta i_k = \frac{(1 + i)[(1 + i)^n - 1] - \dfrac{FV_d}{PMT} \times i}{(n + 1)(1 + i)^n + (1 + i)\left[\dfrac{(1 - (1 + i)^n}{i}\right] - 1} \tag{4-28}$$

To determine new i_{k+1}:

$$i_{k+1} = i_k - \Delta i_k$$

Repeat this procedure until i_{k+1} is equal to i_k, within the desired accuracy.

Remember, if your calculator has one or more memories, this formula can be more easily solved—the formula with i stored in memory 1 and $(1 + i)$ stored in memory 2 is

$$\Delta i_k = \frac{R_2[(R_2)^n - 1] - \dfrac{FV_d}{PMT}(R_1)}{(n + 1)(R_2)^n + R_2\left[\dfrac{1 - (R_2)^n}{R_1}\right] - 1}$$

Now, let's solve a problem using this procedure.

Example 4-15 A company is considering an investment that requires five annual payments of $10,000 at the beginning of each year, for which it will receive a total return of $64,196.65 at the end of the fifth year. What is the return on this investment?

Step 1: Solve for initial i_c.

$$i_0 = \frac{64,196.65}{(10,000)(5)(5)} - \frac{10,000}{64,196.65} = .1010152319$$

Step 2: Solve for Δi_1.

$$\Delta i_0 = \frac{(1.1010152319)[(1.1010152319)^5 - 1] - \dfrac{64,196.65}{10,000}(.1010152319)}{6(1.1010152319)^5 + (1.1010152319)\left[\dfrac{(1 - 1.010152319^5)}{.010152319}\right] - 1}$$

$$= .0161711113$$

Step 3: Solve for i_1.

$$i_1 = .1010152319 - .0161711113$$

$$= .0848441206$$

Repeating steps 2 and 3 for three more iterations:

$$i_2 = .084500127$$

$$i_3 = .0844999747$$

$$i_4 = .0844999747$$

The answer stabilizes with i_4. Computing the FV_d with this interest rate gives

$$FV_d = 10,000(1.084499947)\left[\frac{1.0844999747^5 - 1}{.0844999747}\right]$$

$$= \$64,196.65$$

The FV_d calculated agrees with the stated FV_d; thus the return on this investment is 8.45% (rounded to two decimal places).

4-15 SOLVING FOR i—ANNUITY DUE—PV_d

Solving for i_c given PV_d requires the use of the iteration procedure shown below:

Initial value for i_c:

$$i_0 = \frac{PMT}{PV_d} - \frac{PV_d}{PMT(n)(n)} \tag{4-29}$$

$$\Delta i_k = \frac{(1 + i_c) - (1 + i_c)^{1-n} - \dfrac{PV_d}{PMT}(i_c)}{1 + (n - 1)(1 + i_c)^{-n} + (1 + i_c)\left[\dfrac{(1 + i_c)^{-n} - 1}{i_c}\right]}$$ (4-30)

and

$$i_{k+1} = i_k - \Delta i_k$$

Using two memories for i and $(1 + i)$:

$$\Delta i_k = \frac{R_2 - (R_2)^{1-n} - \dfrac{PV_d}{PMT}(R_1)}{1 + (n - 1)R_2^{-n} + (R_2)\left(\dfrac{R_2^{-n} - 1}{R_1}\right)}$$

Now let's solve an example using these formulas.

Example 4-16 The ABC Company is leasing an asset to the XYZ Company. The lease is for 9 years with $15,000 payments being made at the beginning of each year. The current value of the machine is $82,000. What is the yield of this lease to the ABC Company?

Step 1: Solve for i_0.

$$i_0 = \frac{15,000}{82,000} - \frac{82,000}{15,000(9)(9)}$$

$$= .1154371173$$

Step 2: Compute Δi_0.

$$\Delta i_0 = \frac{(1.1154371173) - (1.1154371173)^{-8} - \dfrac{82,000}{15,000}(.1154371173)}{1 + (8)(1.1154371173)^{-9} + (1.1154371173)\left(\dfrac{1.1154371173^{-9} - 1}{.1154371173}\right)}$$

$$= -.0326470072$$

Step 3: Compute i_1.

$$i_1 = .1154371173 - (-.032647002)$$

$$= .1480841245$$

Repeating steps 2 and 3 until the answer stabilizes gives

$$i_2 = .1513760318$$

$$i_3 = .1514050763$$

$$i_4 = .1514050785$$

$$i_5 = .1514050785$$

The interest rate stabilizes after the fifth iteration. Computing the PV_d with this rate gives

$$PV_d = 15{,}000(1.1514050785)\left(\frac{1 - 1.1514050785^{-9}}{.1514050785}\right) \qquad \text{from Eq. (4-18)}$$

$$= \$82{,}000$$

The lease earns 15.14% (rounded to two places).

4-15.1 Annuities Due—Summary

An annuity due is identified by the timing of the payments at the beginning of the period. Where payments are equal and occur at the beginning of the period (with compounding at the end of the period), a simple annuity due is indicated.

In the preceding sections, procedures and formulas for solving for PV_d, FV_d, n, i_c, and PMT for annuities due were presented. The formulas are constructed to facilitate solution by Level I calculators with y^x and **ln x** keys and one or more memories. Calculators with financial function keys can solve for the values directly, and programs are available for programmable calculators which emulate these financial keys.

4-16 GENERAL RELATIONSHIP BETWEEN ORDINARY ANNUITIES AND ANNUITIES DUE

There is an important general relationship between ordinary annuities and annuities due which will allow us to unify all the preceding equations presented in this chapter into one general formula. The following terms will be used in explaining this relationship.

n = number of periods

i_c = interest rate compounded at the end of each period

PMT = payment made each period

V_K = FV, PV, FV_d, or PV_d of the annuity

K = a factor defined to convert the generalized formula into specific cases

We'll begin by restating the four key equations of this chapter and reviewing their relationships in Time Diagram 4-15.

1. *Ordinary Annuity—FV*

$$FV = PMT \times S(n,i_c) \tag{4-3}$$

Ordinary Annuity—FV

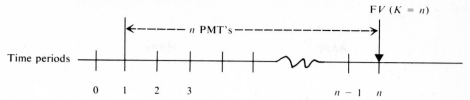

Ordinary Annuity—PV

PV $(K = 0)$

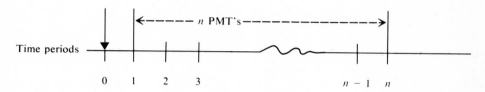

Annuity Due—FV$_d$

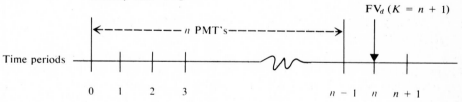

Annuity Due—PV$_d$

PV$_d$ $(K = 1)$

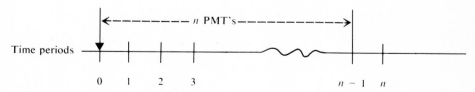

Time Diagram 4-15

The n payments of the amount PMT occur at the end of the time periods and the future value, FV, is located at the end of the nth period.

   2. *Ordinary annuity—PV*

$$PV = PMT \times A(n,i_c) \qquad (4\text{-}5)$$

The n payments of the amount PMT also fall at the end of the time periods and the present value, PV, is evaluated at the beginning of the first time period.

   3. *Annuity due—FV$_d$*

$$FV_d = PMT \times (1 + i_c) \times S(n,i_c) \qquad (4\text{-}17)$$

The n payments of size PMT fall at the beginning of the time periods, but the future value, FV$_d$, is still evaluated at the end of the nth time period.

   4. *Annuity due—PV$_d$*

$$PV_d = PMT \times (1 + i_c) \times A(n,i_c) \qquad (4\text{-}18)$$

The n payments for annuity due occur at the beginning of the periods and the present value, PV$_d$, is evaluated at the beginning of the 1st time period.

4-16.1 The General Formula

In presenting the generalized formula, the relationship between $S(n,i_c)$ and $A(n,i_c)$ will be utilized:

$$S(n,i_c) = (1 + i_c)^n \times A(n,i_c) \qquad (4\text{-}6)$$

   Equation (4-6) permits us to express all four relationships in terms of $S(n,i_c)$:

$$FV_d = (1 + i_c)^1 \times PMT \times S(n,i_c) \qquad (4\text{-}31)$$

$$PV_d = (1 + i_c)^{1-n} \times PMT \times S(n,i_c) \qquad (4\text{-}32)$$

$$FV = (1 + i)^0 \times PMT \times S(n,i_c) \qquad (4\text{-}33)$$

$$PV = (1 + i)^{-n} \times PMT \times S(n,i_c) \qquad (4\text{-}34)$$

   An examination of the four key equations above indicates that they differ only in the exponent of $(1 + i_c)$. We can express all four annuity cases by the following general formula:

$$\boxed{V_K = (1 + i)^{K-n} \times PMT \times S(n,i_c)} \qquad (4\text{-}35)$$

The generalized formula of Eq. (4-35) can be used as follows:

Any of the four cases can be identified and used by the proper selection of the numerical value for K. For instance, if we let $K = n + 1$, we have selected the annuity due—FV$_d$ case, where

$$V_K = V_{n+1} = V(K = n + 1) = (1 + i_c)^1 \times PMT \times S(n,i_c)$$

This format is used for all four cases in Time Diagram 4-15, where V_K represents all the present-value and future-value cases.

The following table presents the assignment of K for the specific cases:

Annuity type	K assignment
Ordinary annuity—FV	$K = n$
Ordinary annuity—PV	$K = 0$
Annuity due —FV_a	$K = n + 1$
Annuity due —PV_a	$K = 1$

These same K assignments are indicated on Time Diagram 4-15. We now have a generalized formula for simple annuities, which is quite useful for programs on a computer or programmable calculator. This one formula can also be used to solve for the PMT, n, or i_c as well as for the values indicated above. However, some additional attention must be given to the calculation procedure when solving for i_c.

4-16.2 Solving for i_c

The objective here is to develop one iterative formula to solve for i_c which will be based upon the generalized formula, Eq. (4-35). The calculation procedure is broken down into the following steps.

Step 1: Rearrange Eq. (4-35) to introduce $f(i)$:

$$f(i) = (1 + i)^K \times [1 - (1 + i)^{-n}] - \frac{V_K \times i}{\text{PMT}} \tag{4-36}$$

(Note that the subscript c has been dropped from i.)

Step 2: Obtain the function $f'(i)$:

$$f'(i) = (n - k) \times (1 + i)^{(K-n-1)} + k(1 + i)^{K-1} + (1 + i)^K \left[\frac{(1 + i)^{-n} - 1}{i} \right] \tag{4-37}$$

[The symbol $f'(i)$, which stands for the derivative of $f(i)$, is explained more fully in Appendix 6A.]

Step 3: Make use of the iterative procedure already discussed in this chapter.

$$i_{k+1} = i_k - \Delta i_k \tag{4-38}$$

where

$$\Delta i_k = \frac{f(i)}{f'(i)} \tag{4-39}$$

Step 4: Obtain an initial value for i.

No new formulas will be given to help select an initial value. One practical approach would be to use one of the formulas already given in the text, such as Eq. (4-13) or (4-15). Another practical approach would be to select an arbitrary value, exercising care to select a value larger than -1 and a value other than zero.

APPENDIX 4A DERIVATION OF FORMULA FOR ORDINARY ANNUITY, FV

In Sec. 4-1 the concept of ordinary annuities was introduced and the following equation was presented:

$$FV = PMT \left[\frac{(1 + i_c)^n - 1}{i_c} \right] \tag{4A-1}$$

This formula will be developed in more detail in this appendix and then reused in later chapters.

We know that for the ordinary annuity case the n payments of current PMT all occur at the end of the periods. The future value cumulated for all n payments must be

$$FV = PMT(1 + i_c)^{n-1} + PMT(1 + i_c)^{n-2} + \cdots + PMT(1 + i_c)^{n-n} \tag{4A-2}$$

Rearranging the terms in the reverse order, we have

$$FV = PMT[(1 + i_c)^0 + (1 + i_c)^1 + \cdots + (1 + i_c)^{n-1}] \tag{4A-3}$$

This is a finite series of the geometric type where the sum is known, as demonstrated in the following section. It is

$$FV = PMT \left[\frac{(1 + i_c)^n - 1}{(1 + i_c) - 1} \right] \tag{4A-4}$$

which, of course, reduces to formula (4A-1).

4A-1 DEMONSTRATION: FINITE GEOMETRIC SERIES

A demonstration will show that the series in brackets of Eq. (4A-3) is the same as the quantity in the brackets of (4A-4). Let

$$V = d^0 + d^1 + d^2 + \cdots + d^{n-1} \tag{4A-5}$$

where d has been substituted for $1 + i_c$. So V is really the same as the quantity in the brackets of Eq. (4A-3), and

$$d \cdot V = d^1 + d^2 + \cdots + d^{n-1} + d^n \tag{4A-6}$$

will be utilized next. Subtracting Eq. (4A-6) from (4A-5) gives

$$V - dV = d^0 - d^n \qquad (4A\text{-}7)$$

or
$$V(1 - d) = 1 - d^n \qquad (4A\text{-}8)$$

Solving for V:

$$V = \frac{1 - d^n}{1 - d} = \frac{d^n - 1}{d - 1} \qquad (4A\text{-}9)$$

Now use $1 + i_c$ for d and we get

$$V = \frac{(1 + i_c)^n - 1}{(1 + i_c) - 1} = \frac{(1 + i_c)^n - 1}{i_c} \qquad (4A\text{-}10)$$

which is indeed the same as the quantity inside the brackets of Eq. (4A-4).

KEYSTROKE SOLUTIONS

This section contains keystroke solutions for selected examples in this chapter. These solutions are organized by *type* of calculator (Type A or Type R) and within each type by *level* (Level I, II, or III).

Type	Level	Example Number	Page
A	I	4-2, 4-8, 4-14	80, 95, 106
	II	4-2, 4-6, 4-8, 4-14	80, 89, 95, 106
	III	4-2, 4-6, 4-8, 4-14	80, 89, 95, 106
R	I	4-2, 4-8, 4-14	80, 95, 106
	II	4-2, 4-6, 4-8, 4-14	80, 89, 95, 106
	III	4-2, 4-6, 4-8, 4-14	80, 89, 95, 106

Type A, Level I keystrokes for Example 4-2

TI-30/50 keystrokes	Display	Comments
C	0.	Clear
100	100.	PMT
×	100.	
(	100.	
1	1.	
−	1.	
1.1	1.1	$1 + i$
y^x	1.1	
3	3.	n
+/−	−3.	$-n$
)	0.2486852	$A(n,i)$
÷	0.2486852	
.1	0.1	
=	248.6852	PV

Type A, Level I keystrokes for Example 4-8

TI-30/50 keystrokes	Display	Comments
C	0.	Step 1—clear
2500	2500.	PMT
÷	2500.	
82000	82000.	PV
−	0.0304878	
82000	82000.	PV
÷	82000.	
2500	2500.	PMT
÷	32.8	
60	60.	n
÷	.54666667	
60	60.	
=	.02137669	i_0
+	.02137669	
1	1.	$1 + i_0$
=	1.0213767	
STO	1.0213767	STO $1 + i_0$ in memory
		Step 2
1	1.	
−	1.	
RCL	1.0213767	$1 + i$
y^x	1.0213767	
60	60.	n
+/−	−60.	$-n$
−	.71891133	
82000	82000.	PV
÷	82000.	
2500	2500.	PMT
×	32.8	
(	32.8	
RCL	1.0213767	$1 + i$
1	1.0213767	
	1.	

TI-30/50 keystrokes	Display	Comments
)	.02137669	
=	.01775577	
÷	.01775577	
(	.01775577	
60	60.	n
×	60.	
RCL	1.0213767	$1 + i$
y^x	1.0213767	
61	61.	$n + 1$
+/−	−61.	$-(n + 1)$
+	16.512341	
(	16.512341	
RCL	1.0213767	$1 + i$
y^x	1.0213767	
60	60.	n
+/−	−60.	$-n$
−	−.28108867	
1	1.	
)	−.71891133	
÷	−.71891133	
(	−.71891133	
RCL	1.0213767	$1 + i$
−	1.0213767	
1	1.	
)	.02137669	
=	−.00103724	Δi
+/−	.00103724	
SUM	.00103724	
RCL	1.0224139	$1 + i_1$

Repeat step 2 until i stabilizes.

$1 + i_2 = 1.0224337$
$1 + i_3 = 1.0224337$

Type A, Level I keystrokes for Example 4-14

TI-30/50 keystrokes	Display	Comments
C		Clear
1.0425	1.0425	$1 + i$
−	1.0425	
150000	150000.	PV
÷	150000.	
35000	35000.	PMT
×	4.2857143	
.0425	0.0425	i
=	.86035714	
ln x	−.15040769	
÷	−.15040769	
1.0425	1.0425	$1 + i$
ln x	.04162168	
=	−3.6136866	
+/−	3.6136866	
+	3.6136866	
1	1.	
=	4.6136866	n $(M.X)$
150000	150000.	PV

TI-30/50 keystrokes	Display	Comments
×	150000.	
1.0425	1.0425	$1 + i$
y^x	1.0425	
4	4.	M
−	177172.17	
35000	35000.	PMT
×	35000.	
(	35000.	
(	35000.	
1.0425	1.0425	$1 + i$
y^x	1.0425	
5	5.	n
−	1.2313466	
1.0425	1.0425	$1 + i$
)	.18884661	
÷	.18884661	
.0425	0.0425	i
)	4.4434498	
=	21651.433	Final payment

Type A, Level II keystrokes for Example 4-2

TI-MBA/BA-II keystrokes	Display	Comments
CA	0	Clear
3	3	n
N	3.	
10	10	$i\%$
%i	10.	
100	100	PMT
PMT	100.	
CPT		
PV	248.6851991	PV

Type A, Level II keystrokes for Example 4-6

TI-MBA/BA-II keystrokes	Display	Comments
CA	0	Clear
9	9	r
÷	9.	
12	12	c
=	0.75	
%i	0.75	i
15000	15000	PMT
PMT	15000.	
750000	750000	
PV	750000.	PV
CPT	750000.	
N	62.90185959	$M.X$
62	62	M
N	62.	
CPT	62.	
PV	741548.1695	PMT $A(M,i)$
+/-	-741548.1695	
+	-741548.1695	
750000	750000	PV
=	8451.83051	PV of partial payment
PV	8451.83051	PV – PMT $A(M,i)$
0	0	Zero out PMT
PMT	0.	
63	63	$M + 1$
N	63.	
CPT	63.	
FV	13532.84891	Final payment

Type A, Level II keystrokes for Example 4-8

TI-MBA/BA-II keystrokes	Display	Comments
CA	0	Clear
60	60	n
N	60.	
2500	2500	PMT
PMT	2500.	
82000	82000	PV
PV	82000.	
CPT	82000.	
%i	2.24371629	i_c

Type A, Level II keystrokes for Example 4-14

TI-MBA/BA-II keystrokes	Display	Comments
CA	0	Clear
8.5	8.5	r
÷	8.5	
2	2	c
=	4.25	$i\%$
%i	4.25	
35000	35000	
PMT	35000.	PMT
150000	150000	
PV	150000.	PV_d
DUE	150000.	
N	4.613686731	$M.X$
4	4	M
N	4.	
DUE		
PV	1316669.1547	$PMT(1+i)A(M,i)$
+/-	-1316669.1547	
+	-1316669.1547	
150000	150000	PV_d
=	18330.84528	PV of partial payment
PV	18330.84528	$PV_d - PMT(1+i)A(m,i)$
0	0	
PMT	0.	Zero out PMT
CPT	0.	
FV	21651.43804	Final payment

Type A, Level III keystrokes for Example 4-2

TI-58/59 keystrokes	Display	Comments
Pgm 19	0.	Call ML-19
E'	0.	Initialize
C'	0.	Select PV case
3	3	
A	3.	n
10	10	
B	10.0000	i%
100	100	
C	100.00	PMT
0	0	
D	248.69	PV

Type A, Level III keystrokes for Example 4-6

TI-58/59 keystrokes	Display	Comments
Pgm 19	0.	Call ML-19
E'	0.	Initialize
C'	0.	Select PV case
9	9	r
÷	9.	
12	12	c
=	0.75	
B	0.7500	i%
15000	15000	
C	15000.00	PMT
750000	750000.	PV
D	750000.	
0	0	
A	62.90185972	$M.X$
62	62	
A	62.	M
0	0	
D	741548.17	$PMT\,A(M,i)A(m,i)$
+/-	-741548.17	
+	-741548.17	
750000	750000	Present value of last payment
=	8451.83	
Pgm 18	8451.83	Call ML-18
E'	8451.83	Initialize
C	8451.83	Enter PV of last payment
63	63	
A	63.00	$M + 1$
0	0	
D	13532.85	Final payment

Type A, Level III keystrokes for Example 4-8

TI-58/59 keystrokes	Display	Comments
PGM 19	0.	Call ML-19
E'	0.	Initialize
C'	0.	Select PV case
60	60	
A	60.	n
2500	2500	
C	2500.00	PMT
82000	82000	
D	82000.00	PV
0	0	
B	2.2434	$i\%$

Type R, Level I keystrokes for Example 4-2

HP-31E/32E keystrokes	Display	Comments
ALL	0.0000	Clear
100	100.	PMT
ENTER↑	100.0000	
1	1.	
ENTER↑	1.0000	
1.1	1.1	$1 + i$
ENTER↑	1.1000	
3	3.	n
CHS	-3.	$-n$
y^x	0.7513	
-	0.2487	
×	24.8685	
.1	0.1	
÷	248.6852	PV

Type A, Level III keystrokes for Example 4-14

TI-58/59 keystrokes	Display	Comments
Pgm 19	0.	Call ML-19
E'	0.	Initialize
D'	0.	Select PV_d case
8.5	8.5	$r\%$
÷	8.5	
2	2	c
=	4.25	
B	4.2500	$i\%$
35000	35000	
C	35000.00	PMT
150000	150000	
D	150000.00	PV_d
0	0	
A	4.613686731	$M.X$
4	4.	
A	4.	M
0	0	
D	131669.15	PV_d of four regular payments
+/-	-131669.15	
+	-131669.15	PV_d
150000	150000	
=	18330.85	PV of last payment
Pgm 18	18330.85	Call ML-18
E'	18330.85	Initialize
C	18330.85	PV
0	0	
D	21651.44	Final payment

Type R Level I keystrokes for Example 4-8

HP-31E/32E keystrokes	Display	Comments
ALL	0.0000	Start step 1
		Clear
2500	2,500.	PMT
ENTER↑	2,500.0000	
82000	82,000.	PV
÷	0.0305	
82000	82,000.	PV
ENTER↑	82,000.0000	
2500	2,500.	PMT
÷	32.8000	PV/PMT stored in R_3
STO 3	32.8000	
60	60.	n
÷	0.5467	
60	60.	n
÷	0.0091	
-	0.0214	Initial guess i_c
STO 1	0.0214	STO i_c in R_1
1	1.	Start step 2
+	1.0214	$1 + i_c$
STO 2	1.0214	STO $1 + i_c$ in R_2
1	1.	
ENTER↑	1.0000	
RCL 2	1.0214	
60	60.	
CHS	-60.	$-n$
y^x	0.2811	
-	0.7189	
RCL 3	32.8000	PV/PMT
ENTER↑	32.8000	
RCL 1	0.0214	i_c
×	0.7012	

HP-31E/32E keystrokes	Display	Comments
-	0.0178	Top term
STO 4	0.0178	
RCL 2	1.0214	$1 + i_c$
60	60.	$-n$
CHS	60.	
y^x	0.2811	
1	1.	
-	-0.7189	
RCL 1	0.0214	i_c
÷	-33.6306	
60	60.	n
ENTER↑	60.0000	
RCL 2	1.0214	$1 + i_c$
61	61.	
CHS	-61.	$-n - 1$
y^x	0.2752	
×	16.5123	
+	-17.1183	
1/x	-0.0584	Bottom term
RCL 4	0.0178	
×	-0.0010	Δi
CHS	0.0010	$-\Delta i$
STO +1	0.0010	Sum to i_0
STO +2	0.0010	Sum to $1 + i_0$
RCL 1	0.024	RCL i_1

Repeat Step 2 until i stabilizes.

$i_2 = 0.02243710$
$i_3 = 0.02243717$
$i_4 = 0.02243717$

Type R, Level I keystrokes for Example 4-14

HP-31E/32E keystrokes	Display	Comments	HP-31E/32E keystrokes	Display	Comments
ALL	0.0000	Clear	(f)4	4.6137	
1.0425	1.0425	$1 + i_c$	1.0425	1.0425	$1 + i_c$
ENTER↑	1.0425		ENTER↑	1.0425	
150000	150,000	PV	5	5.	$M + 1$
ENTER↑	150,000.0000		y^x	1.2313	
35000	35,000	PMT	1.0425	1.0425	$1 + i_c$
÷	4.2857		−	0.1888	
.0425	0.0425	i_c	.0425	0.0425	i_c
×	0.1821		÷	4.4434	
−	0.8604		35000	35,000	PMT
LN	−0.1504		×	155,520.7360	
1.0425	1.0425		CHS	−155,520.7360	
LN	0.0416		1.0425	1.0425	$1 + i_c$
÷	−3.6137		ENTER↑	1.0425	
CHS	3.6137		4	4.	M
1	1.		y^x	1.1811	
+	4.6137		150000	150,000.	PV
(f)9	4.613686732	$n(M·X)$	×	177,172.1738	
			+	21,651.4378	Final partial payment

Type R, Level II keystrokes for Example 4-2

HP-37E/38E keystrokes	Display	Comments
END	0.00	Set payment switch to end
FIN	0.00	Clear financial registers
3	3.	
n	3.00	n
10	10.	
i	10.00	$i\%$
100	100.	
PMT	100.00	PMT
PV	−248.69	PV

Type R, Level II keystrokes for Example 4-6

HP-37E/38E keystrokes	Display	Comments
END	0.00	Set payment switch to end
FIN	0.00	Clear financial registers
9	9.	$r\%$
12 ÷	0.75	$i\%$
15000	15,000.	
PMT	15,000.00	PMT
750000	750,000.	
CHS	−750,000.	
PV	−750,000.00	PV
n	62.90	$M \cdot X$
62	62.	
n	62.00	M
PV	−741,548.17	$A(M,i)\text{PMT}$
750000	750,000.	PV
+	8,451.83	$PV \cdot fM$ payments
CHS	−8,451.83	
PV	−8,451.83	PV of M payments
0	0.	Zero out
PMT	0.00	PMT
63	63.	
n	63.00	$M + 1$
FV	13,532.85	Final payment

Type R, Level II keystrokes for Example 4-8

HP-37E/38E keystrokes	Display	Comments
END	0.00	Set payment switch to end
FIN	0.00	Clear financial registers
60	60.	
n	60.00	n
2500	2,500.	
PMT	2,500.00	PMT
82000	82,000.	
CHS	-82,000.	
PV	-82,000.00	PV
i	2.24	I%

Type R, Level II keystrokes for Example 4-14

HP-37E/38E keystrokes	Display	Comments
BEGIN	0.00	Set payment switch to BEGIN
FIN	0.00	Clear financial registers
8.5	8.5	r%
ENTER↑	8.50	
2	2.	
÷	4.25	i%
i	4.25	i%
35000	35,000.	
PMT	35,000.00	PMT
150000	150,000.	
CHS	-150,000.	
PV	-150,000.00	PV
n	4.61	M.X
4	4.	
n	4.00	n
PV	-13,1669.15	PV of M payments
150000	150,000.	
+	18,330.85	PV of last payment
CHS	-18,330.85	
PV	-18,330.85	PV
0	0.	Zero out
PMT	0.00	PMT
FV	21,651.44	Final payment

Type R, Level III keystrokes for Example 4-2

HP-97/67 keystrokes	Display	Comments
fA	0.00	Program SD-05A
3	3.	Start function
STO A	3.00	n
10	10.	
STO B	10.00	$i\%$
100	100.	
STO C	100.00	PMT
D	248.69	PV

Type R, Level III keystrokes for Example 4-6

HP-97/67 keystrokes	Display	Comments
fA	0.00	Program SD-05A
9	9.	Start function
ENTER↑	9.00	r
12	12.	c
÷	0.75	$i\%$
STO B	0.75	Enter $i\%$
15000	15000.	
STO C	15000.00	Enter PMT
750000	750000.	
STO D	750000.00	Enter PV
A	62.90	$M.X$
62	62.	
STO A	62.00	
D	741548.17	$\mathrm{PMT} \times A(M,i)$
CHS	−741548.17	
750000	750000.	
+	8451.83	Present value of last payment
STO D	8451.83	
0	0.	
STO C	0.00	
63	63.	
STO A	63.00	$M + 1$
E	13532.85	Final payment

Type R, Level III keystrokes for Example 4-14

HP-97/67 keystrokes	Display	Comments
fA	0.00	Program SD-05A
fB	1.00	Start function
8.5	8.5	Select annuity due
ENTER↑	8.50	
2	2.	c
÷	4.25	
STO B	4.25	$i\%$
35000	35000.	
STO C	35000.00	PMT
150000	150000.	
STO D	150000.00	PV_d
A	4.61	$M.X$
4	4.	
STO A	4.00	M
D	131669.15	PV_d for four regular payments
CHS	131669.15	
150000	150000.	PV_d
+	18330.85	
STO D	18330.85	PV
0 STO C	0.	Prepare for single payment calculation
E	21651.44	Final payment

Type R, Level III keystrokes for Example 4-8

HP-97/67 keystrokes	Display	Comments
fA	0.00	Program SD-05A
60	60.	Start function
STO A	60.00	n
2500	2500.	PMT
STO C	2500.00	
82000	82000.	
STO D	82000.00	PV
B	2.24	$i\%$

EXERCISES

Drill on Equations

4-1 Given: $n = 7$, $i\% = 5\%$, PMT = \$176
Find: FV, PV, FV$_d$, PV$_d$
answers: **FV = \$1432.99; PV = \$1018.40; FV$_d$ = \$1504.64; PV$_d$ = \$1069.32**

4-2 Given: $n = 19$, $i = 7.344\%$, PMT = \$345.65
Find: FV, PV, FV$_d$, PV$_d$

4-3 Given: $T = 5$, $f = 6$, $c = 6$, $r = 13.78\%$, PMT = \$5426.83
Find: FV, PV, FV$_d$, PV$_d$
answers: **FV = \$230,682.44; PV = \$116,726.66; FV$_d$ = \$235,980.45; PV$_d$ = \$119,407.48**

4-4 Given: T = $8\frac{1}{2}$, $f = 12$, $c = 12$, $r = 19.45\%$, PMT = \$1247.39
Find: FV, PV, FV$_d$, PV$_d$

4-5 Given: $n = 25$, $i\% = 4\%$, PV = \$31,465.86
Find: PMT
answer: **PMT = \$2014.19**

4-6 Given: $n = 42$, $i\% = 3.4\%$, PV = \$8431.56
Find: PMT

4-7 Given: $n = 36$, $i\% = .5\%$, PV$_d$ = \$453.85
Find: PMT
answer: **PMT = \$13.74**

4-8 Given: $n = 49$, $i\% = 1.7\%$, PV$_d$ = \$5124.85
Find: PMT

4-9 Given: $T = 24$, $r\% = 15$, $f = 6$, $c = 6$, PV = \$24,183.62
Find: PMT
answer: **PMT = \$622.37**

4-10 Given: $T = 30$, $r\% = 9.75\%$, $f = 12$, $c = 12$, PV = \$65,000
Find: PMT

4-11 Given: $T = 25$, $r\% = 13.8\%$, $f = 4$, $c = 4$, PV$_d$ = \$85,000
Find: PMT
answer: **PMT = \$2933.40**

4-12 Given: $T = 19$, $r\% = 14.33\%$, $f = 3$, $c = 3$, PV$_d$ = \$49,455.85
Find: PMT

4-13 Given: $n = 33$, PMT = \$155.42, PV = \$1117
Find: $\%i$
answer: **%i = 13.7138%**

4-14 Given: $n = 43$, PMT = \$2400, PV = \$102,073
Find: $\%i$

4-15 Given: $n = 28$, PMT = \$1256, PV$_d$ = \$21,180
Find: $\%i$
answer: **%i = 4.2604%**

4-16 Given: $n = 240$, PMT = \$1487.56, PV$_d$ = \$118,286.97
Find: $\%i$

4-17 Given: $T = 7$, $f = 12$, $c = 12$, PMT = \$1,655.13, PV = \$113,865.18
Find: $r\%$
answer: **r% = 5.8482%**

4-18 Given: $T = 13$, $f = 12$, $c = 12$, PMT = \$685, PV = \$75,095
Find: $r\%$

4-19 Given: $T = 3$, $f = 12$, $c = 12$, PMT = $20,485, PV = $600,000
Find: $r\%$
answer: **$r\%$ = 13.9259%**

4-20 Given: $T = 4.25$, $f = 4$, $c = 4$, PMT = $13,450, PV = $200,500
Find: $r\%$

4-21 Given: $T = 4$, $f = 12$, $c = 12$, PMT = $1500, PV_d = $62,398.23
Find: $r\%$
answer: **$r\%$ = 7.5235%**

4-22 Given: $T = 6.5$, $f = 12$, $c = 12$, PMT = $421.85, PV_d = $20,868.92
Find: $r\%$

4-23 Given: $n = 134$, $i\% = .0421\%$, FV = $100,000
Find: Payment
answer: **PMT = $725.574**

4-24 Given: $n = 223$, $i\% = .684\%$, FV = $84,250
Find: PMT

4-25 Given: $n = 91$, $i\% = 2.4\%$, FV_d = $133,425
Find: PMT
answer: **PMT = $408.48**

4-26 Given: $n = 163$, $i\% = .9\%$, FV_d = $45,000
Find: PMT

4-27 Given: $T = 21$, $c = 12$, $f = 12$, $r\% = 7.5\%$, FV = $15,000
Find: PMT
answer: **PMT = $24.625**

4-28 Given: $T = 25$, $c = 3$, $f = 3$, $r\% = 10\%$, FV = $41,543
Find: PMT

4-29 Given: $T = 14$, $c = 6$, $f = 6$, $r\% = 5\%$, FV_d = $21,500
Find: PMT
answer: **PMT = $176.290**

4-30 Given: $T = 25$, $c = 12$, $f = 12$, $r\% = 7.5\%$, FV_d = $250,000
Find: PMT

4-31 Given: $n = 19$, PMT = $425, FV = $35,863.32
Find: $\%i$
answer: **$\%i$ = 14.6000%**

4-32 Given: $n = 84$, PMT = $125, FV = $13,499.87
Find: $\%i$

4-33 Given: $n = 28$, PMT = $1425, FV_d = $42,299.72
Find: $\%i$
answer: **$\%i$ = .4000%**

4-34 Given: $n = 72$, PMT = $645, FV_d = $136,110.98
Find: $\%i$

4-35 Given: $T = 6$, $f = 12$, $c = 12$, PMT = $55, FV = $4070
Find: $r\%$
answer: **$r\%$ = .9222%**

4-36 Given: $T = 10$, $f = 12$, $c = 12$, PMT = $100, FV = $23,003.87
Find: $r\%$

4-37 Given: $T = 3$, $f = 3$, $c = 3$, PMT = $3300, FV_d = $33,300
Find: $r\%$
answer: **$r\%$ = 6.8398%**

4-38 Given: $T = 8$, $f = 12$, $c = 12$, PMT = $989, FV_d = $127,528.23
Find: $r\%$

4-39 Given: PMT = \$1425, i_c = .84%, PV = \$28,500
Find: (*a*) *n*
(*b*) number of whole payments and amount of last payment
answers: (*a*) **21.987**; (*b*) **21, \$1407.13**

4-40 Given: PMT = \$384, i_c = .73%, PV = \$50,000
Find: (*a*) *n*
(*b*) number of whole payments and amount of last payment

4-41 Given: PMT = \$1240, i_c = 1.15%, PV_d = \$79,469
Find: (*a*) *n*
(*b*) number of whole payments and amount of last payment
answers: (*a*) **114.066**; (*b*) **114, \$82.75**

4-42 Given: PMT = \$2463, i_c = .96%, PV_d = \$64,650
Find: (*a*) *n*
(*b*) number of whole payments and amount of last payment

4-43 Given: PMT = \$750, i_c = .5625%, FV = \$11,500
Find: (*a*) *n*
(*b*) number of whole payments and amount of last payment
answers: (*a*) **14.749**; (*b*) **14, \$546.05**

4-44 Given: PMT = \$1250, i_c = .48%, FV = \$80,000
Find: (*a*) *n*
(*b*) number of whole payments and amount of last payment

4-45 Given: PMT = \$50, i_c = .523%, FV_d = \$3750
Find: (*a*) *n*
(*b*) number of whole payments and amount of last payment
answers: (*a*) **63.158**; (*b*) **62, \$60.93**

4-46 Given: PMT = \$850, i_c = .486%, FV_d = \$50,000
Find: (*a*) *n*
(*b*) number of whole payments and amount of last payment

4-47 Given: PMT = \$1900, f = 12, c = 12, $r\%$ = 19%, PV = \$100,000
Find: (*a*) *n* and *T*
(*b*) number of whole payments and amount of last payment
answers: (*a*) ***n* = 114.057, *T* = 9.5**; (*b*) **114, \$109.66**

4-48 Given: PMT = \$175, f = 12, c = 12, $r\%$ = 11.5%, PV = \$7950
Find: (*a*) *n* and *T*
(*b*) number of whole payments and amount of last payment

4-49 Given: PMT = \$1850, f = 6, c = 6, $r\%$ = 17%, PV_d = \$35,000
Find: (*a*) *n* and *T*
(*b*) number of whole payments and amount of last payment
answers: (*a*) ***n* = 26.365, *T* = 4.394**; (*b*) **26, \$680.61**

4-50 Given: PMT = \$275, f = 12, c = 12, $r\%$ = 13.8%, PV_d = \$12,584
Find: (*a*) *n* and *T*
(*b*) number of whole payments and amount of last payment

4-51 Given: PMT = \$560, f = 12, c = 12, $r\%$ = 6.77%, FV = \$50,000
Find: (*a*) *n* and *T*
(*b*) number of whole payments and amount of last payment
answers: (*a*) ***n* = 72.51, *T* = 6.04**; (*b*) **72, \$150.15**

4-52 Given: PMT = \$900, f = 6, c = 6, $r\%$ = 5.65%, FV = \$35,500
Find: (*a*) *n* and *T*
(*b*) number of whole payments and amount of last payment

4-53 Given: PMT = \$90, f = 12, c = 12, $r\%$ = 6.3%, FV_d = \$6500
Find: (*a*) *n* and *T*

(*b*) number of whole payments and amount of last payment
answers: (*a*) **n = 61.12, T = 5.09**; (*b*) **61, $18.99**

4-54 Given: PMT = $150, *f* = 3, *c* = 3, *r*% = 7.4%, FV$_d$ = $10,000
Find: (*a*) *n* and *T*
(*b*) number of whole payments and amount of last payment

Application Problems

4-55 A company plans to deposit $15,000 each month in a savings account paying $5\frac{3}{4}$% annual compounded monthly. How much will be in the account after the last payment if
(*a*) 24 end-of-month payments are made?
(*b*) 47 end-of-month payments are made?
(*c*) 19 beginning-of-month payments are made?
(*d*) 58 beginning-of-month payments are made?
answers: (*a*) **$380,552.44**; (*b*) **$788,588.23**; (*c*) **$299,056.99**; (*d*) **$1,004,966.69**
What is the effective annual interest rate for each of the four options above?
answer: **5.90398% for all four cases**

4-56 If you deposit $100 each quarter in a savings account paying 6.2% annual compounded quarterly, what amount will be in the account after
(*a*) 13 end-of-period deposits?
(*b*) 27 end-of-period deposits?
(*c*) 21 beginning-of-period deposits?
(*d*) 68 beginning-of-period deposits?
What is the effective annual interest rate for each of the four options above?

4-57 A firm is evaluating a machine that has a 6-year life and a zero salvage value. The after tax cash flows are $50,000 to acquire the machine and projected yearly savings are $11,500. The company requires a 17% return on projects of this sort.
(*a*) What is the present value of the cash savings?
(*b*) What is the net present value of this project [answer to part (*a*) less $50,000]?
(*c*) What interest rate will make the present value of the savings equal to the $50,000 outlay cost?
answers: (*a*) **$41,275.62**; (*b*) **−$8,724.38**; (*c*) **10.05833%**

4-58 You want to establish an annuity that pays $350 per month for 10 years. Assuming an annual interest rate of 5.7%, how much should be deposited if
(*a*) payments are at the end of the month?
(*b*) payments are at the beginning of the month?
(*c*) If you can purchase the annuity for $33,100, what is the return per month, the nominal annual rate, and the effective annual rate?

4-59 A company wants to lease a machine from you for 6 years. The machine has a current market value of $65,000 but will be worthless at the end of the sixth year. The company has offerred semiannual lease payments of $7500. Assuming you want to earn 12% annual on the lease, what is the present value for two options:
(*a*) beginning-of-period payments?
(*b*) end-of-period payments?
(*c*) What is the return or interest rate for parts (*a*) and (*b*)?
(*d*) If you accept the lease, what option, (*a*) or (*b*), would you select?
answers: (*a*) **66,651.56**; (*b*) **62,878.83**; (*c*) **13.1156%, 10.7999%**; (*d*) **Select option** (*a*)

4-60 You are buying a mortgage as an investment. The monthly payments are $275.23 with 128 end-of-month payments remaining. What is the maximum price you can pay and earn at least 9.4% annual?

4-61 Your rich uncle has died and left you an inheritance, but you must make a choice. You can either receive $200 at the end of each month for 10 years, or you can receive $50,000 at the end of the 10 years. Assuming your maximum investment opportunity is $6\frac{1}{2}\%$ annual compounded monthly, which alternative should you select?

answer: **$50,000 at end of 10 years**

4-62 Your firm's accountants tell you that the equipment you are leasing must be "capitalized," that is, recorded in your books as an asset at an amount equal to the present value of the $895 monthly lease payments made at the beginning of each month. There are 87 payments remaining. What is the present value of the lease assuming an 8% annual compounded monthly rate?

4-63 You are borrowing $65,000 to buy your new house. Assuming a $9\frac{5}{8}\%$ annual interest rate compounded monthly, what is the amount of each end of month payment? Assume that the mortgage will be repaid at the end of 30 years.

answer: **$564.4266**

4-64 You are leasing a truck worth $35,000 to a company for 6 years. The salvage value of the truck will be zero at the end of the sixth year. You want to earn 14.5% annual compounded monthly on the lease. What is the lease payment if

(*a*) payments are made at the beginning of each month?

(*b*) payments are made at the end of each month?

4-65 Using the date in Exercise 4-64, what are the semiannual lease payments if interest is compounded each 6 months?

answers: (*a*) **$4163.60**; (*b*) **$4465.46**

4-66 Your child goes to college in 10 years and you want to have $40,000 in cash by then. Assuming a $5\frac{3}{4}\%$ annual interest rate compounded monthly, what monthly deposit in a savings account is required assuming

(*a*) beginning-of-month payments?

(*b*) end-of-month payments?

4-67 You are buying a new car and must borrow $6500 from a bank which quotes 11.74% annual interest compounded monthly. Assuming end-of-period payments, what is the monthly payment for a

(*a*) 24-month loan?

(*b*) 36-month loan?

(*c*) 48-month loan?

answers: (*a*) **$305.189**; (*b*) **$215.087**; (*c*) **$170.341**

4-68 You have just taken out a 30-year mortgage for $54,000 with $463.94 end-of-month payments. The annual interest rate is $9\frac{3}{4}\%$ compounded monthly. But after reviewing your budget, you decide that you can make monthly payments of $500, which means the difference of $36.06 goes to paying off the principal. How long will it take you to pay off the mortgage with $500 payments and what is the amount of the last payment? What payment is necessary to pay off the mortgage in 25 years?

4-69 You are leasing a machine worth $24,000 which will have a zero salvage value at the end of the lease. Assuming the lessor wants to earn 12.74% annual compounded quarterly, how many payments are necessary if $1500 is paid:

(*a*) at the start of each quarter?

(*b*) at the end of each quarter?

answers: (*a*) ***n* = 21.719**; (*b*) **22.726**

4-70 A company wants to establish a sinking fund to pay off $340,000 of bonds at the end of 20 years. Assuming that they can earn 6.4% annual compounded monthly, how much should they deposit at the

(*a*) end of each month?

(*b*) beginning of each month?

4-71 If the company in Exercise 4-70 deposits $3000 each month, how long will it take to accumulate $340,000 and what is the amount of the last deposit assuming

(*a*) end-of-month payments?

(*b*) beginning-of-month payments?

answers: (*a*) **n = 88.882, 88 at $3000 and 89th at $2433.22**; (*b*) **n = 88.506, 88 at $3000, 89th at $629.51**

4-72 You have been considering an investment which pays $300 monthly for 10 years. This investment opportunity will cost you $10,000. What is the return per month and year for
   (*a*) end-of-month payments?
   (*b*) beginning-of-month payments?

4-73 You have just taken out a $67,500 twenty-five-year mortgage with $596.80 payments made at the end of each month. The annual interest rate is 9.65% compounded monthly. But you had to pay 2 points or 2% of the loan amount to get the loan. What is the nominal annual interest rate you are paying for the mortgage when the points are included? (*Hint*: Subtract the points from the amount borrowed.)
   answer: **r% = 9.90755%**

4-74 You are considering the purchase of a mortgage which has a current balance of $47,557.85 and 296 monthly payments of $384.46 remaining. Assuming that you want to earn 9.5% annual compounded monthly on your investment, how much should you pay for the mortgage?
   If you pay $44,000 for the mortgage, what is your return?

4-75 A copy machine salesman has proposed selling you his brand of copy machine. He claims that the initial net outlay of $5000 will save your company $100 each month in copying costs for the next 5 years. But you can invest the $5000 in another project for 5 years that earns 9% annual compounded monthly.
   (*a*) What is the return on the copy machine project assuming end-of-month savings?
   (*b*) Which project should you select based on the return?
   answers: (*a*) **r% = 7.4201%**; (*b*) **alternative investment**

4-76 A company is establishing a sinking fund to accumulate $500,000 at the end of 8 years. They want to make $6500 monthly deposits in a savings account. What interest rate is necessary to accumulate $500,000 assuuming
   (*a*) beginning-of-month payments?
   (*b*) end-of-month payments?

4-77 A man paid $75 at the beginning of each month for 22 years into a retirement fund. At the end of the 22nd year he had $55,941.95 in his account. What interest rate did he earn over the 22 years?
   answers: **i% = .6863, r% = 8.236%**

4-78 A store has offered to sell you a color TV set for $675 or for 48 payments of $22. Assuming end-of-month payments, what is the nominal annual interest rate?

4-79 A small loan company charges 3% of the amount borrowed as a service fee. This amount is deducted from the amount given to the borrower. For a $1500 loan having 36 monthly payments of $53, what is the nominal interest rate assuming end-of-month payments?
   answers: **i% = 1.5454%, r% = 18.5445%**

Some Mortgage Applications

4-80 Simple mortgage values are computed using the *ordinary annuity—PV case* because payments are normally made at the end of each month. As a result, the amount borrowed is PV, the monthly payment is PMT, the monthly interest rate is i_c, and the number of monthly payments is n. Thus what is the monthly payment for a 30-year mortgage where $65,000 is borrowed at 9½% annual compounded monthly?
   answer: **$546.56**

4-81 What is the monthly payment for a 25-year mortgage where $53,500 is borrowed at 8¾% annual compounded monthly?

4-82 If you can pay $350 a month, how big a mortgage can you afford, assuming a 20-year term and 9⅜% interest compounded monthly?
   answer: **$37,221.81**

4-83 If you can pay $385 a month for 30 years, how big a mortgage can you afford assuming an 8.5% annual interest rate compounded monthly?

4-84 A mortgage of $50,000 has 360 monthly payments of $425.91. What is the monthly compounding rate and the nominal annual rate?

  answers: $i_c\% = .8042\%$, $r\% = 9.65\%$

4-85 A mortgage of $45,000 has 240 monthly payments of $362.52. What is the monthly compounding rate and the nominal annual rate?

4-86 What is the remaining balance of a 30-year $75,000 mortgage after 173 payments if interest is 8.5% annual compounded monthly? The monthly payments are $576.69. (*Hint:* Compute the present value of payments already made and subtract from the loan amount and compound the difference forward to the last payment made.)

  answer: **$59,662.20**

4-87 What is the remaining balance of a 25-year $42,500 mortgage after 104 monthly payments of $297 if interest is $6\frac{7}{8}\%$ annual compounded monthly?

FIVE

GENERAL ANNUITIES

IN THIS CHAPTER

In this chapter, simple annuity applications, in which the compounding period is the same as the payment period, are broadened. *General annuity* applications cover the important class of problems in which payment and compounding periods differ: for example, savings accounts where the payments are made monthly and compounding occurs daily, or mortgage payments made monthly when compounding occurs semiannually. This chapter will show how these general annuity applications can be reduced to the simple annuity solutions given in Chap. 4.

● ● ● ● ●

The simple annuities discussed in Chap. 4 assumed equal time intervals for compounding interest and making payments. As a result, the compound interest rate was equal to the annual rate divided by the number of payments per year. However, some time value of money applications utilize a compounding interval that differs from the payment period. Annuities with this difference are called *general annuities*. Thus a general annuity has n equal payments with the compound interest interval *unequal* to the payment period.

5-1 CLASSIFICATION OF GENERAL ANNUITIES

General annuities are classified in the same manner as simple annuities: a general *ordinary* annuity has payments made at the end of the payment period, while a general annuity *due* has payments occurring at the beginning of the payment period. Here, as before, this classification depends on the timing of the payment within the *payment period,* not the compounding interval. Each type of general annuity also has a future-value case and a present-value case. These four cases are:

1. GFV: general ordinary annuity—future-value case.
2. GPV: general ordinary annuity—present-value case.
3. GFV$_d$: general annuity due—future-value case.
4. GPV$_d$: general annuity due—present-value case.

The basic approach of this chapter will be to develop an equivalency relationship between general and simple annuities that makes it possible to apply the formulas of Chap. 4 to the general annuity cases. However, to underscore the basic structure of general annuity problems, we will begin by applying the straightforward compound interest methods of Chap. 3.

5-2 SOLVING GENERAL ANNUITIES USING BASIC COMPOUND INTEREST METHODS

Many general annuity cases can be solved using conventional compound interest calculations, once the number of compounding periods and payment periods are identified. We will use the following notation:

c = number of compounding periods per year

f = number of payment periods per year

Of course, if $c = f$ (interest compounded when payments are made), we have the simple annuity case covered in Chap. 4. Let's consider an example where $c \neq f$, specifically the general ordinary annuity case.

Example 5-1 You deposit $100 at the end of each 2-month period in a savings account which pays 6% compounded monthly. What is the future value at the end of 1 year?

First, notice how this example differs from a simple annuity. Interest is compounded monthly, which means that the compound rate i_c is expressed in monthly terms, but the payment period is 2 months. Time Diagram 5-1 shows this timing difference, with the payments shown on top and the compound intervals indicated by the symbol Δ. You can see that payment 1 is compounded once before the second payment is made and then compounded again when the payment is received. This pattern is continued until the final payment is received. Table 5-1 provides the future-value calculations. Note that i_c, the interest rate per compounding period, is $.06/12 = .0005$.

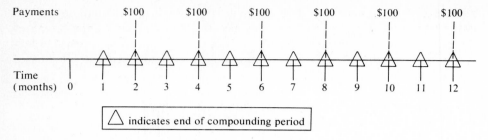

Time Diagram 5-1

Both the time diagram and the table show the relationship among the calendar time period, the payment period, and the compounding interval.

Table 5-1

Payment number	Number of compounding periods	Compound interest factor	×	Payment	=	Future value at end of 12 months
1	10	$(1.005)^{10}$	×	$100	=	$105.1140132
2	8	$(1.005)^{8}$	×	100	=	104.0707044
3	6	$(1.005)^{6}$	×	100	=	103.0377509
4	4	$(1.005)^{4}$	×	100	=	102.0150501
5	2	$(1.005)^{2}$	×	100	=	101.0025
6	0	$(1.005)^{0}$	×	100	=	100
				Total future value		$615.2400186

Now let's consider another example, where the compounding interval is greater than the payment period.

Example 5-2 You deposit $100 at the end of each 3-month period in a savings account that compounds interest every 4 months at 6% annual. What is the future value at the end of 1 year?

Time Diagram 5-2 shows the four payments that are made and the three

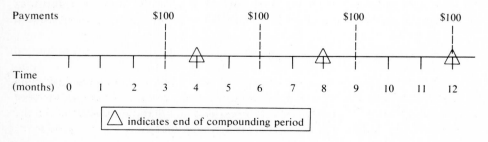

Time Diagram 5-2

Table 5-2

Payment number	Number of compounding periods	Compound interest factor		Payment	Future value at end of 12 months
1	$2\frac{1}{4}$	$(1.02)^{2\ 1/4}$	$\times$	$100	$104.5563434
2	$1\frac{3}{4}$	$(1.02)^{1\ 2/4}$	$\times$	100	103.0149504
3	$\frac{3}{4}$	$(1.02)^{3/4}$	$\times$	100	101.4962809
4	0	$(1.02)^{0}$	$\times$	100	100
				Total future value	$409.0675747

compounding intervals each year. Note that the payments are compounded using fractions in the compound interest formula for future value (see Table 5-2). For example, the first payment is invested for $\frac{1}{4}$ of the first compounding period and is therefore compounded for $2\frac{1}{4}$ periods to compute future value at the end of the year.

Likewise, the second payment is invested for $\frac{1}{2}$ of the second compounding period and is compounded $1\frac{1}{2}$ periods, while the third payment is invested for only $\frac{3}{4}$ of the third and last compounding period. Since the fourth payment is made at the end of the last compounding period, it earns no interest.

5-3 CONVERTING GENERAL ANNUITIES TO SIMPLE ANNUITIES WITH EQUIVALENT INTEREST

In Tables 5-1 and 5-2 the number of compounding periods is determined for each payment; then the remainder of the calculation is identical to the ordinary annuity procedure discussed in Chap. 4. Unfortunately, this process is relatively cumbersome. Therefore, the remainder of this chapter will be based on a simpler approach which involves the *conversion* of general annuities to simple annuities. There are two possible approaches to this conversion process: (1) to convert the interest rate per compounding period (i_c) to *equivalent interest rate per payment period* (i_f) and solve the general annuity as a simple annuity; or (2) to determine the *equivalent payment per compounding period* (PMT_c) and solve as a simple annuity. The first approach, using equivalent interest rates, is generally the simplest and will be emphasized in the remainder of the chapter. A later section will describe the equivalent-payment approach.

5-3.1 Equivalent Interest Rates

To understand the nature of equivalent interest rates, consider the following question. If $1 is invested and compounded c times per year to yield the value FV, what *equivalent* interest rate compounded a different number of times, f, will yield the same FV? We know that compounding c times per year gives

$$FV = \$1 \times (1 + i_c)^c$$

whereas compounding f times per year gives

$$FV = \$1 \times (1 + i_f)^f$$

Since both relationships are to compute the same value for FV, they can be set equal:

$$\$1(1 + i_c)^c = \$1(1 + i_f)^f$$

This equation can then be solved for i_f, the equivalent interest per period f:

$$i_f = (1 + i_c)^{c/f} - 1 \qquad (5\text{-}1)$$

where i_c = interest rate compounded c times per year
i_f = interest rate compounded f times per year

Or, if i_f is known, the relationship to determine i_c is

$$i_c = (1 + i_f)^{f/c} - 1 \qquad (5\text{-}2)$$

Remember, if either interest rate, i_c or i_f, is given, it is possible to solve for the other *equivalent* interest rate. Let's now see how equivalent interest rates can be used to solve general annuities.

In the equivalent-interest-rate approach, the goal is to convert the general annuity to a simple annuity so that the basic formulas in Chap. 4 can be used. The general procedure to solve for the various unknown values in an annuity situation consists of three steps:

1. Identify the variables.
2. Compute the equivalent interest rate.
3. Solve, using the ordinary annuity formulas.

Having converted i_c to i_f, you can then determine values for n, PMT, PV, or FV for ordinary general annuities or general annuities due using the formulas in Chap. 4 in the usual manner. Solving for i_c, however, will require an additional step, because the interest rate determined from the iteration procedure described in Chap. 4 is actually i_f. The value for i_f must be converted to i_c using Eq. (5-2).

Rather than repeat each of the formulas in Chap. 4 for the general annuity, we will simply solve some representative problems to illustrate the three-step procedure. Our notation is:

GFV = future value of a general ordinary annuity
GPV = present value of a general ordinary annuity
GFV_d = future value of a general annuity due
GPV_d = present value of a general annuity due
n = total number of payments

$$T = \text{number of years}$$
$$f = \text{number of payments per year}$$
$$c = \text{number of compounding intervals per year}$$
$$\text{PMT} = \text{payment per payment period}$$
$$i_c = \text{interest rate per compounding interval}$$
$$i_f = \text{interest rate per payment period}$$

This notation allows us to use the same basic symbols shown for simple annuities.

5-3.2 Solving for GPV and GFV—Example 5-3

You have won first place in a contest. As your prize, you may receive either: (1) $150 at the end of each month for 8 years, or (2) $12,000 in cash now. Assuming that you can invest the monthly income at 7% annual compounded quarterly, which option should you select?

This is a general ordinary annuity—PV case.

Step 1: Identify the relevant variables. The values are:

$$T = 8 \text{ years}$$
$$c = 4$$
$$f = 12$$
$$\text{PMT} = \$150$$
$$n = 8 \times 12 = 96$$
$$i_c = \frac{.07}{4} = .0175$$
$$i_f = ?$$
$$\text{GPV} = ?$$

Step 2: Compute the equivalent i_f.

$$i_f = 1.0175^{4/12} - 1 \qquad \text{from Eq. (5-1)}$$
$$= .0057996326$$

Step 3: Solve for GPV using the PV formula for a simple annuity, Eq. (4-4).

$$\text{GPV} = \$150 \times \frac{1 - 1.0057996326^{-96}}{.0057996326}$$
$$= \$150 \times 73.455952$$
$$= \$11,018.39281$$

The present value of $11,018.39 is less than the alternative prize of $12,000. So based on the assumption above, you should select the $12,000 prize.

Another way to view the problem is to compare the *future* value at the end of 8 years for each alternative. Because the first two solution steps are identical, we go directly to the third step, computing GFV, using Eq. (4-1):

$$GFV = \$150 \times \frac{1.0057996326^{96} - 1}{.0057996326}$$

$$= \$150 \times 127.975951$$

$$= \$19,196.3926$$

The future value is $19,196.39 for ninety-six $150 end-of-month payments, compounded quarterly at 7% annual.

The future value of the $12,000 lump-sum payment after 32 compounding periods can be determined using compound interest:

$$FV = \$12,000 \times \left(1 + \frac{.07}{4}\right)^{32}$$

$$= \$12,000 \times 1.742213492$$

$$= \$20,906.562$$

As might be expected, the $12,000 compounds to a greater value than the annuity.

This example can also be used to reinforce the concept of an equivalence relationship between present value and future value, discussed in Chap. 4. We could have computed the future value of the annuity using the present value and compound interest:

$$GFV = \$11,018.39281 \times \left(1 + \frac{.07}{4}\right)^{32}$$

$$= \$11,018.39281 \times 1.742213492$$

$$= \$19,196.3926$$

5-3.3 Solving for PMT and *n*—Example 5-4

A company is arranging a mortgage for a machine, but they have payment terms that are unusual. They want to make a payment at the end of 5-month periods. Interest is 11.7% annual compounded quarterly. The loan is for $195,000. The company wishes to consider two questions: (1) If 25 equal payments are to be made, what is the payment amount? and (2) If $15,000 payments are made, how many are necessary, and what is the final payment amount?

Step 1: Identify the variables for question 1.

$$c = 4$$

$$f = \frac{12}{5}$$

$$i_c = \frac{.117}{4} = .02925$$

$$GPV = \$195,000$$

$$n = 25$$

$$i_f = ?$$

$$PMT = ?$$

Step 2: Compute the equivalent i_f.

$$i_f = 1.02925^{4/(12/5)} - 1$$

$$= 1.02925^{5/3} - 1$$

$$= .0492237826$$

The equivalent interest rate per compounding period is 4.92%.

Step 3: Compute the PMT using the simple ordinary annuity—PV formula. We solve for the payment using the PMT formula, Eq. (4-8), for ordinary annuities, which is

$$PMT = \frac{GPV}{A(n,i_f)}$$

or

$$PMT = GPV \times \frac{i_f}{1 - (1 + i_f)^{-n}}$$

$$= \$195,000 \times \frac{.0492237826}{1 - 1.0492237826^{-25}}$$

$$= \$195,000 \times .0704014729$$

$$= \$13,728.28721$$

To pay off the mortgage in 25 payments requires a \$13,728.29 payment each 5 months for 125 months.

To answer the second question (If \$15,000 payments are made, how many are necessary, and what is the final payment amount?), we'll use the approach for the ordinary annuities—PV case described in Chap. 4.

Step 1: Identify the variables.

$$c = 4$$

$$f = 12/5$$

$$r = 11.7\%$$

$$i^c = .02925$$

$$\text{GPV} = \$195,000$$

$$\text{PMT} = \$15,000$$

$$i_f = .0492237826$$

$$n = \text{?}$$

We already know the value for i_f, so we can go directly to step 3.

Step 3: Solve for the unknown.

The formula to compute n for the ordinary annuity—PV case is Eq. (4-11):

$$n = \frac{-\ln\left(1 - \dfrac{\text{GPV}}{\text{PMT}} \times i_f\right)}{\ln(1 + i_f)}$$

Substituting our values gives

$$n = \frac{-\ln\left(1 - \dfrac{\$195,000}{\$15,000} \times .0492237826\right)}{\ln(1.0492237826)}$$

$$= 21.25672138$$

This answer means that only 21 payments of $15,000 will be made. A final 22nd payment, which will be a smaller amount, is computed using Eq. (4-12):

$$\text{Final payment} = \text{GPV} - \text{PMT} \times A(M, i_f) \times (i + i_f)^{M+1}$$

or

$$\text{Final payment} = \text{GPV} - \text{PMT} \times \frac{1 - (1 + i_f)^{-M}}{i_f} \times (1 + i_f)^{M+1}$$

Remember that the value M represents the number of $15,000 payments, which is 21. Substituting our values in the formula and solving, we obtain

$$\text{Final payment} = \left(\$195,000 - \$15,000 \times \frac{1 - 1.0492237826^{-21}}{.0492237826}\right)$$

$$\times 1.0492237826^{22}$$

$$= \$3919.852195$$

The company can pay off the mortgage by making 21 payments of $15,000 and a final 22nd payment of $3919.85.

5-3.4 General Annuities Due—Example 5-5

Suppose your company is considering the purchase of a lease. The lease payments are $2500 per month, and 65 beginning-of-month payments remain. Using an 18% annual discount rate compounded weekly, what is the maximum price you should pay?

The procedure for solving the annuities-due case for GFV_d, GPV_d, PMT, and n is exactly the same as outlined in the previous examples, except, of course, that simple *annuity due* formulas from Chap. 4 are used. The solution follows the three-step procedure previously discussed.

Step 1: Identify the variables.

$$c = 52$$
$$f = 12$$
$$n = 65$$
$$PMT = \$2500$$
$$r = 18\%$$
$$i_c = \frac{.18}{52} = .003461538$$
$$i_f = ?$$
$$GPV_d = ?$$

Step 2: Compute i_f.

$$i_f = 1.003461538^{52/12} - 1$$
$$= .015086772$$

Step 3: Compute GPV_d or maximum price to pay for the lease using the equivalent monthly interest rate in Eq. (4-18).

$$GPV_d = \$2500 \times 1.015086772 \times \frac{1 - 1.015086772^{-65}}{.015086772}$$
$$= \$2500 \times 1.015086772 \times 41.23957539$$
$$= \$104,654.3694$$

The maximum purchase price the company can pay to yield 18% annual compounded weekly is $104,654.37.

5-3.5 Solving for i_c

It was noted earlier that solving for the interest rate in a general annuity situation also requires the three-step procedure, as follows:

Step 1: Identify the variables (as before).

Step 2: Use the iteration procedure of Chap. 4 to solve for the interest rate per payment period, i_f.

Step 3: Convert i_f to i_c, using Eq. (5-2).

The following example will illustrate the procedure.

Example 5-6 Let's modify the facts of Example 5-5 and solve for the interest rate. If the seller offers to sell the lease for $110,000, what interest rate or yield on the lease is implied? Remember that to solve for i_c we must convert the answer from the simple annuity-due iteration procedure (which will be i_f, in terms of payment periods).

Step 1: Identify the variables.

$$c = 52$$

$$f = 12$$

$$n = 65$$

$$PMT = \$2500$$

$$GPV_d = \$110{,}000$$

$$i_c = ?$$

$$i_f = ?$$

Step 2: Compute i_f using the iteration procedure described in Chap. 4 for the annuity due—PV case. Note that i_f is used in the formulas below, Eqs. (4-15) and (4-16), in place of i_c.

Initial guess for i_f:

$$i_0 = \frac{PMT}{GPV_d} - \frac{GPV_d}{PMT \times n \times n}$$

$$i_{k+1} = i_k - \Delta i_k$$

where

$$\Delta i_k = \frac{(1 + i_f) - (1 + i_f)^{1-n} - \dfrac{GPV_d}{PMT} \times i_f}{1 + (n - 1) \times (1 + i_f)^{-n} + (1 + i_f) \times \dfrac{(1 + i_f)^{-n} - 1}{i_f}} \qquad k = 1, 2, \ldots, n$$

To compute our initial guess for i_f,

$$i_o = \frac{\$2500}{\$110,000} - \frac{\$110,000}{\$2500 \times 65 \times 65}$$

$$= .0123130715$$

Then the first iteration gives

$$\Delta i_1 = \frac{1.0123130715 - 1.0123130715^{-64} - \dfrac{\$110,000}{\$2500} \times .0123130715}{1 + 64 \times 1.0123130715^{-65} + 1.0123130715 \times \dfrac{1.0123130715^{-65} - 1}{.0123130715}}$$

The answers for successive iterations are:

$$\Delta i_1 = -.0008942222$$
$$i_1 = .0132072937$$
$$\Delta i_2 = -0.000016568$$
$$i_2 = .0132238617$$
$$\Delta i_3 = -.0000000055$$
$$i_3 = .0132238672$$
$$\Delta i_4 = 1.7902033 - 12$$
$$i_4 = .0132238672$$
$$i_f = .0132238672$$

The answer stabilizes on the fourth iteration and the interest rate per payment period is 1.32238672%.

Step 3: Convert i_f to i_c using the equivalence relationship, Eq. (5-2):

$$i_c = (1 + i_f)^{f/c} - 1$$

$$= 1.0132238672^{12/52} - 1$$

$$= .0030362605$$

The interest rate per compounding period (weekly) is .30362605%, which means that the yearly rate is $.30362605 \times 52$ or 15.7885548%. As a result, paying \$110,000 for the lease will yield 15.79% (which is less than the desired 18% rate).

5-4 OTHER APPLICATIONS:
CANADIAN MORTGAGES—EXAMPLE 5-7

Canadian mortgages often have interest compounded semiannually but with monthly payments. What is the end-of-month payment for a 25-year $48,000 mortgage where the interest is 8.75% compounded semiannually?

Step 1: Identify the variables.

$$T = 25 \text{ years}$$

$$c = 2$$

$$f = 12$$

$$i_c = \frac{.0875}{2} = .04375$$

$$GPV = \$48,000$$

$$n = 25 \times 12 = 300$$

$$i_f = ?$$

$$PMT = ?$$

Step 2: Compute the equivalent i_f.

$$i_f = (1 + i_c)^{c/f} - 1$$

$$= 1.04375^{2/12} - 1$$

$$= .007162193$$

The equivalent interest rate per payment period is .7162193%.

Step 3: Compute the PMT using the simple ordinary annuity—PV formula, Eq. (4-8a).

$$PMT = \frac{GPV}{A(n,i_f)}$$

$$= GPV \times \frac{i_f}{1 - (1 + i_f)^{-n}}$$

$$= \$48,000 \times \frac{.007162193}{1 - 1.007162193^{-300}}$$

$$= \$389.5748208$$

The monthly payment is $389.57 with interest compounded semiannually.

5-5 CONVERTING GENERAL TO SIMPLE ANNUITIES WITH EQUIVALENT PAYMENTS

It was noted in Sec. 5-3 that there are two possible approaches to convert general to simple annuities. This is by:

1. Converting the interest rate for compounding period (i_c) to the equivalent rate for payment period (i_f).
2. Converting the periodic payments (PMT) to equivalent payments (PMT_c) that coincide with the interest conversion periods (i_c).

The second alternative—the equivalent-payment approach—will receive attention in this section.

5-5.1 Equivalent Payments

The equivalency principal used in Chaps. 3 and 4 and in Sec. 5-3.1 can again be applied. We know that one annuity is *equivalent* to another if the values (such as future values) are the same for a specified date (point in time) and if the same or equivalent interest rates are involved. For instance, consider the following equivalent annuities, where the same future value, FV, is calculated for the same time date, T.

$$\text{General annuity:} \quad \text{GFV} = \text{function of } (\text{PMT}, n, i_c) \qquad (5\text{-}3)$$

$$\text{Simple annuity, } f: \ \text{FV} = \text{PMT} \times S(n, i_f) \qquad (5\text{-}4)$$

$$\text{Simple annuity, } c: \ \text{FV} = \text{PMT}_c \times S(n_c, i_c) \qquad (5\text{-}5)$$

These three annuities are illustrated in Time Diagram 5-3.

The *general annuity* has payments with an elapsed time between payments of $1/f$, measured in years, and n is the number of payments. No subscript is used for either PMT or n. The interest compounding period is specified as $1/c$, measured in years, and i_c represents the interest for the $1/c$ interval. The end of the interest conversion period is indicated by Δ on Time Diagram 5-3. The general annuity can be transformed into either of the two simple annuities.

Simple annuity f retains the n payments PMT with the time interval $1/f$ years. The equivalent interest rate conversion periods become i_f, which means that the compounding periods coincide with the payments, occurring f times per year. The conversion can be made by use of Eq. (5-1):

$$i_f = (1 + i_c)^{c/f} - 1 \qquad (5\text{-}1)$$

However, simple annuity f has already been covered in Sec. 5-3.5 and is not of prime interest in this section.

Simple annuity c retains the original compounding interval, $1/c$ years, but

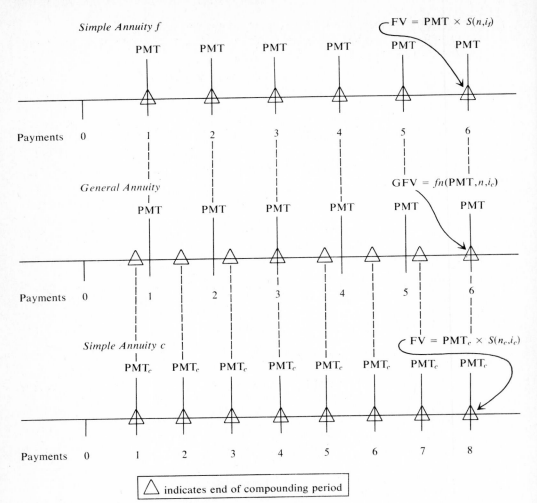

Time Diagram 5-3

modifies the *payment* by introducing the equivalent PMT_c. The subscript c indicates that the payments also occur at interval $1/c$. Of course, the number of payments must also change and is now n_c. The relationship between n and n_c is as follows:

$$T = \frac{n}{f} = \frac{n_c}{c} \tag{5-6}$$

Therefore,

$$n_c = n \times \frac{c}{f} \tag{5-7}$$

To work with simple annuity c, we must first calculate PMT_c.

Since the FV at time T is the same for the two simple annuities, we obtain from Eqs. (5-4) and (5-5),

$$PMT \times S(n,i_f) = PMT_c \times S(n_c,i_c) \tag{5-8}$$

or

$$PMT \times \frac{(1 + i_f)^n - 1}{i_f} = PMT_c \times \frac{(1 + i_c)^{n_c} - 1}{i_c} \tag{5-9}$$

We can then eliminate n and i_f from Eq. (5-9) by using Eqs. (5-7) and (5-1). That is, Eq. (5-8) can be rearranged so that

$$\frac{PMT_c}{i_c}(1 + i_c)^{n_c} - 1 = \frac{PMT}{i_f}(1 + i_c)^{n_c} - 1 \tag{5-10}$$

which leads to

$$\frac{PMT_c}{i_c} = \frac{PMT}{i_f} \tag{5-11}$$

when $i_c \neq 1$.

Now by eliminating i_f from Eq. (5-11), we get

$$PMT_c = PMT\frac{i_c}{(1 + i_c)^{c/f} - 1} \tag{5-12}$$

The symbol $S((c/f),i_c)$, from Eq. (4-2) can be interpreted to mean

$$S((c/f),i_c) = \frac{(1 + i_c)^{c/f} - 1}{i_c} \tag{5-13}$$

and is used to obtain

$$PMT_c = \frac{PMT}{S((c/f),i_c)} \tag{5-14}$$

Let's illustrate the use of Eq. (5-14) by the following example.

Example 5-8 A developer currently has been offered an unusual mortgage contract. It was originally drafted as a general annuity where he would borrow $105,000 at the nominal annual rate of 10.5%, compounded monthly. The contract states that 20 payments of $13,203 will be made, one at the end of each year. The developer would like to know the amount of the equivalent monthly payments.

Step 1: List the data for the general annuity problem using the general annuity symbols of Time Diagram 5-3.

$$n = 20 \text{ payments}$$

$$f = 1$$

$$c = 12$$

$$i_c = \frac{.105}{12} = .00875$$

$$\text{PMT} = 13{,}203$$

Step 2: Identify with the equivalent simple annuity f of Time Diagram 5-3.

$$\text{PMT}_c = ?$$

From Eq. (5-12),

$$\text{PMT}_c = \frac{\text{PMT}}{S(c/f,i_c)} = \frac{13{,}203}{S(12/1,.00875)}$$

$$= \frac{13{,}203}{12.59468005} = \$1048.299754$$

The equivalent monthly payment is $1048.30.

5-5.2 Solving for GFV, GPV, n, or i_c

Based upon the material presented in Sec. 5-5.1, the tools are available to solve for any of the unknowns that relate to a general annuity. We may be interested in determining GFV, GPV, n, i_c, and the related properties for the equivalent simple annuities n_c, PMT_c, or i_f. The particular method of conversion depends upon the problem at hand. In the remainder of the book, most of the general annuity problems will be solved by converting the i_c to i_f, or vice versa. This method often is simpler to visualize and faster to execute on a calculator.

Where the equivalent payment method is used, converting PMT to PMT_c can be accomplished by use of Eq. (5-14). The converse, converting PMT_c to PMT, requires the following companion equation:

$$\text{PMT} = \frac{\text{PMT}_c}{S(f/c,i_f)} \tag{5-15}$$

Working through the exercises at the end of the chapter will provide an opportunity to use the various combinations of the equivalency relationships.

5-6 CONSOLIDATION OF ALL THE ANNUITY RELATIONSHIPS

In Chaps. 4 and 5, a large number of cases were examined, involving various combinations of the following:

1. Simple annuities set up as ordinary annuity or annuity due:
   (a) Solving for FV or FV_d, PV or PV_d.
   (b) Solving for n, PMT, or i_c.
2. General annuities set up as ordinary annuity or annuity due:
   (a) Solving for GFV or GFV_d, GPV or GPV_d.
   (b) Solving for any of the equivalencies n or n_c, PMT or PMT_c, i_f or i_c.

It is difficult enough just to keep these various cases in mind, but it is even more tedious to cope with all these special cases in designing calculator solutions or programs. In order to ease this burden, we have *consolidated* all of these specific cases into one *comprehensive* equation. You'll recall that this type of a consolidation effort was introduced in Sec. 4-16, "General Relationship Between Ordinary Annuities and Annuities Due."

The symbolic relationship for a general annuity was indicated as Eq. (5-3).

$$GFV = \text{function of} (PMT, n, i_c) \qquad (5\text{-}3)$$

where all the terms were defined previously:

n = number of payments over the life of the annuity

f = number of payments per year

c = number of compounding periods

PMT = dollar amount of the payments

i_c = interest rate for the compounding time interval $1/c$

As pointed out in Sec. 5-3, the strategy used for solving a general annuity formulation is to convert it to a simple annuity. Specifically, we wish to convert the relationships in Eq. (5-3) to a consolidated single annuity equation that is identical with Eq. (4-35). In other words, we would like to have the consolidated formula represented as

$$V_K = (1 + i_f)^{K-n} \times PMT \times S(n, i_f) \qquad (5\text{-}16)$$

which is written in terms of i_f rather than i_c. As a reminder, the remaining symbols are

V_K = specific value case: GFV, GPV, GFV_d, GPV_d

with

$$K = n \qquad \text{for general ordinary annuity—GFV case}$$
$$K = 0 \qquad \text{for general ordinary annuity—GPV case}$$
$$K = n + 1 \quad \text{for general annuity due—GFV}_d \text{ case}$$
$$K = 1 \qquad \text{for general annuity due—GPV}_d \text{ case}$$

5-6.1 Solving for V_K or PMT

There is no difficulty in using Eq. (5-16) when i_c is known and c is specified. In such situations we simply use the following steps:

Step 1: Obtain a specific value for i_f from Eq. (5-1).

$$i_f = (1 + i_c)^{c/f} - 1$$

Step 2: Using the specific value obtained for i_f, solve for V_K or PMT, using the correct value for K, which depends upon the problem statement.

5-6.2 Solving for i_c

The only cases not covered is when the interest rate i_c is the unknown quantity in the general annuity problem. The approach is as follows:

First: solve for i_f Solve first for i_f rather than attempting to solve directly for i_c. The computational approach is indicated in Chap. 4, Eqs. (4-36) to (4-39). For convenience the key equations are summarized below.

Step 1: Rearrange Eq. (5-16) to introduce $f(i)$:

$$f(i) = (1 + i)^K \times [1 - (1 + i)^{-n}] - \frac{V_K \times i}{\text{PMT}} \tag{5-17}$$

(Note that the subscript f has been dropped from i.)

Step 2: Obtain the function $f'(i)$:

$$f'(i) = (n - k) \times (1 + i)^{(K-n-1)} + K(1 + i)^{K-1} + (1 + i)^K \frac{(1 + i)^{-n} - 1}{i} \tag{5-18}$$

Step 3: Make use of the iterative procedure already discussed in Chap. 4 as Eqs. (4-38) and (4-39).

$$i_{k+1} = i_k - \Delta i_k$$

where

$$\Delta i_k = \frac{f(i)}{f'(i)}$$

Step 4: Obtain an initial value for i and execute steps 1, 2, and 3 proceeding through the iterative procedures until the desired accuracy is obtained for i_f. No new formulas will be given to help select an initial value. One practical approach would be to use one of the formulas already given in the text, such as Eq. (4-13) or (4-15). One can also select an arbitrary value, as long as it is larger than -1 and a value other than zero.

Second: solve for i_c Now that i_f has been obtained we simply use Eq. (5-2) to solve for i_c.

$$i_c = (1 + i_f)^{f/c} - 1$$

5-6.3 Solving for n

The consolidated formula of Eq. (5-11) is not particularly useful in deriving a consolidated formula for n. The four formulas to be used when solving for n are enumerated below†:

GFV is known ($K = n$):

$$n = \frac{\ln\left(\dfrac{GFV \times i}{PMT} + 1\right)}{\ln(1 + i)} \tag{5-19}$$

which is the same as Eq. (4-9).

GPV is known ($K = 0$):

$$n = \frac{-\ln\left(1 - \dfrac{GPV \times i}{PMT}\right)}{\ln(1 + i)} \tag{5-20}$$

which is the same as Eq. (4-11).

GFV_d is known ($K = n + 1$):

$$n = \frac{\ln\left(\dfrac{GFV_d \times i}{PMT} + 1 + i\right)}{\ln(1 + i)} - 1 \tag{5-21}$$

which is the same as Eq. (4-21).

GPV_d is known ($K = 1$):

$$n = 1 - \frac{\ln\left(1 + i - \dfrac{GPV_d \times i}{PMT}\right)}{\ln(1 + i)} \tag{5-22}$$

which is the same as Eq. (4-24).

---

†In these formulas i is used in place of i_f.

KEYSTROKE SOLUTIONS

This section contains keystroke solutions for selected examples from this chapter. These solutions are organized by *type* of calculator (Type A or Type R) and within each type by *level* (Level I, II, or III).

Type	Level	Example number	Page
A	I	5-3, 5-5	141, 145
	II	5-3, 5-5, 5-6	141, 145, 146
	III	5-3, 5-5, 5-6	141, 145, 146
R	I	5-3, 5-5	141, 145
	II	5-3, 5-5, 5-6	141, 145, 146
	III	5-3, 5-5, 5-6	141, 145, 146

Type A, Level I keystrokes for Example 5-3

TI-30/50 keystrokes	Display	Comments
C	0.	Clear
.07	0.07	r
÷	0.07	
4	4.	c
+	0.0175	
1	1.	
=	1.0175	$1 + i_c$
y^x	1.0175	
(	1.0175	
4	4.	c
÷	4.	
12	12.	f
)	.33333333	
-	1.0057996	$1 + i_f$
1	1.	
=	.00579963	i_f
STO	.00579963	
+	.00579963	
1	1.	
=	1.0057996	
y^x	1.0057996	
96	96.	n
+/-	-96.	

TI-30/50 keystrokes	Display	Comments
-	.57398251	
1	1.	
=	-.42601749	
+/-	.42601749	
÷	.42601749	
RCL	.00579963	
×	73.455959	
150	150.	PMT
=	11018.394	GPV
1	1.	
+	1.	
RCL	.00579963	
=	1.0057996	$1 + i_f$
y^x	1.0057996	
96	96.	n
-	1.7422134	
1	1.	
=	.74221336	
÷	.74221336	
RCL	.00579963	
×	127.97595	i_f
150	150.	PMT
=	19196.393	GFV

Type A, Level I keystrokes for Example 5-5

TI-30/50 keystrokes	Display	Comments	TI-30/50 keystrokes	Display	Comments
C	0.	Clear	1	1.	
1	1.		+	1.	
+	1.		RCL	.01508677	i_f
.18	0.18	r	)	1.0150868	
÷	0.18		y^x	1.0150868	
52	52.	c	65	65.	n
=	1.0034615	$1 + i_c$	+/-	-65.	
y^x	1.0034615		=	.62217197	
(	1.0034615		÷	.62217197	
52	52.		RCL	.01508677	i_f
÷	52.		×	41.239578	
12	12.		(	41.239578	
)	4.3333333		RCL	.01508677	
−	1.0150868		+	.01508677	
1	1.		1	1.	
=	.01508677		)	1.0150868	$1 + i_f$
STO	.01508677	i_f	×	41.86175	
1	1.		2500	2500.	
−	1.		=	104654.37	GPV_d
(	1.				

Type A, Level II keystrokes for Example 5-3

TI-MBA/BA-II keystrokes	Display	Comments
CA	0	Clear
FIX 2	0.00	Set display
4	4	c
n	4.00	
7	7	r%
÷	7.00	
4	4	c
=	1.75	i_c
%i	1.75	
1	1	
PV	1.00	
CPT	1.00	
FV	1.07	
12	12	f
n	12.00	
CPT	12.00	
%i	0.58	i_f
96	96	n
n	96.00	
150	150	PMT
PMT	150.00	
CPT	150.00	
PV	11018.39	GPV
CPT	11018.39	
FV	19196.39	GFV

Type A, Level II keystrokes for Example 5-5

TI-MBA/BA-II keystrokes	Display	Comments
CA	0	Clear
FIX 2	0.00	Set display
52	52	c
n	52.00	
18	18	r%
÷	18.00	
52	52	c
=	0.35	
%i	0.35	
1	1	
PV	1.00	
CPT	1.00	
FV	1.20	f
12	12	
n	12.00	
CPT	12.00	
%i	1.51	$i\%$
65	65	n
n	65.00	
2500	2500	PMT
PMT	2500.00	
DUE	2500.00	
PV	104654.37	GPV_d

Type A, Level II keystrokes for Example 5-6

TI-MBA/BA-II keystrokes	Display	Comments
CA	0	Clear
65	65	
n	65.	n
2500	2500	PMT
PMT	2500.	
110000	110000	GPV_d
PV	110000.	
DUE	110000.	
%i	1.322386732	$i\%$
12	12	f
n	12.	
0	0	
PMT	0.	
1	1	
PV	1.	
CPT	1.	
FV	1.170752077	c
52	52	
n	52.	
CPT	52.	
%i	0.30362606	$i_c\%$
×	0.30362606	c
52	52	$r\%$
=	15.78855512	

Type A, Level III keystrokes for Example 5-3

TI-58/59 keystrokes	Display	Comments
Pgm 19	0.	Call Pgm 19
E'	0.	Initialize
C'	0.	Select PV case
1	1	
+	1.	
.07	0.07	r
÷	0.07	
4	4	
=	1.0175	c
y^x	1.0175	$1 + i_c$
(	1.0175	
4	4	
÷	4.	
12	12	f
)	.333333333	
−	1.005799633	
1	1	
=	.0057996326	i_f
×	.0057996326	
100	100	
=	.5799632569	$i\%$
B	0.5800	
96	96	n
A	96.	
150	150	PMT
C	150.00	
0	0	
D	11018.39	GPV
A'	11018.39	Select FV case
0	0	
D	19196.39	GFV

Type A, Level III keystrokes for Example 5-6

TI-58/59 keystrokes	Display	Comments
Pgm 19	0.	Select Pgm 19
E'	0.	Initialize
D'	0.	Select PV_d case
65	65	n
A	65.	
2500	2500	PMT
C	2500.00	
110000	110000	PV_d
D	110000.00	
0	0	
B	1.3224	i_f
÷	1.3224	
100	100	
+	0.0132	
1	1	
=	1.0132	
y^x	1.0132	
(	1.0132	f
12	12	
÷	12.0000	
52	52	c
)	0.2308	
−	1.0030	$1 + i_c$
1	1	
=	0.0030	i_c
×	0.0030	
100	100	
=	0.3036	$i_c\%$
Fix 9	.3036260417	$i_c\%$

Type A, Level III keystrokes for Example 5-5

TI-58/59 keystrokes	Display	Comments
Pgm 19	0.	Call Pgm 19
E'	0.	Initialize
D'	0.	Select PV_d case
1	1	
+	1.	
.18	0.18	r
÷	0.18	
52	52	c
=	1.003461538	i_c
y^x	1.003461538	
(	1.003461538	
52	52	c
÷	52.	
12	12	f
)	4.333333333	
−	1.015086772	
1	1	
=	.0150867717	i_f
×	.0150867717	
100	100	
=	1.508677172	$i_f\%$
B	1.5087	
65	65.	n
A	65.	
2500	2500	PMT
C	2500.00	
0	0	
D	104654.37	GPV_d

Type R, Level I keystrokes for Example 5-3

HP-31E/32E keystrokes	Display	Comments
ALL	0.0000	
.07	0.07	r
ENTER↑	0.0700	
4	4.	
÷	0.0175	c
1	1.	
+	1.0175	i_c
4	4.	
ENTER↑	4.0000	
12	12.	
÷	0.3333	f
y^x	1.0058	
1	1.	
−	0.0058	
STO 0	0.0058	i_f
1	1	
+	1.0058	
96	96.	
CHS	−96.	n
y^x	0.5740	

HP-31E/32E keystrokes	Display	Comments
1	1.	
−	−0.4260	
CHS	0.4260	
RCL 0	0.0058	
÷	73.4560	
150	150.	PMT
×	11,018.3926	GPV
1	1.	
ENTER↑	1.0000	
RCL 0	0.0058	i_f
+	1.0058	
96	96.	n
y^x	1.7422	
1	1.	
−	0.7422	
RCL 0	0.0058	
÷	127.9760	
150	150.	PMT
×	19,196.3931	GFV

Type R, Level I keystrokes for Example 5-5

HP-31E/32E keystrokes	Display	Comments
ALL	0.0000	Clear
.18	0.18	r
ENTER↑	0.1800	
52	52.	c
÷	0.0035	i_c
1	1.	
+	1.0035	
52	52.	c
ENTER↑	52.0000	
12	12.	f
÷	4.3333	
y^x	1.0151	
STO 0	1.0151	$1 + i_f$
1	1.	
−	0.0151	i_f
STO 1	0.0151	
RCL 0	1.0151	
65	65.	n
CHS	−65.	
y^x	0.3778	
1	1.	
−	−0.6222	
CHS	0.6222	
RCL 1	0.0151	
÷	41.2396	
RCL 0	1.0151	
×	41.8617	
2500	2,500	PMT
×	104,654.3742	GPV_d

Type R, Level II keystrokes for Example 5-3

HP-37E/38E keystrokes	Display	Comments
END		Sets payment switch
ALL	0.00	Clear
4	4.	c
n	4.00	
7	7.	$r\%$
ENTER↑	7.00	
4	4.	
÷	1.75	c
i	1.75	i_c
1	1.	
PV	1.00	
FV	−1.07	
12	12.	f
n	12.00	
i	0.58	i_f
96	96.	
n	96.00	n
150	150.	
PMT	150.00	PMT
0	0.	
FV	0.00	
PV	−11,018.39	GPV
0	0.	
PV	0.00	
FV	−19,196.39	GFV

Type R, Level II keystrokes for Example 5-5

HP-37E/38E keystrokes	Display	Comments
BEGIN	0.00	Sets payment switch
ALL	0.00	Clear
52	52.	c
n	52.00	
18	18.	r%
ENTER↑	18.00	
52	52.	c
÷	0.35	
i	0.35	i_c
1	1.	
PV	1.00	
FV	-1.20	
12	12.	
n	12.00	f
i	1.51	i%
65	65.	n
n	65.00	
2500	2,500.	
PMT	2,500.00	PMT
0	0	
FV	0.00	
PV	-104,654.37	GPV_d

Type R, Level II keystrokes for Example 5-6

HP-37E/38E keystrokes	Display	Comments
BEGIN	0.00	Set payment switch
ALL	0.00	Clear
65	65.	n
n	65.00	
2500	2,500.	
CHS	-2,500.	
PMT	-2,500.00	PMT
110000	110,000.	
PV	110,000.00	GPV_d
i	1.32	i%
12	12.	f
n	12.00	
0	0.	
PMT	0.00	
1	1.	
PV	1.00	
FV	-1.17	
52	52.	c
n	52.00	
i	0.30	i_c%
52	52.	r%
×	15.79	r%
(f)9	15.78855482	

Type R, Level III keystrokes for Example 5-5

HP-97/67 keystrokes	Display	Comments
fA	0.00	Program SD-05A
fB	1.00	Start function
52	52.	Annuity due mode
STO A	52.00	c
18	18.	
ENTER↑	18.00	$r\%$
52	52.	
÷	0.35	c
STO B	0.35	
1	1.	i_c
STO D	1.00	
E	1.20	
12	12.	FV
STO A	12.00	f
B	1.51	
65	65.	$i\%$
STO A	65.00	
2500	2500.	
STO C	2500.00	PMT
0	0.	
STO E	0.00	
D	104654.37	GPV_d

Type R, Level III keystrokes for Example 5-3

HP-97/67 keystrokes	Display	Comments
fA	0.00	Program SD-05A
4	4.	Start function
STO A	4.00	c
7	7.	
ENTER↑	7.00	$r\%$
4	4.	
÷	1.75	c
STO B	1.75	i_c
1	1.	
STO D	1.00	
E	1.07	
12	12.	f
STO A	12.00	
B	0.58	i_f
96	96.	
STO A	96.00	
150	150.	
STO C	150.00	PMT
0	0.	
STO E	0.00	
D	11018.39	GPV
0	0.	
STO D	0.00	
E	19196.39	GFV

Type R, Level III keystrokes for Example 5-6

HP-97/67 keystrokes	Display	Comments
fA	0.00	Program SD-05A
fB	1.00	Start function
65	65.	Annuity due mode
		n
STO A	65.00	
2500	2500.	PMT
STO C	2500.00	
110000	110000	GPV_d
STO D	110000.00	
B	1.32	$i\%$
12	12.	
STO A	12.00	
0	0.	
STO C	0.00	
1	1.	
STO D	1.00	
E	1.17	
52	52.	c
STO A	52.00	
B	0.30	$i_c\%$
52	52.	
×	15.79	$r\%$
DSP 9	15.78855200	$r\%$

EXERCISES

Drill on Equations†

5-1 Given: $i_c = .01$, $n = 60$, PMT = $1250, $c = 4$, $f = 12$
Find: GFV
GPV
GFV_d
GPV_d
answers: **GFV = 82,845.89, GPV = 67,895.89, GFV$_d$ = 83,121.13, GPV$_d$ = 68,121.46**

5-2 Given: $i_c = .045$, $n = 360$, PMT = $346.52, $c = 2$, $f = 12$
Find: GFV
GPV
GFV_d
GPV_d

5-3 Given: $i_c = .008$, $n = 100$, PMT = $25.85, $c = 12$, $f = 52$
Find: GFV
GPV
GFV_d
GPV_d
answers: **GFV = 2835.32, GPV = 2359.09, GFV$_d$ = 2840.54, GPV$_d$ = 2363.43**

5-4 Given: $i_c = .0145$, $n = 29$, PMT = $746.19, $c = 12$, $f = 4$
Find: GFV
GPV
GFV_d
GPV_d

5-5 Given: $r = 9\%$, $n = 160$, PMT = $193.84, $c = 3$, $f = 12$
Find: GFV
GPV
GFV_d
GPV_d
answers: **GFV = 59,116.78, GPV = 18,122.65, GFV$_d$ = 59,555.25, GPV$_d$ = 18,257.07**

5-6 Given: $r = 9.3\%$, $n = 300$, PMT = $402.95, $c = 2$, $f = 12$
Find: GFV
GPV
GFV_d
GPV_d

5-7 Given: PV = $42,500, $i_c = .04$, $n = 300$, $c = 2$, $f = 12$
Find: PMT
answer: **$324.37**

5-8 Given: PV = $64,850, $i_c = .0167$, $n = 240$, $c = 6$, $f = 2$
Find: PMT

5-9 Given: FV = $10,000, $i_c = .0011$, $n = 100$, $c = 52$, $f = 12$
Find: PMT
answer: **$78.25**

5-10 Given: FV = $1,450,000, $i_c = .031$, $n = 44$, $c = 2$, $f = 12$
Find: PMT

†In the following exercises the interest rate is expressed in decimal form except in those cases where a % sign is indicated.

5-11 Given: $PV_d = \$85,000$, $i_c = .015$, $n = 7$, $c = 12$, $f = 1$
Find: PMT
answer: **$19,486.44**

5-12 Given: $PV_d = \$104,000$, $i_c = .065$, $n = 60$, $c = 2$, $f = 12$
Find: PMT

5-13 Given: $FV_d = \$12,000$, $i_c = .005$, $n = 84$, $c = 12$, $f = 6$
Find: PMT
answer: **$90.81**

5-14 Given: $FV_d = \$155,000$, $i_c = .03$, $n = 100$, $c = 4$, $f = 6$
Find: PMT

5-15 Given: $FV = \$45,000$, $r = 9\%$, $T = 6$, $c = 12$, $f = 52$
Find: PMT
answer: **$108.99**

5-16 Given: $FV = \$145,500$, $r = 7\%$, $T = 24$, $c = 12$, $f = 2$
Find: PMT

5-17 Given: $PV = \$65,000$, $r = 8.58\%$, $T = 30$, $c = 2$, $f = 12$
Find: PMT
answer: **$496.60**

5-18 Given: $PV = \$94,250$, $r = 14.7\%$, $T = 10$, $c = 6$, $f = 4$
Find: PMT

5-19 Given: $FV_d = \$2,549.53$, $r = 5.75\%$, $T = 2$, $c = 365$, $f = 12$
Find: PMT
answer: **$100.00**

5-20 Given: $FV_d = \$50,000$, $r = 6.01\%$, $T = 10$, $c = 4$, $f = 6$
Find: PMT

5-21 Given: $PV_d = \$45,000$, $r = 17\%$, $T = 5$, $c = 2$, $f = 12$
Find: PMT
answer: **$1089.64**

5-22 Given: $PV_d = \$165,000$, $r = 11\%$, $T = 10$, $c = 6$, $f = 3$
Find: PMT

5-23 Given: $FV = \$25,000$, $i_c = .0052$, $PMT = \$75$, $c = 12$, $f = 4$
Find: n and final payment
answers: **$n = 117.54$; 116, $325.24**

5-24 Given: $FV = \$180,000$, $i_c = .051$, $PMT = \$10,000$, $c = 2$, $f = 12$
Find: n and final payment

5-25 Given: $PV = \$91,450$, $i_c = .036$, $PMT = \$4000$, $c = 5$, $f = 6$
Find: n and final payment
answers: **$n = 39.07$; 39, $287.90**

5-26 Given: $PV = \$50,000$, $i_c = .045$, $PMT = \$416.23$, $c = 2$, $f = 12$
Find: n and final payment

5-27 Given: $FV_d = \$41,000$, $i_c = .041$, $PMT = \$100$, $c = 12$, $f = 6$
Find: n and final payment
answers: **$n = 43.38$; 42, $1272.93**

5-28 Given: $FV_d = \$125,000$, $i_c = .021$, $PMT = \$300$, $c = 3$, $f = 4$
Find: n and final payment

5-29 Given: $PV_d = \$74,000$, $i_c = .05$, $PMT = \$1565$, $c = 2$, $f = 12$
Find: n and final payment
answers: **$n = 59.37$; 59, $583.38**

5-30 Given: $PV_d = \$271,500$, $i_c = .0136$, $PMT = \$8000$, $c = 12$, $f = 7$
Find: n and final payment

5-31 Given: FV = $14,500, r = 5.75%, PMT = $250, c = 365, f = 6
Find: n and final payment
answers: **n = 46.3; 45, $367.19**

5-32 Given: FV = $350,000, r = 7.75%, PMT = $10,000, c = 6, f = 12
Find: n and final payment

5-33 Given: PV = $91,000, r = 11.9%, PMT = $6000, c = 12, f = 10
Find: n and final payment
answers: **n = 16.83; 16, $4968.81**

5-34 Given: PV = $180,000, r = 9.8%, PMT = $7500, c = 2, f = 12
Find: n and final payment

5-35 Given: FV_d = $25,000, r = 5.65%, PMT = $125, c = 365, f = 52
Find: n and final payment
answers: **n = 180.189; 179, $260.56**

5-36 Given: FV_d = $68,000, r = 6.73%, PMT = $725, c = 6, f = 12
Find: n and final payment

5-37 Given: PV_d = $149,000, r = 19.4%, PMT = $18,000, c = 12, f = 2
Find: n and final payment
answers: **n = 14.81; 14, $14,628.72**

5-38 Given: PV_d = $75,000, r = 10.6%, PMT = $710.21, c = 2, f = 12
Find: n and final payment

5-39 Given: FV = $14,000, n = 25, PMT = $500, c = 12, f = 3
Find: i_f, i_c, and r%
answers: **i_f = .9301%, i_c = .2317%, r% = 2.7807%**

5-40 Given: FV = $91,872, n = 240, PMT = $149.25, c = 2, f = 12
Find: i_f, i_c, and r%

5-41 Given: FV = $138,900, T = 12, PMT = $1240, c = 12, f = 6
Find: i_f, i_c, and r%
answers: **i_f = 1.16997%, i_c = .5833%, r% = 6.9994%**

5-42 Given: PV = $43,250 n = 360, PMT = $365.45, c = 2, f = 12
Find: i_f, i_c, and r%

5-43 Given: PV = $36,975, n = 240, PMT = $1500, c = 12, f = 2
Find: i_f, i_c, and r%
answers: **i_f = 4.0565%, i_c = .6649%, r% = 7.9792%**

5-44 Given: PV = $28,100, T = 5, PMT = $8500, c = 12, f = 1
Find: i_f, i_c, and r%

5-45 Given: FV_d = $8100, n = 50, PMT = $135, c = 52, f = 12
Find: i_f, i_c, and r%
answers: **i_f = .6977%, i_c = .1606%, r% = 8.3499%**

5-46 Given: FV_d = $81,250, n = 51, PMT = $1250, c = 6, f = 8
Find: i_f, i_c, and r%

5-47 Given: FV_d = $63,197, T = 108, PMT = $5000, c = 12, f = 1
Find: i_f, i_c, and r%
answers: **i_f = −7.3299%, r% = −7.5883%, i_c = −.6324%**

5-48 Given: PV_d = $444,600, n = 48, PMT = $12,500, c = 12, f = 6
Find: i_f, i_c, and r%

5-49 Given: PV_d = $60,743.04, n = 300, PMT = $455, c = 2, f = 12
Find: i_f, i_c, and r%
answers: **i_f = .644%, i_c = 3.9267%, r% = 7.8534%**

5-50 Given: PV_d = $267,989, T = 6, PMT = $15,000, c = 5, f = 4
Find: i_f, i_c, and r%

Application Problems

5-51 What is the end-of-month payment for a $73,000 Canadian mortgage having a 30-year term where interest is compounded semiannually? The annual interest rate is 8.95%.

    answer: **$576.25**

5-52 A company plans to deposit $1000 every other month for 5 years in a savings account paying 6.2% interest annual compounded monthly. What is the future value at the end of 5 years, assuming

    (*a*) end-of-month deposits?

    (*b*) beginning-of-month deposits?

5-53 You deposit $25 a week in a savings account paying 5.87% annual interest compounded daily. Given 365 days in a year, what is the balance in the account after 150 weeks assuming

    (*a*) beginning-of-period payments?

    (*b*) end-of-period payments?

    answers: (*a*) **$4088.47**; (*b*) **$4083.86**

5-54 Your mortgage payment is currently $405 paid at the end of each month. The interest rate is 9.45% annual compounded semiannually. What equivalent yearly payment will replace the 12 monthly payments?

5-55 Convert a loan with $14,500 semiannual payments to monthly payments. Assume end-of-period payments. Interest is 10.87% annual compounded semiannually. What is the equivalent monthly payment?

    answer: **$2363.69**

5-56 An investment returns $600 a month for 15 years. Assuming that interest is compounded daily at 6.5% annual. Given 365 days in a year, what is the present value or cost of this investment assuming

    (*a*) beginning-of-period payments?

    (*b*) end-of-period payments?

5-57 A machine is being leased for 8 years, at which time its salvage value is zero. The semiannual lease payment is $4500. Assuming that interest is 11.3% annual compounded daily (365 days in a year), what is the present value of the lease if

    (*a*) payments occur at the beginning of each period?

    (*b*) payments occur at the end of each period?

    answers: (*a*) **$48,747.80**; (*b*) **$46,070.32**

5-58 A division manager has proposed a project to the main office. The project has monthly after-tax savings of $4600 and they should continue for 5 years, which is the life of the project. The salvage value of the machinery is zero at the end of 5 years. The discount rate is 18% compounded weekly.

    (*a*) What is the present value of the cash savings?

    (*b*) If the project costs $186,755, what is the internal rate of return?

5-59 A mortgage with monthly payments of $202.90 is being purchased. Interest is compounded semiannually. The current loan balance is $18,292.49 with 139 end-of-month payments remaining.

    (*a*) What price should be paid to yield 9% annual compounded semiannually?

    (*b*) What was the interest rate on the original loan?

    answers: (*a*) **$17,616.86**; (*b*) i_f = **.6719%**, i_c = **4.1%**, r = **8.2%**

5-60 A company wants to accumulate $1,000,000 in a 20-year sinking fund to retire a bond issue. Assuming that the interest rate is 6.78% annual compounded monthly, what is the amount of the payment if

    (*a*) four payments a year are made at the beginning of each period?

    (*b*) two payments a year are made at the end of each period?

5-61 You want to accumulate $50,000 in a college fund for your child. She starts to college in 14 years. If interest is 5¾% annual compounded daily (assume 365 days per year), what is the monthly payment

    (*a*) if deposits are made at the end of each month?

(*b*) if deposits are made at the beginning of each month?

answers: (*a*) **$194.20;** (*b*) **$193.27**

5-62 You purchase an annuity for $10,000. Interest is compounded weekly with an annual interest rate of 5.65%. What is the amount of the end-of-month payment at the end of 10 years?

5-63 A truck is being leased for 6 years, at which time its salvage will be zero. The truck has a current value of $25,000. The lessor wants to earn 14.6% annual compounded monthly. What is the amount of the payment if

(*a*) payments are made four times a year at the beginning of each period?

(*b*) payments are made six times a year at the end of each period?

answers: (*a*) **$1532.20;** (*b*) **$1052.79**

5-64 A trust fund of $1,000,000 is inherited by Bert. The fund will earn 5.75% annually compounded weekly and pay all principal and interest to Bert over 30 years in end-of-month payments. What is the amount of the monthly payment?

5-65 You can lease a car for 3 years with $276.66 beginning-of-month payments or purchase the car for $8,500. You can earn 6% annually compounded weekly at a local savings and loan association. Ignoring taxes and salvage, should you lease or purchase?

answer: **Buy car because interest rate on lease is 11.20%.**

5-66 You want to save $10,000 by making $200 deposits each month in an account paying $5\frac{7}{8}$% interest annually compounded quarterly. How many payments are necessary and the amount of the final payment if deposits are made:

(*a*) at the beginning of each month?

(*b*) at the end of each month?

5-67 A lessor leased a machine worth $84,000. The lessee pays $5000 quarterly. Interest is 12.5% annual, compounded semiannually. What is the number of beginning-of-period payments and the amount of the final payment?

answers: **n = 22.97, 22 regular payments, 23rd of $4866.92**

5-68 Bob wants to borrow $125,000 at $10\frac{3}{4}$% annual compounded semiannually, but he can only afford monthly payments of $1300. How many end-of-month payments are necessary to pay off the loan and the amount of the final payment?

5-69 A new machine is expected to save $900 after taxes at the end of each quarter. The machine cost $15,585. The company expects such projects to earn 22% annually, compounded monthly. How many months of savings are necessary for the machine to pay for itself?

answer: **n = 64.33**

5-70 A pension fund offers a redemption value of $50,000 after 20 years of monthly payments equaling $128.34. Assuming that you can invest the money in a savings account paying 5.5% interest annual, compounded quarterly, which option earns the highest yield? What is the yield on the pension plan?

5-71 A capital budgeting project has been proposed which generates $1200 after taxes each quarter for 6 years. The project requires an initial outlay of $19,500. What is the annual interest rate, assuming that the salvage value is zero at the end of 6 years and PV = $19,500? Assume end-of-quarter payments and yearly compounding.

answers: **i_f = 3.3874%, i_c = 14.2536%**

5-72 An appliance dealer offers to sell a stove for $650 or $20 down and 24 end-of-month payments of $45. If interest is compounded quarterly, what is the annual rate of interest being charged?

SIX

CONTINUOUS COMPOUNDING AND/OR CONTINUOUS PAYMENTS

IN THIS CHAPTER

In this chapter the concepts of annuities with discrete payments and for discrete compounding periods are extended to continuous payments or continuous compounding or both. Continuous compounding is becoming more popular for use in business applications such as savings accounts and capital budgeting.

● ● ● ● ●

Previous chapters have considered discounting and compounding for discrete time periods. Throughout these chapters, it was assumed that all compounding or discounting is accumulated (or computed) at the *end* of a compounding period. There were a discrete and finite number of periods, and discrete compounding was assumed to occur at the end of each of these periods; hence the name "discrete compounding." Chapter 3 covered discrete compounding for single payments, while Chaps. 4 and 5 dealt with multiple payments, or annuities.

This discrete approach is the one most often used for the evaluation of investments, ammortization of debt, interest payments into savings accounts, sinking fund requirements, and many other practical applications. Even for very short compounding periods, the discrete approach is still a sufficiently accurate and a practical way of comparing present and future sums of money.

However, an alternative to the discrete compounding approach, called *continuous* compounding, is sufficiently important in both practical and theoretical applications to warrant a chapter in this book. The continuous compounding and discounting approach is most frequently used in the following situations:

1. In contract agreements which call for interest accumulation based on continuous compounding.
2. In theoretical investment models which use continuous discounting primarily because of its convenience in mathematical analysis.

The concept of continuous compounding has been developed for discrete cash payments and also a comparable theory has been developed for *continuous cash payments*. Thus this chapter considers the combination of three possible new cases:

1. Discrete payments with continuous compounding.
2. Continuous payments with discrete compounding.
3. Continuous payments with continuous compounding.

The fourth possible case, combining discrete payments and discrete compounding, is not treated here, since that was the topic of Chaps. 3 to 5.

CONTINUOUS COMPOUNDING

6-1 CONTINUOUS COMPOUNDING OF SINGLE PAYMENTS

To introduce continuous compounding, we'll use as a reference point some of the basic equations introduced in Chap. 3. There, the formula for a single payment with discrete compounding was given as:

$$FV = PV \times (1 + i_c)^n \qquad (6\text{-}1)$$

where PV = original principal amount or present value
FV = compound amount of PV, or the future value at a specified later date
n = total number of periods where compound interest is calculated
i_c = interest rate for the time period when compound interest calculations are made

For further development, it is useful to express the interest rate in formula (6-1) on an annual basis:

$$FV = PV \times \left(1 + \frac{r}{c}\right)^n \qquad (6\text{-}2)$$

where r = annual nominal interest rate (with compounding interval specified)
c = number of compounding periods per year

6-1.1 One-Year Time Period

Consider first a 1-year time period. If we wish to compound funds a given number of times (c) during the 1-year period, then

$$FV = PV \times \left(1 + \frac{r}{c} \right)^{1 \times c} \tag{6-3}$$

Of course, the future value (FV) depends on c, the number of compounding periods chosen, as the following example will demonstrate.

Example 6-1 Suppose $1 is deposited in an account which pays a nominal interest rate of 7.5% per year. How much will be accumulated in the account after 1 year when compounding takes place (1) yearly, (2) quarterly, (3) monthly, (4) weekly, or (5) daily?

1. Yearly: $FV = (1 + .075/1)^1 = 1.075$.
2. Quarterly: $FV = (1 + .075/4)^4 = 1.077135866$.
3. Monthly: $FV = (1 + .075/12)^{12} = 1.077632599$.
4. Weekly: $FV = (1 + .075/52)^{52} = 1.0778259 \wr 11.$†
5. Daily: $FV = (1 + .075/365)^{365} = 1.077875 \wr 872.$†

Notice that the future value increases slowly but regularly as the number of compounding periods increases. Let's go on to hourly and minutely compounding.

$$\text{Hourly: } FV = (1 + .075/8760)^{8760} = 1.07788 \wr 3737†$$

$$\text{Minutely: } FV = (1 + .075/525{,}600)^{525{,}600} = 1.0778 \wr 87514†$$

The pattern is clear; the future value continues to increase as (c) increases in Eq. (6-3). A graph indicating how the future value of Eq. (6-3) is influenced by the number of compounding periods per year is shown in Fig. 6-1. As the number of compounding periods increases from 1, 4, 12, 52, etc., times per year, the future value first increases rapidly and then slowly approaches an asymptotic limit.

It is the limit that is of special interest when we talk about continuous compounding. This limit can be determined precisely by letting the number of payments per year increase to infinity. That is,

$$\lim_{c \to \infty} \left(1 + \frac{r}{c} \right)^{1 \times c} = e^r \tag{6-4}$$

†Numerical errors can creep into this type of calculation as we shorten the compounding period. The digits to the right of the wavy line are suspect because of numerical errors. Notice how the wavy line shifts to the left as the compound period becomes shorter. The reasons for this are related to the number of significant digits stored in registers and the accuracy of the **y^x** key for values close to 1. The results will vary somewhat for different calculators.

Figure 6-1 Influence of compounding periods on future value

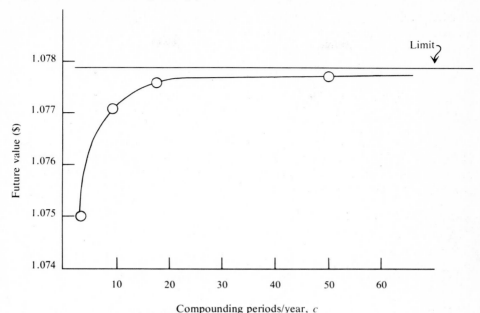

where $e = 2.718281 \ldots$ is known as the base of the natural logarithm system. Equation (6-4) can be interpreted as follows. As the number of compounding periods per year increases, compounding occurs more frequently, becoming continuous compounding in the limit as c goes to infinity. For $1 invested for 1 year at the nominal annual rate r, the continuously compounded value at the end of 1 year is e^r.

By utilizing the information gained from Eq. (6-4), Eq. (6-3) becomes

$$FV = PV \times e^r \qquad (6\text{-}5)$$

Let's illustrate the application of this equation by an example. In Example 6-1 where $r = .075$, the limit for FV is†

$$FV = 1 \times e^{1 \times .075} = 1.077884151$$

This limit is useful in several ways. First, the two quantities c and r in discrete compounding have been replaced by the single quantity e^r, which represents a simplification. Second, it is frequently useful to evaluate two investment alternatives by comparing their respective limit values computed by continuous compounding. Finally, the function e^r has proven to be very useful in the

---

†The FV computed using continuous compounding is smaller than the FV computed using discrete compounding by the minute. This difference illustrates the error that can result when compounding for very small periods, such as a minute or a second.

development of mathematics of finance. For these reasons calculators which have y^x, $\ln x$, and e^x functions are particularly useful in financial applications.

6-1.2 Multiple-Year Time Periods

It is a relatively simple matter to extend the concept of the preceding paragraph so that it will be applicable for any time interval. Suppose a single payment is made and held for exactly 2 years. Then the future value for the nominal annual interest rate, r, becomes

$$FV = PV \times (e^r \times e^r) = PV \times e^{r \times 2}$$

where 2 represents the time interval of 2 years. Generalizing this concept,

$$FV = PV \times e^{r \times t} \tag{6-6}$$

where t represents any nonnegative time period, either whole years or fractions.

Example 6-2 Let's reexamine Example 3-5 with continuous compounding. Suppose you deposit $100 in a savings account where interest is compounded continuously at the annual nominal rate of 7%. What will be the balance in the account at the end of first, second, third, and fourth years?

End of year	Yearly interest	Cumulative interest	End-of-year balance
0	$0.	$0.	$100
1	7.2508	7.2508	107.2508
2	7.7766	15.0274	115.0274
3	8.3404	23.3678	123.3678
4	8.9452	32.3130	132.3130

This table can be compared with that of Example 3-5. The only entry of real interest is the end-of-year balance, which can be checked by means of Eq. (6-6).

Balance at end of year 4 = $100 \times e^{.07 \times 4} = 100 \times e^{.28} = \$132.3130^{\dagger}$

Example 6-3 How much will $1500 accumulate to in 15 years at an annual nominal rate of 6%, compounded continuously?

$$FV = PV \times e^{rt} = 1500 \times e^{.06 \times 15} = 1500 \times 2.459603$$

$$= \$3689.4047$$

---

†In this example and others to follow, the calculations are rounded to four places.

This answer can be compared with the semiannual compounding of the same amounts in Example 3-7.

Example 6-4 How much will $1500 accumulate to in 182 months at an annual nominal rate of 6%, compounded continuously?

$$t = \frac{182}{12} = 15.16667 \text{ years}$$

$$FV = 1500 \times e^{.06 \times 15.16667} = 1500 \times e^{.91}$$

$$= 1500 \times 2.4843225$$

$$= \$3726.4838$$

This answer can be compared to Example 6-3. Note that Eq. (6-6) can be applied with *fractional* time periods.

6-2 CONTINUOUS DISCOUNTING

Equation (6-6) can also be rearranged for the purpose of continuous *discounting* by solving for the present value.

$$PV = \frac{FV}{e^{rt}} = FV \times e^{-rt} \tag{6-7}$$

Example 6-5 As in Example 3-9, suppose $25,000 will be made available in 2 years. What is its value today if money is worth 8.75% as nominal annual rate, compounded continuously?

$$PV = 25,000 \times e^{-.0875 \times 2} = 25,000 \times e^{-.175}$$

$$= 25,000 \times 0.83945702 = \$20,986.4255$$

Example 6-6 As in Example 3-8, find the present value of a promissory note which pays $12,000 on a date 5 years from now. Money is assumed to have a time value of 9% per year, compounded continuously. Then

$$PV = FV \times e^{-rt} = 12,000 \times e^{-.09 \times 5} = 12,000 \times e^{-.45}$$

$$= 12,000 \times .63762815 = \$7651.54$$

6-3 EQUIVALENT RELATIONSHIPS

The equivalent relationships under continuous compounding are essentially the same as described in Chap. 3 for the discrete compounding case. This section will describe equivalent-value diagrams, equivalent payments, and equivalent interest rates for continuous compounding.

6-3.1 Equivalent-Value Diagrams

Suppose a sum of money, V_0, is due at a stated time, t_0. Then there is an equivalent value, V_n, due at a later number of years, t_n, provided the value has been compounded according to the formula of Eq. (6-6). Likewise, there is an equivalent value, V_{-n}, due at an earlier date (earlier by the amount t_{-n}) and expressed by Eq. (6-7).

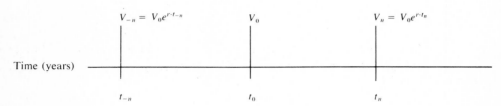

Time Diagram 6-1

These relationships can be illustrated by Time Diagram 6-1. One interpretation of this diagram is that an investor who seeks the rate of return r is indifferent as to whether to accept the amount V_0 at time t_0 or wait until time t_n to accept V_n.

Example 6-7 As in Example 3-10, suppose a payment of $2000 is due at the end of 2 years and another payment of $2500 is due after 5 years. If the time value of money is 8.75%, compounded continuously, determine the value of both amounts under the following conditions:
  (a) Both amounts are paid now.
  (b) Both amounts are paid at end of 2 years.
  (c) Both amounts are paid at end of 5 years.

	(a) Present	(b) End of 2 years	(c) End of 5 years
First amount	$2000e^{-.0875\times2}$	$2000e^{0}$	$2000e^{.0875\times3}$
Second amount	$2500e^{-.0875\times5}$	$2500e^{-.0875\times3}$	$2500e^{0}$

Results of the indicated computations are:

	Present	End of 2 years	End of 5 years
1st amount	$1678.914	$2000.	$2600.353
2nd amount	1614.121	1922.816	2500.
Totals	$3293.035	$3922.816	$5100.353

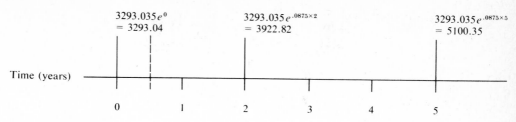

Time Diagram 6-7

These totals represent equivalent values, as shown in Time Diagram 6-7. This is the same type of diagram that was first developed in Chap. 3 and used repeatedly in Chaps. 4 and 5.

6-3.2 Equivalent Payments

When two separate amounts of money are due on different dates it is often desirable to replace one or both of them with an equivalent payment on a given common date, so that comparisons can be made. Consider the following example (taken from Example 3-11) to illustrate this type of situation where continuous compounding is involved.

Example 6-8 Suppose you owe $1500 which is due in 2 years and $4000 which is due in 5 years on two separate notes (promises to pay). You reach an agreement with the creditor to whom the money is owed that you will pay off both notes 1 year from now, by stipulating that you will pay the *equivalent* amounts at an annual rate of 6% compounded continuously.

Amount to be paid
on first note $= 1500e^{+.06 \times (-1)} = \$1412.6468$

Amount to be paid
on second note $= 4000e^{+.06 \times (-4)} = \underline{3146.5114}$

Total amount paid
1 year from now $\underline{\$4559.1582}$

6-3.3 Equivalence Between Continuous and Discrete Interest Rates

In Chap. 3 equivalent interest rates were established for two different compounding periods but where both involved discrete compounding. Here we'll set up an equivalent discrete rate that can be used as a substitute for the continuous rate e^r. We have been using in this chapter the symbol r to represent the nominal annual rate for continuous compounding and i_c to represent the interest rate for a compounding period that occurs c times per year.

The equivalence between i_c and e^r can be obtained by the use of Eqs. (3-7) and (6-6):

$$FV = PV(1 + i_c)^n = PV(1 + i_c)^{c \times t} \qquad (3\text{-}7)$$

$$FV = PV \times e^{r \times t} \qquad (6\text{-}6)$$

If the future values and present values are equal, respectively, then

$$(1 + i_c)^{c \times t} = e^{r \times t}$$

or $$(1 + i_c) = e^{r/c} \qquad (6\text{-}8)$$

where r = nominal annual rate compounded continuously

$\qquad i_c$ = equivalent discrete interest rate for the compounding interval $1/c$

Let's consider a specific example that demonstrates how either the discrete or continuous rate can be used to calculate a specific future value.

Example 6-9 What is the future value when \$1800 is deposited in a savings account for 7 years and interest is compounded continuously at the nominal annual rate of 8.4%? Solve the problem first by using only Eq. (6-6) and then by the combination of Eqs. (6-8) and (3-7).

From Eq. (6-6)

$$FV = 1800e^{.084 \times 7} = 1800 \times 1.80038 = \$3240.69128$$

Alternatively, using the equivalency relationship (6-8) to solve for i_c, where c is arbitrarily assigned the value of 1, we have

$$i_c = e^{r/c} - 1 = e^{.084} - 1 = .08763$$

Then, solving for FV using Eq. (3-7), we obtain

$$FV = 1800(1 + .08763)^7 = 1800 \times 1.80038 = \$3240.69128$$

As expected, the same answer was obtained for FV regardless of whether the interest rate was expressed in continuous or the equivalent discrete form. One important practical application for this equivalence relationship is that the user has a choice as to which way to formulate and solve a problem. For instance, if one wishes to solve a continuous interest problem by use of the equivalent discrete relationship, then all the material of Chaps. 3 to 5 is applicable as well as the financial function keys of the Level II calculators and the computer programs for the Level III calculators.

6-4 THE FOUR UNKNOWNS: FV, PV, r, AND t, FOR A SINGLE PAYMENT

The key formulas in the discussion above are Eqs. (6-6) and (6-7). They enable us to solve for any one of the four variables FV, PV, r, or t provided the other three are known. By using Eq. (6-8), we could solve for any of these unknowns by means of an equivalency relationship and discrete equations. However, in the following section the continuous form will be used.

6-4.1 Solving for FV or PV

We have already used Eqs. (6-6) and (6-7) to solve for FV or PV, respectively. See Examples 6-2 and 6-5.

6-4.2 Solving for Continuous Nominal Interest Rate, *r*

Suppose we want to solve for *r* where FV, PV, and *t* are known. By rearranging Eq. (6-6),

$$e^{rt} = \frac{FV}{PV} \tag{6-9}$$

$$r \times t = \ln\left(\frac{FV}{PV}\right) \tag{6-10}$$

$$r = \left(\frac{1}{t}\right) \times \ln\left(\frac{FV}{PV}\right) \tag{6-11}$$

Consider an example.

Example 6-10 Solve for the nominal annual interest rate, compounded continuously, at which $22,150 will accumulate to $42,180 in 8 years. (See Example 3-13.)

$$PV = \$22,150 \qquad FV = \$42,180 \qquad t = 8$$

$$r = (\tfrac{1}{8}) \times \ln\left(\frac{42,180}{22,150}\right) \qquad \text{from Eq. (6-11)}$$

$$= .080514 \text{ or } 8.0514\%$$

6-4.3 Solving for the Time Span, *t*, in Years

To solve for *t*, the elapsed time (in years) between the PV and FV dates, we begin with Eq. (6-10):

$$r \cdot t = \ln\left(\frac{FV}{PV}\right)$$

Then

$$t = \left(\frac{1}{r}\right) \times \ln\left(\frac{FV}{PV}\right) \tag{6-12}$$

Example 6-11 In Example 6-10, how long will it take for the FV to accumulate to $84,175 if the PV remains at $22,150 and the interest rate is still the nominal 8.0514% compounded continuously?

$$PV = \$22,150 \qquad FV = \$84,175$$

$$r = .080514$$

$$t = \left(\frac{1}{.080514}\right) \ln\left(\frac{84,175}{22,150}\right)$$

$$= 16.5817 \text{ years}$$

6-5 CONTINUOUS COMPOUNDING FOR ORDINARY ANNUITIES

Up to this point this chapter has dealt with single payments with continuous compounding or discounting. We now turn to *multiple* payments with continuous compounding. Multiple-level payments are now a familiar subject, having been developed quite thoroughly in Chaps. 4 and 5. Since compounding is now continuous, there is not a "compounding period" and we need make no distinction between simple annuities (Chap. 4) and general annuities (Chap. 5). We'll begin with the case in which multiple-level payments are made at the end of successive periods—an ordinary annuity.

As in Chap. 4, we will develop the multiple-payment concepts by starting with a formula (6-6) for single-payment relationships,

$$FV = PV \times e^{rt} \tag{6-6}$$

and applying it to a specific example involving multiple payments.

Example 6-12 As in Example 4-1, suppose you invested $100 at the end of each year for 3 years at the nominal annual rate of 10% compounded continuously. How much will be on deposit at the end of the third year?†

In Table 6-1, we note that:

1. The first payment of $100 compounds continuously for 2 years.
2. The second payment of $100 compounds for 1 year.
3. The third payment invested at the end of the third year is not compounded at all.

The method used in Table 6-1 is to compute the individual future value for each payment and then sum all the future values.

---

†As was pointed out in Chap. 4, it is quite useful to sketch out time diagrams for payments and equivalent payments when dealing with annuities. The time diagram for this example is given in Time Diagram 4-1 and will not be duplicated here.

Table 6-1

End of year	Time for continuous compounding	Formula		Future value at end of year 3
1	2	$100 \times e^{.10 \times 2}$	=	$122.1403
2	1	$100 \times e^{.10 \times 1}$	=	110.5171
3	0	$100 \times e^{0}$	=	100.
		Total future value at end of year 3		$332.6574

The computational approach used above to solve Example 6-12 involves the same tabular format introduced at the beginning of Chaps. 3, 4, and 5, respectively. However, a much more practical approach to solve annuity problems with calculators is to develop and use the appropriate formula. Such a formula is developed as Eq. (6A-3) in Appendix 6A of this chapter. That is, when calculating the future value of an ordinary annuity with continuous compounding, the formula is

$$FV = PMT \times \frac{e^{(r/f) \times n} - 1}{e^{(r/f)} - 1} \qquad (6\text{-}13)$$

where r = nominal annual rate compounded continuously
f = number of payments per year
n = number of payments

Now let's rework Example 6-12 by making use of Eq. (6-13):

$$r = .10 \qquad n = 3 \qquad f = 1 \qquad PMT = \$100$$

$$FV = 100 \times \frac{e^{(.10) \times 3} - 1}{e^{(.01)} - 1} = 100 \times 3.326574 = \$332.6574$$

The answer is the same as the future value calculated in Table 6-1.

6-5.1 Converting Continuous to Discrete Interest Rates

Earlier, in Sec. 6-3.1 we demonstrated that an equivalency can be set up between discrete and continuous compounding *for single-payment situations.* We now wish to extend the "continuous to discrete interest equivalency" so that it will be applicable for *multiple-payment situations,* such as annuities. To convert from continuous to discrete it is necessary to specify the compounding interval that will be used for the equivalent discrete interest rate. For simplicity the interval is chosen to coincide with the time interval between payments, that is, $c = f$ and $i_c = i_f$. Then, for convenience, let's define j as:

$$j = \frac{r}{f} \qquad (6\text{-}14)$$

Thus the equivalency relationship [from Eq. (6-8)] can be written as:

$$i_f = e^j - 1 \tag{6-15}$$

Now let's solve Example 6-12 a third time utilizing Eq. (6-15). Recall that $r = .10$, $n = 3$, $f = 1$, PMT = \$100. From Eq. (6-15),

$$i_f = e^j - 1 = e^{r/f} - 1 = e^{.10} - 1 = .105170918$$

$$FV = PMT \times \frac{(1 + i_f)^n - 1}{i_f} \quad \text{from Eq. (4-1)}$$

$$= 100 \times \frac{1.105170918^3 - 1}{.105170918} = \$332.6574$$

which, of course, is again the same as the answer given in Table 6-1. We can now use these equivalency relationships to develop a general approach for solving ordinary annuities with continuous compounding.

6-5.2 Calculation Procedure for FV, PV, PMT, and n

Part of the objective of this chapter is to indicate the computational procedures available for solving annuity-type problems involving continuous compounding. Two choices are presented:

Choice 1 Use the formulas containing the continuous rate factor, e^r. This approach was demonstrated above, and is developed in detail in Appendix 6A. [See Eqs. (6A-3) to (6A-9).]

Choice 2 Develop a procedure to calculate FV, PV, PMT, or n that is based upon the discrete interest formulas of Chap. 4. This simple approach allows us to use the entire body of knowledge and formulas already presented in Chaps. 4 and 5, the financial function keys for the Level II calculator, and the library programs for the Level III calculators. The procedure is:

Step 1: Convert the continuous interest rate j to its discrete equivalent i_f:

$$i_f = e^j - 1 = e^{r/f} - 1$$

Step 2: Insert this i_f into the simple annuity formulas in Chap. 4 to solve for FV, PV, PMT, or n.

The simple annuity formulas will not be repeated in this chapter. However, the series of examples below will be used to demonstrate their application with continuous compounding. Since the illustrative example in the last section involved FV, we will begin with a calculation of PV for an ordinary annuity.

Example 6-13: PV of an ordinary annuity As in Example 4-2, assume you received \$100 at the end of each year for 3 years. What is the present value for this series of three level payments where the nominal annual rate of 10% is discounted continuously?

From Eq. (4-4) with $i_f = e^j - 1 = e^{.10} - 1 = .10517$,

$$PV = PMT \times \frac{1 - (1 + i_f)^{-3})}{i_f} = 100 \times \frac{1 - 1.10517^{-3}}{.10517}$$

$$= \$246.4386$$

Note that the present value of $246.44 for the continuous case is slightly less than for the discrete case (*$248.69* from Example 4-2).

Example 6-14: PMT for an ordinary annuity As in Example 4-3, a company is establishing a sinking fund. They will make a deposit at the end of each quarter in a savings account that pays 8% a year compounded continuously. To accumulate $150,000 at the end of 5 years, how much should be deposited each quarter?

$$i_f = e^j - 1 = e^{r/f} - 1 = e^{.08/4} - 1 = .02020134$$

From Eq. (4-7b)

$$PMT = \frac{FV \times i_f}{(1 + i_f)^n - 1} = \frac{150,000 \times .02020134}{(1.02020134)^{4 \times 5} - 1}$$

$$= \$6161.1404$$

Again, with continuous compounding, the payments are $6161.14, which is lower than the amount shown in Example 4-3 for discrete compounding.

Example 6-15: *n* for an ordinary annuity As in Example 4-5, a company deposits $10,000 at the end of each month in a savings account paying 6% nominal, compounded continuously. They want to accumulate $200,000. How many payments are required?

$$i_f = e^j - 1 = e^{r/f} - 1 = e^{.06/12} - 1 = .005012521$$

Then, from Eq. (4-9),

$$n = \frac{\ln\left(\dfrac{FV \times i_f}{PMT} + 1\right)}{\ln(1 + i_f)} = \frac{\ln\left(\dfrac{200,000 \times .005012521}{10,000} + 1\right)}{\ln(1.005012521)}$$

$$= 19.1076$$

We note that n is not an integer. However, it is assumed in the problem statement that payments must be made on a monthly basis. The two options, as explained for Example 4-5, are:

Option 1 Let the payment at $n = 19$ be the final payment. But 19 payments at $10,000 will not accumulate as much as the required $200,000. There will be a shortfall. To calculate the future value at the end of the 19th period, using Eq. (4-1) or (4-3):

$$FV_{19} = 10,000 \times S(n,i_f) = 10,000 \times S(19,.005012521)$$

$$= \$198,819.83$$

So the future value at $n = 19$ is only $198,819.83, whereas $200,000 is needed. So the shortfall of $1180.17 must be added to the last regular $10,000 payment; that is, the 19th payment becomes

$$\$10,000 + 1180.17 = \$11,180.17$$

Option 2 Make a regular $10,000 payment at the 19th period and make up the shortfall at the end of the 20th period. To calculate the size of the payment at the 20th period, first advance the future value at $n = 19$ to $n + 1 = 20$, using Eq. (6-6):

$$FV_{19} \times e^{r \times t} = \$198,819.8254 \times e^{(.06/12) \times 1}$$

$$= \$199,816.4140$$

At the end of the 20th period the cumulated payments, continuously compounded, are $199,816.42, but still short of the $200,000 by $183.58. The 20th payment makes up this difference; for this option there are 19 regular payments of $10,000 and a final payment of $183.58.

6-5.3 Solving for r

The procedure illustrated above to solve for FV, PV, PMT, and n must be altered to solve for r, the interest or discount rate. The procedure for r is:

Step 1: Compute as the unknown quantity the equivalent discrete interest rate, i_f, using the iterative procedure described in Chap. 4.

Step 2: Convert i_f to its continuous equivalent j, Eq. (6-15):

$$i_f = e^j - 1$$

which solved for j gives

$$j = \ln(1 + i_f) \tag{6-16}$$

Consider an example.

Example 6-16 As in Example 4-8, a company is evaluating a project which returns $2500 at the end of each month for 60 months. The project requires an $82,000 investment at the beginning of the first period. What is the project's yield based on continuous compounding?

In Example 4-8, the iteration procedure was used to obtain

$$i_f = .0224337163$$

Using Eq. (6-16), we can compute j, the equivalent continuous compounding rate:

$$j = \ln(1 + i_f) = \ln(1.0224337163) = .0221857814$$

Of course, j is a continuous interest rate expressed on the basis of *monthly* payment periods. The equivalent nominal annual rate for continuous compounding is obtained by multiplying the number of payments per year, f:

$$r = j \times f = .0221857814 \times 12 = .2662293769$$

The yield is 26.6299% compounded continously. This is slightly lower than the annual return on a discrete basis obtained in Example 4-8.

CONTINUOUS PAYMENTS

Business or financial applications rarely involve payments that are truly continuous. Nevertheless, there is merit in considering continuous payments, for several reasons:

1. Although continuous annuities do not actually occur in business, they are closely approximated in many cases, such as relatively small individual collections from a large number of consumers,
2. Discrete payments may have a short enough time interval between payments (say daily payments) that the error in using continuous payment analysis is negligible.
3. In many classes of problems, the mathematical analysis is facilitated when continuous payments are assumed.

There are two cases of continuous payments to consider: (1) where compounding is also continuous, and (2) where compounding is discrete.

6-6 CONTINUOUS PAYMENTS WITH CONTINUOUS COMPOUNDING

The combination of continuous payments as well as continuous compounding requires some additional analysis.† However, as we shall see, the continuous–continuous situation is not difficult to analyze provided that the interest rate is known and one of the other quantities, such as FV, PV, or T, is the un-

---

†Some readers at this point may wish to scan the analysis in Appendix 6C. However, it is not necessary to do so to work through the following material.

known quantity. The key formula for the continuous payments with continuous compounding is developed as Eq. (6C-4) of Appendix 6C:

$$FV = g \times \frac{e^{rT} - 1}{r} \qquad (6\text{-}17)$$

where T = life of the annuity, years
$\quad r$ = nominal annual interest rate compounded continuously
$\quad g$ = continuous payments, \$/year

Use will be made of Eq. (6-17) to solve various annuities involving continuous payments.

6-6.1 Solving for FV

If r, T, and g are known, it is a simple matter to solve for FV in Eq. (6-17). However, suppose we insist instead upon transforming both the g and r to their discrete equivalents, respectively, and then solve for the FV by use of the techniques of Chap. 4.

Let's determine discrete equivalent payments that occur f times per year. Then Eq. (6-17) can be modified to include the term f:

$$FV = \frac{g}{f} \times \frac{e^{rT} - 1}{r/f} \qquad (6\text{-}18)$$

If we define p as the continuous payment per equivalent discrete payment period:

$$p = \frac{g}{f} \qquad (6\text{-}19)$$

then Eq. (6-18) becomes

$$FV = p\left(\frac{e^{rT} - 1}{r/f}\right) \qquad (6\text{-}20)$$

Equation (6-20) can be used to solve for the FV. However, suppose we still insist upon transforming both p and r to their discrete equivalents, respectively, so that we can use the calculation procedures of Chap. 4. Then the equivalent payment made f times per year can be developed and becomes

$$PMT_e = p\left(\frac{e^{(r/f)} - 1}{r/f}\right) \qquad (6\text{-}21)$$

where $T = 1/f$. Solving for p in Eq. (6-21),

$$p = PMT_e \times \frac{r/f}{e^{(r/f)} - 1} \qquad (6\text{-}22)$$

Substituting p from Eq. (6-22) into (6-20), we obtain

$$FV = PMT_e \times \frac{r/f}{e^{(r/f)} - 1} \times \frac{e^{rT} - 1}{r/f} \tag{6-23}$$

Next, let $T = n/f$, since the FV is calculated at the end of the nth payment. So after canceling r/f,

$$FV = PMT_e \times \frac{e^{(r/f)n} - 1}{e^{(r/f)} - 1} \tag{6-24}$$

We have now accomplished half of the objectives of this section; namely, the FV formula is in terms of the equivalent payment PMT_e. The other half is to express $e^{r/f}$ in terms of the equivalent i_f where $c = f$.

Substituting $1 + i_f$ for $e^{r/f}$, Eq. (6-24) becomes

$$FV = PMT_e \times \frac{(1 + i_f)^n - 1}{i_f} \tag{6-25}$$

The use of Eqs. (6-20) and (6-25) is illustrated by the following example.

Example 6-17 Suppose an electric utility collects $54,750,000 per year in cash flows that are almost continuous and constant throughout the year. What is the anticipated future value of this cash flow stream 2 years from now if money is compounded continuously at nominal 7.5% per year?

Assume there are 365 days in a year and that the daily payments are considered to be continuous.

$$f = 1$$

$$p = \frac{g}{f} = \frac{54{,}750{,}000}{1} = 54{,}750{,}000$$

$$\frac{r}{f} = \frac{.075}{1} = .075$$

$$T = 2 \text{ years}$$

This example will be solved twice, using alternative approaches.

Alternative 1 Solve for FV using Eq. (6-17), which expresses both payment and compounding in the continuous form:

$$FV = g \times \frac{e^{r \times T} - 1}{r} = \$54{,}750{,}000 \times \frac{e^{.075 \times 2} - 1}{.075}$$

$$= \$118{,}138{,}997.2$$

Alternative 2 Solve for FV using Eq. (6-25), which expresses both payment and compounding in the discrete form.

Step 1: Convert the continuous interest rate to the equivalent discrete rate, i_f.

$$i_f = e^{r/f} - 1$$

$$= e^{.075} - 1$$

$$= .0778841509$$

Step 2: Convert the continuous payment p to the equivalent discrete amount PMT_e using Eq. (6-21).

$$PMT_e = p\frac{e^{r/f} - 1}{r/f}$$

$$= \$54,750,000 \times \frac{.0778841509}{.075}$$

$$= \$56,855,430.15$$

Step 3: Using the value of 2 (T/f) for n and the equivalent i_f and PMT_e calculated above, substitute into Eq. (6-25).

$$FV = PMT_e \times \frac{(1 + i_f)^n - 1}{i_f}$$

$$= \$56,855,430.15 \times \frac{(1 + .0778841509)^2 - 1}{.0778841509}$$

$$= \$118,138,997.2$$

The simplicity of alternative 1 is obvious when solving for FV or PV.

6-6.2 Solving for *g* or *T*

There are no difficulties encountered when using Eq. (6-17) to solve for either g or T. The equations are

$$g = FV \times \frac{r}{e^{rT} - 1} \tag{6-26}$$

and

$$T = \frac{\ln[((FV \times r)/g) + 1]}{r} \tag{6-27}$$

6-6.3 Solving for *r*, the Continuous Compounding Rate

To solve for r with both continuous payments and continuous compounding, a trial-and-error procedure is required. Again there are two alternative methods, but only the continuous method is discussed here.† The new iteration formulas are derived from Eq. (6-17), which is the continuous (g)–continuous (r) form, and are very similar to Eqs. (6A-1) and (6B-3) to (6B-5) in Appendix 6B.

$$\Delta r_k = \frac{1 - \dfrac{\text{FV} \times r}{g(e^{rT} - 1)}}{r + 1/r - T}$$

is used in the relationship (6B-5):

$$r_{k+1} = r_k - \Delta r_k$$

6-7 CONTINUOUS PAYMENTS WITH DISCRETE COMPOUNDING

The final case to be considered in this chapter is continuous payments with discrete compounding. Annuities for this case can be solved along the general lines of Sec. (6-6), except that computing an equivalent interest rate is not necessary.

The starting point to calculate the future value is Eq. (6-18) for continuous payments and compounding.

$$\text{FV} = \frac{g}{f} \times \frac{e^{rT} - 1}{r/f}$$

For discrete compounding, the continuous payment per compounding period is g/c, where $c = f$. The interest rate is i_c, and the number of compounding periods is $n = c \times T$. Substituting $(1 + i_c)^n$ for e^{rT}, $\ln(1 + i_c)$ for r/f, and g/c for g/f, we get

$$\text{FV} = \frac{g}{c} \times \frac{(1 + i_c)^n - 1}{\ln(1 + i_c)} \tag{6-28}$$

The other approach is to convert the continuous g to the discrete PMT_e. The equivalency relationship between the continuous payment, g, and discrete payment, PMT_e, for this case is given by

$$\text{PMT}_e = \frac{g}{c} \times \frac{i_c}{\ln(1 + i_c)} \tag{6-29}$$

---

†The first method, which is illustrated, is based on the continuous formula of Eq. (6-17). The second method, which is not illustrated, is based on the discrete formula of Eq. (6-25).

6-7.1 Solving for FV, PV, or *n*

To solve for unknown FV, PV, or n,† simply compute the equivalent PMT, and enter the appropriate values (including i_c and n) into the appropriate annuity equations from Chap. 4. To solve for the continuous payment, g, first obtain PMT_e and obtain the equivalent g using a restated (6-29).

$$g = \frac{\text{PMT}_e \times c \times \ln(1 + i_c)}{i_c} \qquad (6\text{-}30)$$

Let's illustrate this procedure with a FV example.

Example 6-18 Repeat Example 6-17, assuming that discrete compounding takes place four times per year, so

$$g = \$54,750,000 \text{ per year}$$

$$c = f = 4$$

$$i_c = \frac{r}{c} = \frac{.075}{4} = .01875$$

$$n = T \times c = 2 \times 4 = 8$$

$$\text{PMT}_e = \frac{g \times i_c}{c \times \ln(1 + i_c)} = \frac{\$54,750,000 \times (.01875)}{4 \times \ln(1 + .01875)}$$

$$= \$13,815,423.03$$

From Eq. (6-25),

$$\text{FV} = \text{PMT}_e \times \frac{(1 + i_c)^n - 1}{i_c}$$

$$= \$13,815,423.03 \times \frac{(1.01875)^8 - 1}{.01875}$$

$$= \$118,054,943.8$$

A comparison of Example 6-18 with Example 6-17 shows that the FV under quarterly compounding is slightly less than for continuous compounding.

6-7.2 Solving for i_c

Solving for i_c under conditions of continuous payments p and discrete interest rate i_c presents no additional difficulties that deserve mention. Refer back to Eq. (6-28), which is repeated below:

$$\text{FV} = \frac{g}{c} \times \frac{(1 + i_c)^n - 1}{\ln(1 + i_c)}$$

---

†Perhaps it should be emphasized once again that for the annuity cash flow stream with level continuous payments, no distinction can be made between the *ordinary* and *due* annuities.

We note that it is possible to solve for i_c in the equation above using a trial-and-error approach when g, c, and FV are known. This equation can also be used to solve for i_c with Newton-Raphson methods similar to those described in Chaps. 4 and 5 and Appendix 6B.

APPENDIX 6A ANNUITY FORMULAS FOR CONTINUOUS COMPOUNDING, DISCRETE PAYMENTS

This appendix contains a derivation of annuity formulas for continuous compounding with discrete payments.

It will begin by deriving the basic equation (6-13) for the future value (FV) of an ordinary annuity.

6A-1 ORDINARY ANNUITIES—FV

We begin with the formula for single payments, Eq. (6-6):

$$FV = PV \times e^{rt} \qquad (6\text{-}6)$$

and expand the relationship for a series of equal annual payments. Recall that the method of analysis used in Table 6-1 was simply to compute the future value for each of a series of payments and then sum all those future values. This type of calculation can be generalized to

$$FV = PMT \times e^{r\times 0} + PMT \times e^{r\times 1} \times \cdots + PMT \times e^{r(n-1)}$$

or, using summation notation,

$$FV = PMT \times \sum_{h=0}^{n-1} e^{r\times h} \qquad (6A\text{-}1)$$

where PMT = amount of each payment
r = nominal annual interest rate, compounded continuously
n = total number of payment in the annuity problem
h = dummy index to indicate summation

By going through a modest amount of algebraic manipulation this equation can now be generalized from the special case of annual payment to a general case where payments can be made on any regular time period basis. So let:

n = total number of payments
f = number of payments per year
T = total time the annuity is in force, years

Suppose we wish to determine the future value at the time when the last payment occurs. We know that the time for the first payment is $1/f$ and the time for the last payment is n/f. For continuous compounding at the nominal annual rate r, we have

$$FV = PMT \times [e^{r((n-1)/f)} + e^{r((n-2)/f)} + \cdots + e^{r((n-n)/f)}] \qquad (6A\text{-}2)$$

Rearranging the terms, we obtain

$$FV = PMT \times [e^{(r/f)\times 0} + e^{(r/f)\times 1} + e^{(r/f)\times(n-1)}] \qquad (6A\text{-}2)$$

Note that the series in the brackets has a finite sum which was given in Appendix 4A; therefore,

$$FV = PMT \times \frac{e^{(r/f)\times n} - 1}{e^{(r/f)} - 1} \qquad (6A\text{-}3)$$

Equation (6A-3) appears in Sec. 6-5.1 as Eq. (6-13).

6A-2 ORDINARY ANNUITIES—PV

The formula for the present value of an ordinary annuity can be developed following the same pattern used in Sec. 6A-1 for future value.

$$PV = e^{-r(n/f)} \times FV \qquad (6A\text{-}4)$$

or

$$PV = e^{-(r/f)n} \times \frac{e^{(r/f)n} - 1}{e^{r/f} - 1} \qquad (6A\text{-}5)$$

which reduces to

$$PV = PMT \times \frac{1 - e^{-(r/f)n}}{e^{r/f} - 1} \qquad (6A\text{-}6)$$

6A-3 SOLVING FOR PMT, ORDINARY ANNUITIES

Solving for the payments, PMT, of an ordinary annuity is simply making use of Eq. (6A-3) or (6A-6), depending on whether FV or PV is given. Use

$$PMT = \frac{FV \times (e^{r/f} - 1)}{e^{(r/f)\times n} - 1} \qquad (6A\text{-}7)$$

or

$$PMT = \frac{PV \times (e^{r/f} - 1)}{1 - e^{-(r/f)\times n}} \qquad (6A\text{-}8)$$

6A-4 SOLVING FOR NUMBER OF PAYMENTS, ORDINARY ANNUITY

The formula to solve for the number of payments comes from either Eq. (6A-3) or (6A-6), depending on whether FV or PV is known. If FV is known, Eq. (6A-3) can be restated as follows:

$$e^{(r/f) \times n} - 1 = \frac{FV}{PMT}(e^{r/f} - 1)$$

$$e^{(r/f) \times n} = \frac{FV}{PMT}(e^{r/f} - 1) + 1$$

$$n \ln(e^{r/f}) = \ln \left[\frac{FV}{PMT}(e^{r/f} - 1) + 1 \right]$$

$$n = \frac{\ln[(FV/PMT)(e^{r/f} - 1) + 1]}{\ln(e^{r/f})}$$

Since $\ln(e^{r/f}) = r/f$, this equation becomes

$$n = \frac{\ln[(FV/PMT)(e^{r/f} - 1) + 1]}{r/f} \tag{6A-9}$$

6A-5 SOLVING FOR r

You have seen that the key formula for an ordinary annuity with continuous compounding is Eq. (6A-3):

$$FV = PMT \times \frac{^{(r/f) \times n} - 1}{e^{(r/f)} - 1} \tag{6A-3}$$

As shown in previous sections, we can start with this formula to solve for any of the unknown variables FV, PMT, n, or (r/f) provided the other three are known. Solving for FV, PMT, or n was relatively straightforward because it is possible to develop an explicit formula for each of them, where the three known quantities are on the "right-hand side." See Eqs. (6A-3), (6A-7), and (6A-9), respectively.

A different situation exists when solving for (r/f) in Eq. (6A-3), because this term appears twice, both in the numerator and in the denominator, so it is not possible to solve for r explicitly. Therefore, a trial-and-error method, an iteration method, similar to that used in Chap. 4, is required. Appendix 6B describes a method, known as the Newton–Raphson method, to solve for the interest rate r for the ordinary annuity case when FV, PMT, n, and f are known.

APPENDIX 6B THE NEWTON-RAPHSON METHOD

This appendix introduces the reader to the Newton-Raphson method of solving for an unknown interest rate. Although specific formulas for finding interest rates were introduced in Chaps. 4 and 5, the more detailed explanations and analysis were deferred to this appendix for treatment.

To solve for j (or r/f) in Eq. (6A-3),

$$FV = PMT \times \frac{e^{r/f \times n} - 1}{e^{r/f} - 1} \tag{6A-3}$$

where the other three variables, FV, PMT, and n, are known requires a trial-and-error method, similar to the iteration routine described in Chap. 4.

Essentially, the problem reduces to that of finding a root for an equation of the type $f(j) = 0$, where $f = 1$ so $r = j$.

6B-1 FINDING A ROOT OF $f(r) = 0$

Let's first consider a simple approach to finding the root, $\bar{r}$, of $f(r) = 0$. First, we'll rearrange Eq. (6A-3) into the form $f(r) = 0$, with $f = 1$, so that

$$f(r) = PMT \times \frac{e^{r \times n} - 1}{e^r - 1} - FV = 0 \tag{6B-1}$$

To illustrate Eq. (6B-1) as a curve, we'll select specific numerical values and plot them.

6B-1.1 Curve Plotting

From Example 4-7, PMT = $1200, $f = 1$, $n = 10$, and FV = $17,800. Suppose our objective is to find a value of r for continuous compounding such that $f(r) = 0$ in Eq. (6B-1). The most direct approach is to calculate values of $f(r)$ for specified value of r and plot them on graph paper, as in Fig. 6-2.

A characteristic of this curve is that values of $f(r)$ start out as a negative values for $r = 0$, provided suitable values are given to PMT, n, and FV. Note that Eq. (6B-1) cannot be used directly to get a value for $f(r)$ with $r = 0$. Instead, it is necessary to know that for $r = 0$,

$$f(0) = PMT \times n - FV \tag{6B-2}$$

If $f(0) < 0$, then PMT $\times n <$ FV and a positive root, $\bar{r}$, will exist. Indeed, in Example 4-7, PMT $\times n$ is less than FV (1200 $\times$ 10 < 17,800), so there *is* a positive interest rate root, $\bar{r}$.

Next plot the calculated values of $f(r)$ for assumed values of r. We then

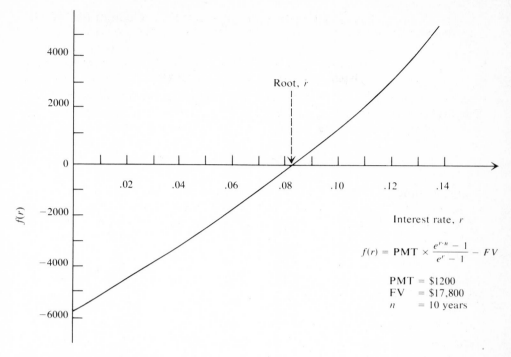

Figure 6-2 Use of $f(r)$ to find root, $\bar{r}$

examine the plotted curve, noting the value of r where $f(r) = 0$. From Fig. 6-2, $\bar{r}$ is approximately equal to .081 or 8.1% compounded continuously.

Although this method is easy to understand, it can be time consuming to execute if you want $\bar{r}$ to be accurate to (say) three significant figures, especially if a large number of cases are to be solved. The Newton-Raphson method provides a more systematic approach.

6B-2 THE NEWTON-RAPHSON METHOD

The solution to an equation $f(r) = 0$ may often be found by a simple procedure known as the Newton-Raphson method. In fact, the annuity equations, as described in Chaps. 4 to 6 are especially good candidates for this method. That is why this method is generally used in the built-in circuits or in the library programs of Level II and III calculators.

6B-2.1 Graphical Illustration

To illustrate the method, we will use Fig. 6-3. Select a starting value of r, called r_0. Let's take $r_0 = .05$; then we calculate $f(r)$ at $r = .05$, or $f(.05)$, and also the *slope* of the *tangent* to the curve at $f(r_0)$. Calculation of the tangent, which is shown graphically in Fig. 6-3, is explained in the next section. Then this tangent with slope $f'(r_0)$ is extended to intersect the r axis at $r_1 = .0851$.

By inspection of Fig. 6-3, the value r is different from the real root $\bar{r}$, so the process is repeated. Once again, the tangent is drawn at $f(r_1)$ and this second tangent intersects the r axis at $r_2 = .0816$, a value much closer to $\bar{r}$. The procedure can be repeated to find an improved approximation to $\bar{r}$. However, while this graphical method is useful as a way of visualizing what is going on, it is not very practical. It is far more useful to apply the Newton-Raphson procedure using hand-held calculators of Levels II and III.

6B-2.2 Analytical Approach

Start with the relationship from Eq. (6A-3):

$$f(r) = \text{PMT} \times \frac{e^{r \times n} - 1}{e^r - 1} - \text{FV}$$

Now we need a relationship for the slope of the tangent, $f'(r)$:

$$f'(r) = \text{PMT}\frac{[(e^r - 1)e^{r \times n} \times n - (e^{r \times n} - 1)e^r]}{(e^r - 1)^2}$$

.where $f'(r)$ denotes the derivative of $f(r)$ with respect to r. The ratio $f(r)/f'(r)$ is needed to find the next approximation to the root r:

$$\frac{f(r)}{f'(r)} = \frac{(e^{rn} - 1) - (\text{FV}/\text{PMT})(e^r - 1)}{ne^{r \times n} - e^r \times \left(\dfrac{e^{rn} - 1}{e^r - 1}\right)} \tag{6B-3}$$

The following calculation procedure can now be used.

Step 0: Make an initial estimate of r and call it r_0.

Step 1: Calculate $f(r_0)/f'(r_0)$ from Eq. (6B-3).

Step 2: Calculate an improved approximation for r by use of the equation

$$r_1 = r_0 - \frac{f(r_0)}{f'(r_0)} \tag{6B-4}$$

where r_1 is the improved value.

Step 3: Equation (6B-4) can be used repeatedly to find an improved approximation to the root $\bar{r}$. The formula above is generalized to

$$r_{k+1} = r_k - \frac{f(r_k)}{f'(r_k)} \tag{6B-5}$$

where r_{k+1} is the $(k + 1)$st improvement over e_k to find the real root $\bar{r}$.

Step 4: The iterative sequence can be terminated whenever you feel that the approximation is close enough to the real root $\bar{r}$ to be of practical value. (This termination decision is made for you in Level II and III calculators.)

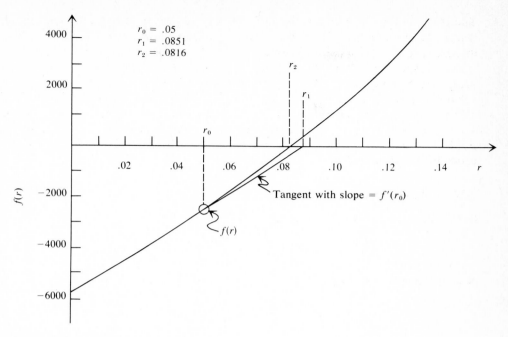

Figure 6-3 Newton-Raphson method

The next example demonstrates these steps for the numerical example of Fig. 6-3.

Example 6-19 This example is based upon the same numerical values plotted in Fig. 6-3. That is,

$$\text{PMT} = \$12,000 \qquad n = 10 \text{ years} \qquad f = 1 \qquad \text{FV} = \$17,800$$

Solve for r.

The necessary equations need not be repeated here. These equations can be solved with any level calculator. The actual computations were made with a Level III programmable, and the results tabulated in Table 6-2. The initial value for r at $k = 0$ was selected as .05 in order to agree with r_0 in Fig. 6-3.

Table 6-2

Iteration No k	r_k	$f(r_k)$	$f'(r_k)$	r_{k+1}
0	.05	−2616.679	74561.86	.085094
1	.085094	329.1128	94155.61	.081599
2	.081599	3.83556	91970.36	.081557
3	.081557	.00054	91944.63	.081557

Then using Eqs. (6A-1), (6B-3), and (6B-4), r was calculated to be .085094. Several more iterations were carried out until there was essentially no change in r_k (within a certain tolerance). So we accept $r_3 = .081557$ as the root that satisfies Eq. (6A-3).

APPENDIX 6C CONTINUOUS PAYMENTS– CONTINUOUS DISCOUNTING

To derive the formulas for continuous payments and continuous discounting, we will define:

$g(t)$ = continuous payments, \$/year
t = time, years
T = life of the annuity, years
dt = very small time interval
r = nominal annual interest rate

From Fig. 6-4, we note that $g(t)$ represents continuous payments of the same amount. For example, if a large number of consumers were putting coins into a vending machine, it could be assumed that the money flows in continuously and, in this case, at a constant rate measured in \$/year.

Between the time intervals t and $t + \Delta t$, the small inflow is $g(t) \times \Delta t$, which is compounded from t to T. The future value for this small inflow is

$$\Delta FV = g(t) \times \Delta t \times e^{r(T-t)} \tag{6C-1}$$

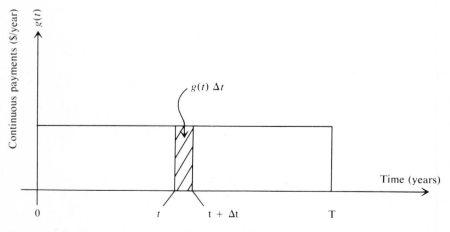

Figure 6-4 Continuous payments and continuous discounting

Using methods of calculus, it is a straightforward matter to add up or integrate all the ΔFV increments for all values of t. That is,

$$FV = \int_0^T g(t)e^{r(T-t)}dt \tag{6C-2}$$

Since all the cash flows are constant $[g(t) = \text{constant} = g]$,

$$FV = g \times \int_0^T e^{r(T-t)}dt \tag{6C-3}$$

The integration of Eq. (6C-3) leads to the result

$$FV = g \times \frac{e^{rT} - 1}{r} \tag{6C-4}$$

From this point it is also routine to determine the PV at $t = 0$.

$$PV = FV \times e^{-rT} \tag{6C-5}$$

Substituting Eq. (6A-9) into (6A-10),

$$PV = g \times \frac{e^{r \times T} - 1}{r} \times e^{-rT} \tag{6C-6}$$

$$= g \times \frac{1 - e^{-r \times T}}{r} \tag{6C-7}$$

KEYSTROKE SOLUTIONS

This section contains keystroke solutions for selected examples in this chapter. These solutions are organized by *type* of calculator (Type A or R) and within each type by *level* (Level I, II, or III).

Type	Level	Example number	Page
A	I	6-4, 6-12, 6-17, 6-18, 6-19	177, 182, 189, 192, 199
	II	6-4, 6-12, 6-17, 6-18, 6-19	177, 182, 189, 192, 199
	III	6-4, 6-12, 6-17, 6-18, 6-19	177, 182, 189, 192, 199
R	I	6-4, 6-12, 6-17, 6-18, 6-19	177, 182, 189, 192, 199
	II	6-4, 6-12, 6-17, 6-18, 6-19	177, 182, 189, 192, 199
	III	6-4, 6-12, 6-17, 6-18, 6-19	177, 182, 189, 192, 199

Type A, Level I keystrokes for Example 6-4

TI-30/50 keystrokes	Display	Comments
C	0.	Clear
1500	1500.	PV
×	1500.	
(	1500.	
.06	0.06	r
×	0.06	
182	182.	n
÷	10.92	
12	12.	f
)	0.91	
INV ln x	2.4843225	
=	3726.4838	FV

Type A, Level I keystrokes for Example 6-12

TI-30/50 keystrokes	Display	Comments
C	0.	Clear
.1	0.1	r
×	0.1	
3	3.	n
=	0.3	
INV ln x	1.3498588	
−	1.3498588	
1	1.	
=	.3498588	
÷	.3498588	
(	.3498588	
.1	0.1	
INV ln x	1.1051709	
−	1.1051709	
1	1.	
)	.10517092	
×	3.3265737	
100	100.	PMT
=	332.65737	FV

Type A, Level I keystrokes for Example 6-17

TI-30/50 keystrokes	Display	Comments
C	0.	Clear
54750000	5475000	g
×	54750000.	
(	54750000.	
(	54750000.	
.075	0.075	r
×	0.075	
2	2	T
)	0.15	
INV ln x	1.1618342	
−	1.1618342	
1	1	
)	0.16183424	
÷	8860424.8	
.075	0.075	
=	1.1814 08	1.1814×10^8 FV

Type A, Level I keystrokes for Example 6-18

TI-30 keystrokes	Display	Comments
C	0.	Clear
54750000	54750000.	g
×	54750000.	
(	54750000.	
(	54750000.	
1	1.	
+	1.	
.075	0.075	r
÷	0.075	
4	4.	c
)	1.01875	
y^x	1.01875	
8	8.	n
−	1.1602217	
1	1.	
)	.16022168	
÷	8772136.8	
(	8772136.8	
4	4.	
×	4.	
(	4.	
1	1.	
+	1.	
.075	0.075	
÷	0.075	
4	4.	
)	1.01875	
ln x	.01857639	
=	1.1805 08	1.1806×10^8

Type A, Level I keystrokes for Example 6-19

TI-30/50 keystrokes	Display	Comments
C	0.	Clear
.05	0.05	First guess r_0
STO	0.05	STO r_0
RCL	0.05	
×	0.05	
10	10.	n
=	0.5	
INV ln x	1.6487213	
−	1.6487213	
1	1.	
=	.64872127	
−	.64872127	
17800	17800.	FV
÷	17800.	
1200	1200.	PMT
×	14.833333	
(	14.833333	
RCL	0.05	r
INV ln x	1.0512711	
−	1.0512711	
1	1.	
)	0.0512711	
=	−.11179998	$f(r)$
÷	−.11179998	
(	−.11179998	
10	10.	n
×	10.	
(	10.	
RCL	0.05	r
×	0.05	
9	9.	$n-1$
)	0.45	

TI-30/50 keystrokes	Display	Comments
INV ln x	1.5683122	
+	15.683122	
(	15.683122	
1	1.	
−	1.	
(	1.	
RCL	0.05	
×	0.05	
10	10.	
)	0.5	
INV ln x	1.6487213	
)	−.64872127	
÷	−.64872127	
(	−.64872127	
RCL	0.05	
INV ln x	1.0512711	
−	1.0512711	
1	1.	
)	0.0512711	
=	−.03689337	$f(r)/f'(r)$
+/−	.03689337	Δr_1
SUM	.03689337	
RCL	.08689337	r_1

Repeating the iterations:

$r_2 = .08117572$

$r_3 = .0815897$

$r_4 = .08155416$

$r_5 = .08155717$

$r_6 = .08155692$

$r_7 = .08155694$

Type A, Level II keystrokes for Example 6-4

TI-MBA/BA-II keystrokes	Display	Comments
CA	0	Clear
FIX 2	0.00	Set display
1500	1500	PV
PV	1500.00	
182	182	n
N	182.00	
.06	0.06	r
÷	0.06	
12	12	f
=	.01	j
e^x	1.01	
−	1.01	
1	1	
=	0.01	
×	0.01	
100	100	
=	0.50	$i_c\%$
%i	0.50	
CPT	0.50	
FV	3726.48	FV

Type A, Level II keystrokes for Example 6-12

TI-MBA/BA-II keystrokes	Display	Comments
CA	0	Clear
FIX 2	0.00	Set display
3	3	n
N	3.00	
.1	0.1	r/f
e^x	1.11	
−	1.11	
1	1	
=	0.11	
×	0.11	
100	100	
=	10.52	$i_c\%$
%i	10.52	
100	100	PMT
PMT	100.00	
CPT	100.00	
FV	332.66	FV

Type A, Level II keystrokes for Example 6-17

TI-MBA/BA-II keystrokes	Display	Comments
CA	0	Clear
FIX 2	0.00	
.075	0.075	r/f
e^x	1.08	
−	1.08	
1	1	
=	0.08	
STO 0	0.08	i_c
÷	0.08	
.075	0.075	
×	1.04	
54750000	54750000	g
=	56855430.16	Equivalent discrete payment
PMT	56855430.16	
2	2.00	T
N		
RCL 0	.08	
×	.08	
100	100	
=	7.79	
%i	7.79	$i_c\%$
CPT	7.79	
FV	118138997.2	FV

Type A, Level II keystrokes for Example 6-18

TI-MBA/BA-II keystrokes	Display	Comments
CA	0	Clear
FIX 2	0.00	
7.5	7.5	r
÷	7.50	
4	4	c
=	1.88	
%i	1.88	$i_c\%$
÷	1.88	
100	100	
=	0.02	i_c
STO 0	0.02	
+	0.02	
1	1	
=	1.02	
ln x	0.02	
1/x	53.83	
×	53.83	
RCL 0	0.02	
÷	1.01	
4	4	
×	0.25	
54750000	54750000	
=	13815423.02	Equivalent discrete payments
PMT	13815423.02	
8	8	n
N	8.00	
CPT	8.00	
FV	118054943.8	FV

Type A, Level II keystrokes for Example 6-19

TI-MBA/BA-II keystrokes	Display	Comments
CA	0	Clear
FIX 2	0.00	Set display
10	10	n
N	10.00	
1200	1200	PMT
PMT	1200.00	
17800	17800	FV
FV	17800.00	
CPT	17800.00	
%i	8.50	$i_c\%$
÷	8.50	
100	100	
+	0.08	$1 + i_c$
1	1	
=	1.08	r/f
ln x	0.08	
FIX 8	0.08155694	Eight-digit display

Type A, Level III keystrokes for Example 6-4

TI-58/59 keystrokes	Display	Comments
CMs	0.	Clear memories
Pgm 18	0.	Call compound interest program
E'	0.00	Initialize
1500	1500	PV
C	1500.00	
182	182	n
A	182.00	
.06	0.06	r
÷	0.06	
12	12	
=	0.01	j
INV ln x	1.01	
−	1.01	
1	1	
=	0.01	i_c
×	0.01	
100	100	
=	0.50	$i_c\%$
B	0.50	
O	0	
D	3726.48	FV

Type A, Level III keystrokes for Example 6-12

TI-58/59 keystrokes	Display	Comments
CMs	0.	Clear memory
Pgm 19	0.	Call annuity program
E'	0.	Initialize
A'	0.	Select FV case
3	3	n
A	3.	
100	100	PMT
C	100.00	
.1	0.1	r/f
INV ln x	1.11	
−	1.11	
1	1	
=	0.11	i_c
×	0.11	
100	100	
=	10.52	$i_c\%$
B	10.5171	
0	0	
D	332.66	FV

Type A, Level III keystrokes for Example 6-17

TI-58/59 keystrokes	Display	Comments
CMs	0.	Clear memories
Pgm 19	0.	Call annuity program
E'	0.	Initialize
A'	0.	Select PV case
.075	0.075	r/f
INV ln x	1.077884151	
−	1.077884151	
1	1	
=	.0778841509	i_c
STO 25	.0778841509	
×	.0778841509	
100	100.	
=	7.788415088	$i_c\%$
B	7.7884	
RCL 25	0.0779	
÷	0.0779	
.075	0.075	
×	1.0385	
54750000	54750000	
=	56855430.15	g
C	56855430.15	Equivalent discrete payment
2	2	T
A	2.	
0	0	
D	118138997.2	FV

Type A, Level III keystrokes for Example 6-19

TI-58/59 keystrokes	Display	Comments
CMs	0.	Clear memories
Pgm 19	0.	Call annuity program
E'	0.	Initialize
A'	0.	Select FV case
10	10	n
A	10.	
1200	1200	PMT
C	1200.00	
17800	17800	FV
D	17800.00	
0	0	
B	8.4975	$i_c\%$
÷	8.4975	
100	100	
+	0.0850	i_c
1	1	
=	1.0850	
ln x	0.0816	r/f
Fix 9	.0815569403	Full-digit display

Type A, Level III keystrokes for Example 6-18

TI-58/59 keystrokes	Display	Comments
CMs	0.	Clear memories
PGM 19	0.	Call annuity program
E'	0.	Initialize
A'	0.	Select FV case
7.5	7.5	r
÷	7.5	
4	4	c
=	1.875	$i_c\%$
B	1.8750	
÷	1.8750	
100	100	
=	0.0188	i_c
STO 25	0.0188	
÷	0.0188	
4	4	c
÷	0.0047	
(	0.0047	
1	1	
+	1.0000	
RCL 25	0.0188	
)	1.0188	
ln x	0.0186	
×	0.2523	
54750000	54750000	g
=	1381542303	Equivalent discrete payment
C	1381542303	
8	8.	n
A	8.	
0	0	
D	118054943.8	FV

Type R, Level I keystrokes for Example 6-4

HP-31E/32E keystrokes	Display	Comments
ALL	0.0000	Clear
.06	0.06	r
ENTER↑	0.0600	
182	182.	n
×	10.9200	
12	12.	f
÷	0.9100	
e^x	2.4843	
1500	1,500.	PV
×	3,726.4838	FV

Type R, Level I keystrokes for Example 6-12

HP-31E/32E keystrokes	Display	Comments
ALL	0.0000	Clear
.1	0.1	r
ENTER↑	0.1000	
3	3.	n
x	0.3000	
e^x	1.3499	
1	1.	
−	0.3499	
.1	0.1	
e^x	1.1052	
1	1.	
−	0.1052	
÷	3.3266	PMT
100	100.	
×	332.6574	FV

Type R, Level I keystrokes for Example 6-18

HP-31E/32E keystrokes	Display	Comments
ALL	0.0000	Clear
.075	0.075	r
ENTER↑	0.0750	c
4	4.	
÷	0.0188	
1	1	
+	1.0188	
8	8.	n
y^x	1.1602	
1	1.	
−	0.1602	
4	4	
÷	0.0401	
.075	0.075	
ENTER↑	0.0750	
4	4.	
÷	0.0188	
1	1.	
+	1.0188	
LN	0.0186	
÷	2.1563	
54750000	54,750,000.	g
×	118,054,943.5	FV

Type R, Level I keystrokes for Example 6-17

HP-31E/32E keystrokes	Display	Comments
ALL	0.0000	Clear
.075	0.075	r
ENTER↑	0.0750	T
2	2.	
×	0.1500	
e^x	1.1618	
1	1.	
−	0.1618	
.075	0.075	
÷	2.1578	
54750000	54,750,000	g
×	118,138,997.4	FV

Type R, Level I keystrokes for Example 6-19

HP-31E/32E keystrokes	Display	Comments	HP-31E/32E keystrokes	Display	Comments
ALL	0.0000	Clear	RCL 1	0.0500	
.05	0.05	First guess r_0	10	10.	n
STO 1	0.0500		×	0.5000	
RCL 1	0.0500		e^x	1.6487	
10	10.		−	−0.6487	
×	0.5000		RCL 1	0.0500	r_0
e^x	1.6487		e^x	1.0513	
1	1.		1	1.	
−	0.6487	n	−	0.0513	
17800	17,800.	FV	÷	−12.6528	
ENTER↑	17,800.0000		+	3.0304	$f'(r)$
1200	1,200.	PMT	STO 3	3.0304	
÷	14.8333		RCL 2	−0.1118	
RCL 1	0.0500		RCL 3	3.0304	
e^x	1.0513		÷	−0.0369	$f(r)/f'(r)$
1	1.		CHS	0.0369	
−	0.0513		STO + 1	0.0369	Δr_1
×	0.7605		RCL 1	0.0869	
−	−0.1118	$f(r)$	(f)9	0.086893374	r_1
STO 2	−0.1118				
RCL 1	0.0500				
9	9.	$n-1$			
×	0.4500				
e^x	1.5683				
10	10.	n			
×	15.6831				
1	1.				
ENTER↑	1.0000				

The remaining iteration values are

$i_2 = 0.081175718$
$i_3 = 0.081589705$
$i_4 = 0.081554160$
$i_5 = 0.081557177$
$i_6 = 0.081556920$
$i_7 = 0.081556942$
$i_8 = 0.081556940$

Type R, Level II keystrokes for Example 6-4

HP-37E/38E keystrokes	Display	Comments
ALL	0.00	Clear
END	0.00	Set payment switch to end
.06	0.06	r
ENTER↑	0.06	
12	12.	
÷	0.01	j
e^x	1.01	$1 + i_c$
1	1.	
−	0.01	i_c
100	100.	
×	0.50	
i	0.50	
1500	1,500	PV
PV	1,500.00	
182	182.	
n	182.00	n
FV	−3,726.48	FV

Type R, Level II keystrokes for Example 6-12

HP-37E/38E keystrokes	Display	Comments
ALL	0.00	Clear
END	0.00	Set payment switch to end
3	3.	n
n	3.00	
100	100.	PMT
PMT	100.00	
.1	0.1	r/f
e^x	1.11	
1	1.	
−	0.11	i_c
100	100.	
×	10.52	i_c
i	10.52	
FV	−332.66	FV

213

Type R, Level II keystrokes for Example 6-17

HP-37E/38E keystrokes	Display	Comments
ALL	0.00	Clear
END	0.00	Set payment switch
.075	0.075	r/f
e^x	1.08	
1	1.	
−	0.08	i_c
STO 1	0.08	
.075	0.075	
÷	1.04	
54750000	54,750,000	g
×	56,855,430.25	Equivalent discrete payment
PMT	56,855,430.25	
RCL 1	0.08	
100	100.	
×	7.79	$i_c\%$
i	7.79	
2	2.	T
n	2.00	
FV	−118,138,997.4	FV

Type R, Level II keystrokes for Example 6-18

HP-37E/38E keystrokes	Display	Comments
ALL	0.00	Clear
END	0.00	Set payment switch
7.5	7.5	r
ENTER↑	7.50	
4	4.	c
÷	1.88	
i	1.88	$i_c\%$
RCL i	1.88	
100	100.	
÷	0.02	i_c
STO 1	0.02	
4	4.	c
÷	0.005	
RCL 1	0.02	
1	1.	
+	1.02	
LN	0.02	
÷	0.25	
54750000	54,750,000.	g
×	13,815,423.03	Equivalent discrete payment
PMT	13,815,423.03	
8	8.	n
n	8.00	
FV	−118,054,943.8	FV

Type R, Level II keystrokes for Example 6-19

HP-37E/38E keystrokes	Display	Comments
ALL	0.00	Clear
END	0.00	Set payment switch
10	10.	
n	10.00	n
1200	1,200	
PMT	1,200.00	PMT
17800	17,800.	
CHS	−17,800.	
FV	−17,800.00	FV
i	8.50	
100	100.	$i_c\%$
÷	0.08	
1	1	i_c
+	1.08	
LN	0.08	j
(f)9	0.081556941	j full-digit display

Type R, Level III keystrokes for Example 6-4

HP-97/67 keystrokes	Display	Comments
fA	0.00	Program SD-05A
1500	1500.	Start function
STO D	1500.00	PV
182	182.	
STO A	182.00	n
.06	0.06	
ENTER↑	0.06	r
12	12.	
÷	0.01	f
e^x	1.01	j
1	1.	
−	0.01	i_c
100	100.	
×	0.50	
STO B	0.50	$i_c\%$
E	3726.48	FV

Type R, Level III keystrokes for Example 6-12

HP-97/67 keystrokes	Display	Comments
fA	0.00	Program SD-05A
3	3.	Start function
STO A	3.00	
100	100.	
STO C	100.00	n
.1	0.1	PMT
e^x	1.11	f/f, which is the same as j
1	1.	
-	0.11	i_c
100	100.	
×	10.52	
STO B	10.52	$i_c\%$
E	332.66	FV

Type R, Level III keystrokes for Example 6-17

HP-97/67 keystrokes	Display	Comments
fA	0.00	Program SD-05A
.075	0.075	Start function
e^x	1.08	r/f, which is the same as j
1	1.	
-	0.08	i_c
STO 2	0.08	
100	100.	
×	7.79	
STO B	7.79	$i_c\%$
RCL 2	0.08	
.075	0.075	
÷	1.04	
54750000	54750000	g
×	56855430.25	Equivalent discrete payment
STO C	56855430.25	
2	2.	
STO A	2.00	T
E	118138997.4	FV

Type R, Level III keystrokes for Example 6-18

HP-97/67 keystrokes	Display	Comments
		Program SD-05A
fA	0.00	Start function
7.5	7.5	
ENTER↑	7.50	
4	4.	
÷	1.88	$i_c\%$
STO B	1.88	
100	100.	
÷	0.02	i_c
STO 2	0.02	
1	1.	
+	1.02	
LN	0.02	
4	4.	c
×	0.07	
1/x	13.46	
RCL 2	0.02	i_c
×	0.25	
54750000	54750000	g
×	13815425.03	Equivalent discrete payments
STO C	13815423.03	
8	8.	
STO A	8.00	
E	118054943.8	FV

Type R, Level III keystrokes for Example 6-19

HP-97/67 keystrokes	Display	Comments
		Program SD-05A
fA	0.00	Start function
10	10.	
STO A	10.00	n
1200	1200.	
STO C	1200.00	PMT
17800	17800.	
STO E	17800.00	FV
B	8.50	$i_c\%$
100	100.	
÷	0.08	i_c
1	1.	
+	1.08	
LN	0.08	r/f, which is the same as j
DSP 9	0.081556941	Full-digit display

217

EXERCISES

Drill on Equations

Compound interest

6-1 Given: PV = $5000, T = 6, j = .0575
   Find: FV
   answer: **$7059.95**

6-2 Given: FV = $800, T = 17, j = .005
   Find: PV

6-3 Given: FV = $800, PV = 450, j = .06
   Find: T
   answer: **9.589**

6-4 Given: FV = $1950, PV = 450, T = 9
   Find: j

Discrete payments and continuous compounding

6-5 Given: PMT = 645, j = .03, n = 24
   Find: FV, PV, FV_d, and PV_d
   answers: **$22,331.96, $10,870.13, $23,012.07, $11,201.18**

6-6 Given: PMT = 175, j = .0275, n = 60
   Find: FV, PV, FV_d, and PV_d

6-7 Given: PMT = $1400, r = 6.75%, f = 2, T = 5
   Find: FV, PV, FV_d, and PV_d
   answers: **$16,372.88, $11,682.90, $16,934.90, $12,083.93**

6-8 Given: PMT = 245, r = 8.75%, f = 12, T = 30
   Find: FV, PV, FV_d, and PV_d

6-9 Given: FV = $60,500, r = 9.4%, f = 12, T = 20
   Find: PMT
   answer: **$85.67**

6-10 Given: PV = $25,375, r = 18.5%, f = 1, T = 8
   Find: PMT

6-11 Given: FV_d = $14,000, r = 7%, f = 52, T = 10
   Find: PMT
   answer: **$18.58**

6-12 Given: PV_d = $185,000, r = 14%, f = 2, T = 6
   Find: PMT

6-13 Given: PMT = $1950, f = 12, $r\%$ = 18%, PV = $105,000
   Find: (*a*) n and T
   answers: **112.055; 9.338**
   (*b*) number of whole payments and amount of last payment
   answers: **112, $108.50**

6-14 Given: PMT = $170, f = 6, $r\%$ = 11.2%, PV_d = $8500
   Find: (*a*) n and T
   (*b*) number of whole payments and amount of last payment

6-15 Given: PMT = $550, f = 6, $r\%$ = 5.5%, FV = $38,000
   Find: (*a*) n and T
   answers: **53.717, 8.953**
   (*b*) number of whole payments and amount of last payment
   answers: **53, $295.97**

6-16 Given: PMT = $90, $f = 12$, $r\% = 6.5\%$, $FV_d = \$7800$
Find: (*a*) n and T
(*b*) number of whole payments and amount of last payment

6-17 Given: $n = 20$, PMT = $415, FV = $34,000
Find: j
answer: **12.3129%**

6-18 Given: $n = 74$, PMT = $635, $FV_d = \$135,500$
Find: j

6-19 Given: $n = 43$, PMT = $2385, PV = $101,800
Find: j
answer: **.03363%**

6-20 Given: $n = 28$, PMT = $1250, $PV_d = \$20,750$
Find: j

6-21 Given: $T = 10$, $f = 12$, PMT = $100, FV = $24,500
Find: $j\%$ and $r\%$
answers: **1.08297%, 12.99563%**

6-22 Given: $T = 3$, $f = 3$, PMT = $3300, $FV_d = \$33,800$
Find: $j\%$ and $r\%$

6-23 Given: $T = 4.25$, $f = 4$, PMT = $13,325, PV = $200,350
Find: $j\%$ and $r\%$
answers: **1.39008%, 5.56032%**

6-24 Given: $T = 6$, $f = 12$, PMT = $425, $PV_d = \$20,750$
Find: $j\%$ and $r\%$

Continuous payments and compounding

6-25 Given: $p = \$750$, $r = 6\%$, $f = 4$, $T = 10$
Find: FV and PV
answers: **$41,105.94, $22,559.42**

6-26 Given: $p = \$1075$, $r = 11\%$, $f = 52$, $T = 5$
Find: FV and PV

6-27 Given: FV = $150,000, $r = 7\%$, $f = 4$, $T = 8$
Find: p
answer: **$3496.86**

6-28 Given: PV = $85,000, $r = 13\%$, $f = 6$, $T = 5$
Find: p

6-29 Given: FV = $74,500, $p = \$1500$, $f = 12$, $r = 15\%$
Find: n and T
answers: **38.635, 3.22**

6-30 Given: $p = \$1000$, $f = 52$, $r = 7.8\%$, PV = $156,087
Find: n and T

6-31 Given: FV = $95,854.35, $p = \$2300$, $f = 6$, $T = 5$
Find: $r\%$
answer: **12.5%**

6-32 Given: PV = $1,576,798.196, $p = \$22,000$, $f = 12$, $T = 8$
Find: $r\%$

Continuous payments and discrete compounding ($f = 1$)

6-33 Given: $g = \$500$, $r\% = 8.5\%$, $c = 12$, $T = 5$
Find: FV and PV
answers: **$3112.74, $2038.07**

6-34 Given: g = $1800, $r\%$ = 14.5%, c = 1, T = 21
Find: FV and PV

6-35 Given: FV = $65,000, $r\%$ = 6%, c = 6, T = 20
Find: g
answer: **$1686.95**

6-36 Given: PV = $155,000, $r\%$ = 19%, c = 4, T = 6
Find: g

6-37 Given: FV = $25,000, g = $575, $r\%$ = 6.4%, c = 12
Find: n and T
answers: **249.749, 20.812**

6-38 Given: PV = $90,000, g = $6,000, $r\%$ = 15%, c = 4
Find: n and T

6-39 Given: FV = $28,118.29, g = $865, c = 2, T = 15
Find: $r\%$
answer: **9.475%**

6-40 Given: PV = $27,072.04, g = $7550, c = 4, T = 5
Find: $r\%$

Applications

6-41 A company plans to deposit $20,000 each month in a savings account paying 6.25% annual compounded continuously. What is the balance in the account after the last payment if:
  (*a*) 53 end-of-month payments are made?
  answer: **$1,217,570.39**
  (*b*) 60 beginning-of-month payments are made?
  answer: **$1,412,329.26**

6-42 If you deposit $300 semiannually in a savings account paying 5.78% annual compounded continuously, what amount will be in the account after:
  (*a*) 20 end-of-period deposits?
  (*b*) 33 end-of-period deposits?
  (*c*) 15 beginning-of-period deposits?
  (*d*) 29 beginning-of-period deposits?

6-43 A company is evaluating a machine that has an 8-year life and a zero salvage value. The after-tax cash flow necessary to acquire the machine is $78,000, while the projected quarterly after-tax savings are $4800. The company requires an 18% annual return on such projects.
  (*a*) What is the present value of the cash saving assuming
    (1) continuous compounding and end-of-period discrete payments?
    (2) continuous compounding and payments?
  answers: (1) **$79,576.73**; (2) **$81,394.37**
  (*b*) What interest rate makes the present value of the savings equal to the $78,000 outlay cost assuming
    (1) continuous compounding and end-of-period discrete payments?
    (2) continuous compounding and payments?
  answers: (1) **18.6289%**; (2) **19.4022%**

6-44 A company needs to establish a sinking fund to redeem a bond issue in 15 years. What quarterly payment is necessary to accumulate $1,500,000 to retire the issue after 15 years if interest is compounded continuously at $6\frac{3}{4}\%$ annually?
  (*a*) For beginning-of-period payments.
  (*b*) For end-of-period payments.

6-45 A lessor is leasing a machine for 7 years, at which time the salvage will be zero. The machine has a current market value of $78,000 and the lessor wants an annual return of 11.7% annual compounded continuously. Assuming monthly payments, what is the monthly payment if (*a*) beginning-of-period payments?

(*b*) end-of-period payments?

answers: (*a*) **$1353.55**; (*b*) **$1366.81**

6-46 Work Exercise 4-61 assuming interest is compounded continuously.

6-47 Work Exercise 4-62 assuming interest is compounded continuously.

answer: **$59,280.81**

6-48 Work Exercise 4-66 assuming interest is compounded continuously.

6-49 Work Exercise 4-67 assuming interest is compounded continuously.

answers: (*a*) **$305.36**; (*b*) **$215.27**; (*c*) **$170.52**

6-50 Work Exercise 4-69 assuming interest is 14.55% annual compounded continuously.

6-51 Work Exercise 4-70 assuming interest is 6.3% annual compounded continuously.

answers: **$708.67**; **$704.96**

6-52 Work Exercise 4-74 assuming interest is compounded continuously.

6-53 Work Exercise 4-76 assuming interest is compounded continuously and accumulates $1,000,000.

answers: (*a*) **$10.891%**; (*b*) **11.091%**

6-54 A vending machine company is evaluating a new line of machines, each of which should generate approximately $100 a week in cash flow after expenses. The machines will be placed in airports and should generate the cash flows on a continuous basis.

(*a*) If each machine costs $9500 and the company expects a 16.5% return compounded continuously, how many weeks are necessary before the present value equals the outlay cost?

(*b*) Assuming an $8750 cost per machine and a 3-year life for each machine, what is the internal rate of return (what interest rate makes the present value of the earnings equal to the outlay cost)?

(*c*) If the earnings are overestimated by 10%, what are the answers to parts (*a*) and (*b*)?

(*d*) If the payments are compounded using a discrete interest rate, what are the answers to parts (*a*), (*b*) and (*c*)?

6-55 A Las Vegas Hotel is considering a new addition for slot machines which will cost $1,000,000 including the machines. They estimate that the slot machines in the room will net $1000 a day. The hotel wants to earn a 17.6% return on their investment assuming a 6-year life for the slot machine. Assume that there are 365 days in a year.

(*a*) What is the present value of the cash flows assuming continuous cash flows and compounding?

answer: **$1,352,481.77**

(*b*) What is the internal rate of return?

answer: **30.7226%**

(*c*) What are the answers to parts (*a*) and (*b*) assuming discrete compounding and continuous flows?

answers: (*a*) **$1,352,624.14**; (*b*) **30.7355%**

SEVEN

VARIABLE CASH FLOWS AND INTERNAL RATE OF RETURN

IN THIS CHAPTER

In this chapter the scope of the book is extended to include payments of unequal amounts—time-value-of-money situations involving variable cash flows. In contrast to previous chapters, wherein the payment amounts were equal each period (annuity situations), we will now allow payments to vary from period to period. Although equal payments are satisfactory for many business problems, there are a number of important applications which require analysis using variable cash flows or unequal payments. Examples include personal savings programs with unequal deposits, capital budgeting decisions with unequal cash flows, and mortgages or leases with unequal payments.

$\bullet \quad \bullet \quad \bullet \quad \bullet \quad \bullet$

7-1 INTRODUCTION

We will explain how to solve for the three basic unknowns in variable-cash-flow problems; the future value, the present value, and the interest rate. Both discrete and continuous interest compounding are discussed, as well as continuous variable cash flows.

We'll begin with a simple variable-cash-flow situation and then develop and generalize the relationships involved to include the many variations possible with variable cash flows.

As a starting point we will provide some structure to the variable-cash-flow situations by making the following assumptions:

1. Payments occur on a regular periodic basis, where each payment may be for a different amount.
2. Payments are made at the end of the periods.
3. Interest is computed or converted at the end of each payment period.
4. Periods for payment and interest conversion are of 1-year duration.

7-2 FUNDAMENTALS OF VARIABLE CASH FLOW

Our objective in this section is to develop a means for calculating either the present value, the future value, or the interest rate, and to understand their relationship, under the conditions imposed by the assumptions listed above. In subsequent sections of this chapter most of these assumptions are relaxed.

7-2.1 Net Present Value

The concept of present value, PV, was introduced for a single payment in Chap. 3 and then used extensively for annuities in Chaps. 4, 5, and 6. In all annuity cases, the PV was defined to be the accumulation of all payments, *discounted* back to the *beginning of the first period*. It is customary to retain this definition for PV when working with variable cash flows; that is, PV is calculated at the *beginning* of the first period ($t = 0$), regardless of whether payments occur at the end or at the beginning of the periods.

At this point it is worthwhile to examine cash flows from the viewpoint of a prospective investor. Proposed investments are attractive only if the prospective cash flows will return the investment plus a satisfactory amount of interest.

As an illustration, consider the possibility that an investor makes an initial cash outlay with the anticipation of receiving a future cash inflow, occurring as end-of-year payments. According to our definition as applied to the investor, the present value discounts only the promised future payments. In that sense the PV, as defined above, represents a *gross* present value, since it does not include the initial outlay. As expected, the *net* present value adds the initial negative outlay to the positive discounted present value; that is,

$$\text{net present value} = \text{original outlay} + \text{PV} \tag{7-1}$$

The sign convention used in Eq. (7-1) is that the initial cash outlay is represented by a negative value and the cash inflow by a positive value.† This point is illustrated in the following example.

Example 7-1 An investor is contemplating an original outlay of \$10,000 with the expectation of receiving end-of-year payments for the next 5 years of

---

†It is also possible to reverse the signs on the outflow and inflow, respectively, and arrive at the same results.

Table 7-1 Net-present-value calculations for Example 7-1

Year	Cash flow	Present value (8%)
0	−$10,000	−$10,000
1	2,000	1,851.85
2	2,400	2,057.61
3	2,800	2,222.73
4	3,450	2,535.85
5	2,800	1,905.63
	Net present value	$ 573.68

$2000, $2400, $2800, $3450, and $2800, respectively. What is the net present value if money is discounted annually at 8%?

The present-value calculations for each outlay and inflow are presented in Table 7-1. The net present value, which includes the initial outlay, is $573.68 and the PV, which excludes the initial outlay, is $10,573.68.

If all payments are end-of-period payments, as they are in this example, there is no difficulty in incorporating the initial outlay into a formula for the net present value, NPV. That is,

$$\text{NPV} = CF_0 + CF_1(1 + i_f)^{-1} + \cdots + CF_n(1 + i_f)^{-7} \quad (7\text{-}2)$$

which can be expressed as

$$\text{NPV} = \sum_{h=0}^{n} CF_h(1 + i_f)^{-h} \quad (7\text{-}3)$$

where CF_0 = initial inflow or outflow at beginning of the *first* period
CF_h = cash inflow or outflow at the end of period h

There is no difficulty, of course, in using Eq. (7-3) to solve Example 7-1.

There are several direct uses of net-present-value calculations:

1. Placing a prospective dollar evaluation on an investment proposal.
2. Comparing and ranking two or more alternative investment opportunities.
3. Making trial-and-error calculations to determine unknown interest rates of return that make the net present value equal to zero. This concept is developed further in the next section.

7-2.2 Internal Rate of Return

This section deals with the methods for solving for the interest rate when the NPV is specified. Although there are many types of applications, it is often desirable to compute the internal rate which makes the *net present value of an investment exactly zero*. Different names are applied to this type of computation; internal rate of return, investor's rate of return, IRR, and discounted-cash-flow method, among others. Regardless of the name selected, the manual calculations involve a trial-and-error process: selecting two or more interest rates and then determining the net present value for each, following the procedure in Example 7-1. Hopefully, one of the interest rates selected will lead to a positive NPV and another interest rate selected will lead to a negative NPV. Then the internal rate of return, IRR, for which NPV = 0 is found by interpolation; the following example may clarify the procedure.

Example 7-2 Using the initial outlay and the end-of-year cash flow streams given in Example 7-1, determine the internal rate of return, IRR.

To calculate the approximate rate of return, set up Table 7-2 following the pattern used in Table 7-1. Then calculate the net present value, NPV, for $i = 8\%$ and then for 12%. Since the NPV for $i = 8\%$ was calculated in Table 7-1, that information is duplicated in Table 7-2. It is noted that in Table 7-2 the NPV for 8%, NPV(8%), is $573.68 and the NPV(12%) is −$526.70. Thus it is reasonable to assume that the interest rate, IRR, that makes NPV = 0 can be found somewhere between 8 and 12%. By linear interpolation the rate of return is calculated in Table 7-2 to be 9.91%. However, this answer is only an approximate one, because of the relatively large jump in interest rates between 8 and 12%. By continuing the trial-and-error procedure a more accurate answer can be determined.

It should not come as a surprise that the Newton-Raphson method, which was used in Chaps. 4, 5, and 6, is applicable for computing a more accurate value for IRR. In the following paragraphs all the necessary equations will be given to program or execute manually the Newton-Raphson method when solving for IRR, which, when applied to Example 7-2, gives the more accurate IRR of 10.00%.

The starting point for using the Newton-Raphson method is to express Eq. (7-3) in the form

$$NPV = f(i) = \sum_{h=0}^{n} CF_h(1 + i)^{-h} \tag{7-4}$$

Table 7-2 Internal-rate-of-return calculation

Year	Cash flow	NPV ($i = 8\%$)	NPV ($i = 12\%$)
0	−$10,000	−$10,000	−$10,000
1	2,000	1,851.85	1,785.71
2	2,400	2,057.61	1,913.27
3	2,800	2,222.73	1,992.98
4	3,450	2,535.85	2,192.54
5	2,800	1,905.63	1,588.80
		NPV(8%) $ 573.68	NPV(12%) −$ 526.70

$$\text{approx. IRR} = 8\% + \frac{\$526.70}{\$526.70 + \$573.68} \times (12 - 8) = 9.91\%$$

where $i = i_f$. To solve for IRR, we wish to solve Eq. (7-4) for the unknown value, i, where NPV is set equal to zero. Next we need a value for $f'(i)$, following the methods described in Appendix 6B,

$$f'(i) = -\sum_{h=0}^{n} h \times CF_h(1 + i)^{-(h+1)} \tag{7-5}$$

Next we use the relationship

$$i_{k+1} = i_k - \frac{f(i_k)}{f'(i_k)} \tag{7-6}$$

where an arbitrary value for i_0 is selected. The iterative computations are given for the following example.

Example 7-3 Recompute Example 7-2 to obtain a more accurate value for IRR.
   Step 0: Start with $i_0 = .08$, using the information gained from Example 7-2.

$$\frac{f(i_0)}{f'(i_0)} = -.0191778468$$

   Step 1:

$$i_1 = i_0 - \frac{f(i_0)}{f'(i_0)} = .08 - (-.0191778468) = .0991778468$$

   Step 2:

$$i_2 = .10000984$$

$$i_3 = .100011303$$

$$i_4 = .100011303$$

$$i = .10 \text{ or } 10.00\% \qquad \text{rounded to two decimal places}$$

IRR = 10.00%.

7-2.3 Net Future Value

Based upon the discussions given above on net present value, there should be no difficulty in extending the concepts to cover the net-future-value case. The future value, FV, is still accumulated at the end of the last payment period. As before, end-of-period payments are assumed and if an initial outlay occurs at the beginning of the first period, then we are justified in introducing the concept of a net future value, NFV. Of course the initial outlay, as well as all other payments, must be compounded forward to the time representing the end of the last payment period, as indicated in the next example.

Table 7-3 Net-future-value calculations for Example 7-4

Year	Cash flow	Future value (8%)
0	−$10,000	−$14,693.28
1	2,000	2,720.98
2	2,400	3,023.31
3	2,800	3,265.92
4	3,450	3,726.00
5	2,800	2,800.00
	Net future value	$ 842.93

Example 7-4 Using all the data given in Example 7-1, determine the net future value, NFV. The future-value calculations for each payment are accumulated in Table 7-3 to give a net future value of $842.93. As a check we can discount the $842.93 back to present value and obtain the net present value of Example 7-1. That is,

$$\text{NPV} = (1 + i)^{-n} \times \text{FV} = 1.08^{-5} \times 842.93 = \$573.68$$

The generalized formula for NFV is

$$\text{NFV} = \sum_{h=0}^{n} \text{CF}_h (1 + i_f)^{n-h} \qquad (7\text{-}7)$$

where the terms have been defined above.

Following the pattern used in Chaps. 4, 5, and 6, it is possible to use trial-and-error methods to compute an unknown interest rate when the NFV is specified. Interestingly enough, it is possible to determine the internal interest rate, IRR, by setting the NFV = 0. Although it is quite common to evaluate IRR based on setting NPV = 0, there are situations in practice where IRR could be evaluated based on setting NFV = 0.

7-3 TRANSITION TO CONSOLIDATED FORMULAS

The primary reasons for developing the various consolidated formulas are twofold:

1. To facilitate the development of efficient, compact programs on Level III calculators.
2. To unfold, in a comprehensive manner, the options introduced in Chaps. 4, 5, and 6, including:
   a. End-of-period payments.
   b. Beginning-of-period payments.

    c. Compounding period different from the payment periods; that is, $c \neq f$.

    d. Continuous payments with discontinuous jumps.

    e. Continuous compounding.

There is no easy way to present so many different options. The approach used presents the options systematically and relies heavily on consolidated equations. A rather large number of examples and end-of-chapter exercises are provided to help in the understanding of the consolidated equations.

However, many cases are clumsy to handle, even with the financial function keys of the Level II calculators or the standard library programs of the Level III calculators. Therefore, we also developed a customized program for a Level III calculator. Sufficient information will be provided in this chapter so that you can use the program as presented, or modify it for use in your own programmable calculator or computer.

7-4 CONSOLIDATED FORMULAS FOR PRESENT AND FUTURE VALUES

We will first discuss the generalized variable-cash-flow model necessary to compute FV or PV. This model does not require identification of end- or beginning-of-period payments, but it does require proper placement of cash flows in the period during which they occur.

Second, we discuss an approach to computing FV or PV using an equivalence relationship which is very useful with Level II and III calculators.

For both approaches we assume discrete payments but allow in turn for (1) discrete compounding where $f = c$, (2) discrete compounding where $f \neq c$, and (3) continuous compounding. A final method considered assumes both continuous cash flow payments and compounding. Computing FV and PV for this situation requires a modification of the equivalency approach.

Because of the multitude of cases presented in this chapter, the consolidated formulas dealing only with calculating present value or future value are presented in this section. After all the PV or FV equations are derived and illustrated, we will go on to a similar presentation for computing interest rates.

7-4.1 Discrete Cash Flows—Discrete Compounding

We will consider first the most common situation, where both payments and compounding are discrete. Later, most of the combinations of continuous and discrete payments and/or compounding will be discussed.

7-4.1.1 Shifting payments manually. One choice that must be made in setting up a variable-cash-flow problem is whether to locate the payments at the *end* or the *beginning* of the periods. In this section the same formula is used for both end- and beginning-period cases; however, use of this formula does require that the user shift the payments manually.

There is an obvious similarity with the annuity cases of Chaps. 4, 5, and 6. However, the variable-cash-flow model differs from the annuity model because the payments are different for some or all periods. Since the payments or cash flows vary, the future value and present value are computed using the basic compound interest formula applied to each cash flow.

If we assume that a cash flow occurs at the *end of each discrete time period* with compounding occurring at that time, the variable-cash-flow model is stated as

$$V_K = \sum_{h=0}^{n} CF_h (1 + i_f)^{(K - h)} \tag{7-8}$$

where n = number of payments *and* periods
  CF_h = cash flow at *end* of period
  i_f = interest rate per period
  K = n for FV
    = 0 for PV
  V_K = FV if $K = n$
    = PV if $K = 0$

As an aid to understanding the model, examine Fig. 7-1. You see that the *only* difference between the two diagrams is where the unknown, V_K, is located. Both have n cash flows, as well as n compounding periods. This variable-cash-flow model has only two cases—FV and PV—with a cash flow assumed to occur at the *end* of each period, including time period zero.

$K = n$, FV case

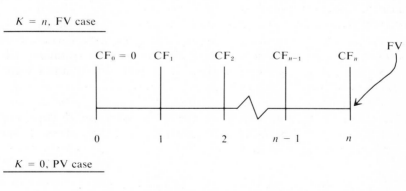

$K = 0$, PV case

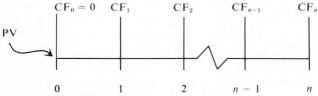

Figure 7-1 End-of-period payments

K = n, FV case

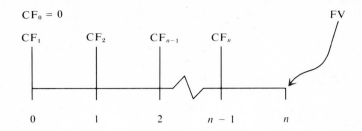

K = 0, PV case

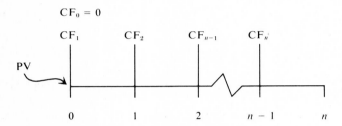

Figure 7-2 Beginning-of-period payments

Each time period number 0 to n, which represents the end of a period, must have a positive, negative, or zero cash flow. The model requires an explicit value for CF_0 even if it is zero.

If we assume that a cash flow occurs at the *beginning of each period,* then the same formula, Eq. (7-8), is used, except that the same payments must be manually shifted and refixed in place at the beginning of the periods. The relocation is shown in Fig. 7-2. The PV and FV are still located at the beginning of the first period and end of the last period, respectively. Also, the proper value for CF_0 must be selected, usually $CF_0 = 0$.

In this model cash flows are simply placed where they occur; zero payments are entered for periods without cash flows. Example 7-5 solves the FV and PV cases to demonstrate Eq. (7-8).

Example 7-5 Given four unequal annual cash flows: $1400, $1900, $1500, and $1700. If interest is compounded annually at 10%, compute the FV and PV cases assuming that:

(*a*) Cash flows occur at the end of the period.

(*b*) Cash flows occur at the beginning of the period.

For part (a), cash flows at the end of the period, a zero cash flow must be entered for time period $n = 0$ because the model assumes that a cash flow occurs at the end of each time period, and that the first payment occurs at n

Time Diagram 7-5a End-of-period payments

= 1. The remaining cash flows are entered in the time periods where they occur, as shown in Time Diagram 7-5a.

Next, the FV and PV are computed using the generalized formula of Eq. (7-8). For the FV case, $K = n$, the value is

$$FV = 0(1.1)^{(4-0)} + 1400(1.1)^{(4-1)} + 1900(1.1)^{(4-2)} + 1500(1.1)^{(4-3)}$$
$$+ 1700(1.1)^{(4-4)}$$

$$= \$7512.40$$

For the PV case, the K value is 0 and the PV is

$$PV = 0(1.1)^{-0} + 1400(1.1)^{-1} + 1900(1.1)^{-2} + 1500(1.1)^{-3} + 1700(1.1)^{-4}$$

$$= \$5131.07$$

Part (b) of Example 7-5 assumes that the first cash flow occurs at the beginning of the period. This assumption means that the first cash flow is CF_1 and occurs at time 0. Time Diagram 7-5b shows that the cash flows have been in effect "shifted" to the left one time period from where they were in Time Diagram 7-5a. (Now time period $n = 4$ has the zero payment.) After shifting the payments, Eq. (7-8) can be applied without difficulty.

As a result, the FV and PV may be computed as previously shown:

$$FV = 1400(1.1)^{(4-0)} + 1900(1.1)^{(4-1)} + 1500(1.1)^{(4-2)} + 1700(1.1)^{(4-3)}$$
$$+ 0(1.1)^{(4-4)}$$

$$= \$8263.64$$

$$PV = 1400(1.1)^{-0} + 1900(1.1)^{-1} + 1500(1.1)^{-2} + 1700(1.1)^{-3} + 0(1.1)^{-4}$$

$$= \$5644.18$$

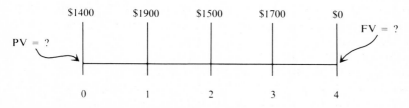

Time Diagram 7-5b Beginning-of-period payments

Thus the basic variable-cash-flow formula allows the same computation of FV or PV whether cash flows are at the *beginning* or *end* of the period. However, some additional notation is desirable to avoid confusion.

When cash flows are assumed to occur at the end of the period, the future and present values will be designated as FV_E and PV_E. Where cash flows occur at the beginning of the period, the notation is FV_B and PV_B. This notation is consistent with the ordinary annuity and annuity due notation used previously.

7-4.1.2 Shifting payments automatically. In Sec. 7-4.1.1 it was possible to solve for either PV or FV by specifying a value for K in the basic formula. If you wanted to switch from *end-of-period* payments to *beginning-of-period* payments, you had to reposition all the payments manually, as indicated in going from Fig. 7-1 to 7-2 or from Time Diagram 7-5a to 7-5b.

In this section we will modify Eq. (7-8) so that it is no longer necessary to shift the location of the payments manually. This shifting will take place automatically, simply by specifying the appropriate values for K in a modified formula.

The modified relationship to solve for future value or present value is

$$V_K = \sum_{h=1}^{n} CF_h (1 + i_f)^{K-h} \tag{7-9}$$

where V_K = future value or present value
$\quad CF_h$ = cash flow for period h
$\quad\quad i_f$ = interest rate per payment period
$\quad\quad n$ = total number of payments
$\quad\quad h$ = counter, which varies as $h = 1, 2, 3, \ldots, n$
$\quad\quad K$ = setting for various cases, where:

For case:	K
FV_E	n
PV_E	0
FV_B	$n + 1$
PV_B	1

$\quad E$ = payments made at end of each period
$\quad B$ = payments made at beginning of each period

This equivalent relationship is in a form that is satisfactory for programmable calculators or computers but can be reduced further to simplify calculations on less sophisticated calculators, as shown below.

First, recall that we developed a generalized relationship for annuities,

$$V_K = (1 + i_f)^{K-n} \times \text{PMT} \times S(n, i_f) \tag{7-10}$$

Since the term $(1 + i_f)^{K-n}$ in Eq. (7-10) proved to be useful in Chap. 4, we wish to arrange Eq. (7-9) so that the same $(1 + i_f)^{K-n}$ term is shown explicitly:

$$V_K = (1 + i_f)^{K-n} \sum_{h=1}^{n} \text{CF}_h (1 + i_f)^{n-h} \tag{7-11}$$

7-4.1.3 Fixing payments at end of period. Although Eq. (7-11) corresponds to the form illustrated at the end of Chap. 4, its use is somewhat awkward on a Level I calculator. We can, however, change the equation to facilitate manual calculations on Level I and gain other benefits for Level II and III calculators. In this revised model, payments are assumed to be made only at the *end* of each period.

$$V_K = (1 + i_f)^K \sum_{h=1}^{n} \text{CF}_h (1 + i_f)^{-h} \tag{7-12}$$

where i_f = interest rate per payment period
$K = n$ for FV_E
$\quad = 0$ for PV_E
$\quad = n + 1$ for FV_B
$\quad = +1$ for PV_B

In this relationship the index term h simply starts at 1 and ends with the last period, n. This means that for the end-of-period cases there is no provision for an initial payment at the beginning of the first period, CF_0. However, this omission is of minor significance because an initial payment of CF_0, for end-of-period payment cases, can be accounted for by proper adjustment of PV_E to a net present value and likewise for FV_E to a net future value.

Also, note that for PV_E the term K is equal to zero. This particular case, solving for PV_E where $K = 0$, is the most common use of Eq. (7-12). You may wish to confirm that Eq. (7-12) with $K = 0$ reduces to Eq. (7-3), except that the CF_0 has to be inserted, as discussed in the preceding paragraph. Many Level II and III calculators have internal routines or programs which compute the PV_E of variable cash flows. Hence only the correction factor $(1 + i_f)^K$ is necessary to convert the PV_E answer obtained from these routines to the other cases, FV_E, FV_B, or PV_B. In the next section we'll describe a simplified calculation procedure for Level I calculators.

7-4.1.4 Simplified calculation methods. In Example 7-4 we used the y^x key to compute the future value for cash flows. On some calculators the use of this key may be awkward and result in errors. A simpler method for variable cash flows omits the use of the y^x key for calculating answers with Eq. (7-12).

Two examples will be given to demonstrate the use of Eq. (7-12). Both examples follow the two steps given below:

Step 1: Solve Eq. (7-12) for the PV_E case, which means set $K = 0$. (Most Level II and Level III calculators have routines to carry out this step.)

Step 2: Multiply the PE_E value by $(1 + i)^K$ for the appropriate value of K, depending on whether the answer calls for FV_E, PV_B, or FV_B.

Example 7-6 The BG Company is evaluating a lease for a machine. They are interested in the present value using an 18% annual discount factor (interest rate) compounded semiannually with tax effects and depreciation being omitted. The lease payments are made at the *beginning* of each 6-month period.

Semiannual periods	Cash flow
1	$15,800
2	15,000
3	14,500
4	13,400
5	12,600
6	12,000

We note from the problem statement that the PV_B case must be computed because the payments occur at the beginning of each period. Nevertheless, we compute the PV_E case first in step 1, using a procedure that does not require raising the term $(1 + i)$ to a power with the **y^x** key:

Step 1: Compute PV_E.

Period 6:	$12,000.	+ $	0 = 12,000.	÷ 1.09 =	$11,009.17431
Period 5:	11,009.17431 +	12,600 = 23,609.17431	÷ 1.09 =	21,659.79295
Period 4:	21,659.79295 +	13,400 = 35,059.79295	÷ 1.09 =	32,164.94766
Period 3:	32,164.94766 +	14,500 = 46,664.94766	÷ 1.09 =	42,811.87858
Period 2:	42,811.87858 +	15,000 = 57,811.87858	÷ 1.09 =	53,038.42072
Period 1:	53,038.42072 +	15,800 = 68,838.42072	÷ 1.09 =	63,154.51442

So $PV_E = \$63{,}154.51442$.

Now that the PV_E value is computed, let's convert it to the PV_B case. First, the value of K is determined and it is 1 for the PV_B case. Next, perform step 2.

Step 2: Let $K = 1$ to solve for PV_B.

$$PV_B = (1.09)^1 \times \$63{,}154.51442$$

$$= \$68{,}838.4207$$

The present value of the lease is $68,838.42.

To compute the FV_E and FV_B cases:

FV_E case, $K = n = 6$:

$$FV_E = (1.09)^6 \times \$63,154.51442$$

$$= \$105,916.4431$$

FV_B case, $K = n + 1 = 7$

$$FV_B = (1.09)^7 \times \$63,154.51442$$

$$= \$115,448.9230$$

The next example follows the same computational pattern to solve for FV_B.

Example 7-7 If the following amounts are deposited in a savings account at the *beginning* of each year and if interest is compounded annually at 10%, what is the FV_B?

Year	Deposit
1	$100
2	75
3	60
4	85
5	40

Step 1: Compute PV_E.

Year 5:	$ 40.	+ $	0 =	$ 40.	÷ 1.1 =	$ 36.3636364
Year 4:	36.3636364	+	85 =	121.3636364	÷ 1.1 =	110.3305785
Year 3:	110.3305785	+	60 =	170.3305785	÷ 1.1 =	154.8459805
Year 2:	154.8459805	+	75 =	229.8459805	÷ 1.1 =	208.9508913
Year 1:	208.9508913	+	100 =	308.9508913	÷ 1.1 =	280.8644467

The result of this step is $PV_E = \$280.8644$.†

Step 2: To convert the PV_E value obtained in step 1 to FV_B requires a substitution of $n + 1 = 6$ for K. Then

$$FV_B = (1.1)^{+6} \times \$280.8644467$$

$$= \$497.5685$$

† To check this result, we could compute this value using the **y**^{x} key, as follows:

Year 1:	$100 × 1.1^{-1} =	$90.90909091
Year 2:	75 × 1.1^{-2} =	61.98347107
Year 3:	60 × 1.1^{-3} =	45.07888805
Year 4:	85 × 1.1^{-4} =	58.05614371
Year 5:	40 × 1.1^{-5} =	24.83685292
	Total PV	$280.864446

Both procedures give the same answer.

To illustrate the other possible cases in Example 7-7:
    FV_E case: $K = n$

$$FV_E = (1.1)^5 \times \$280.8644467$$
$$= \$452.3350$$

PV_B case: $K = 1$

$$PV_B = (1.1)^{+1} \times \$280.8644467$$
$$= \$308.9509$$

7-4.2 Unequal Payment and Compounding Periods

We can utilize the same general method outlined in Sec. 7-4.1 for solving variable-cash-flow cases with unequal compounding and payment periods (as for general annuities). The equivalent interest rate per payment period i_f is determined and used in the formula. The i_f equivalence relationship, from Chap. 5, is

$$i_f = (1 + 1_c)^{c/f} - 1 \tag{7-13}$$

where i_f = decimal interest rate per payment period
    i_c = decimal interest rate per compounding period
    f = number of payments per year
    c = number of compounding periods per year

Let's consider an example.

Example 7-8 A company makes five unequal deposits at the end of successive quarters in an account paying 6.5% interest annually compounded every 4 months. Given the cash flows below, what is the amount in the account after the last payment is made (i.e., the future value, FV)?

Quarter	Payment
1	$125
2	175
3	250
4	300
5	450

As shown in Time Diagram 7-8, four payments and three compounding periods occur each year. The interest rate per compounding period is $i_c = .065$

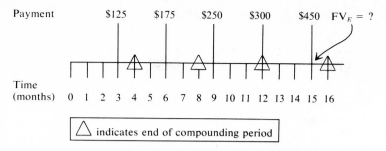

Time Diagram 7-8

$\div$ 3 or .0216666667. With this information we can compute the equivalent interest rate per payment period as follows:

$$i_f = (1.0216666667)^{3/4} - 1$$

$$= .0162063821$$

where $c = 3$
   $f = 4$
   $i_c = .0216666667$

  Given i_f, we compute the PV_E value of \$1227.257066, using one of the procedures discussed previously. Then to convert to FV_E:

$$K = n = 5$$

$$FV_E = 1.0162063821^5 \times \$1227.257066$$

$$= \$1329.980066$$

  The company will have \$1329.98 in their account at the end of 15 months (assuming that the savings institution pays interest for fractional periods).

  Note that solving for the FV and PV where the compounding and payment periods are unequal requires only converting i_c to i_f. The remainder of the process is identical to the previous section. However, up to this point, we have assumed discrete compounding. Our next step is to consider continuous compounding.

7-4.3 Discrete Cash Flows with Continuous Compounding

Continuous compounding theory and applications, including the concept of *equivalence* between a discrete rate and continuous rate, were discussed in detail in Chap. 6. By converting a continuous rate to its equivalent discrete rate, the formula for variable cash flows, Eq. (7-12), can be used for continuous compounding. Recall that the equivalency relationship is

$$i_f = e^{r/f} - 1 \qquad\qquad (7\text{-}14)$$

where i_f = equivalent interest rate per payment period
$\qquad f$ = number of payments per year
$\qquad r$ = annual continuous interest rate

The four cases FV_E, PV_E, FV_B, and PV_B are again possible, because the cash flows are discrete and can be at the beginning or end of each period. Each case is solved using the same approach as before once the equivalent i_f is calculated. To demonstrate this procedure, consider the following example.

Example 7-9 Suppose that you are considering an investment returning 10% annually compounded continuously. At the start of each 6 months you invest the amounts shown below. At the end of 2 years your investment and interest is returned. What is the amount you receive?

Period	Cash flow
1	$10,000
2	15,000
3	23,000
4	17,500

In this example the FV_B value is the unknown. First, we must compute the equivalent discrete interest rate, using Eq. (7-14):

$$r = 10\%$$

$$f = 2$$

$$i_f = e^{.10/2} - 1$$

$$= .0512710964$$

Now that we have the equivalent discrete interest rate, the rest of the solution follows the approach used previously.

The PV_E value is computed, using Eq. (7-12), as $57,208.92715. To calculate FV_B, we use a K value of $n + 1 = 5$.

$$FV_B = 1.051271096^5 \times \$57,208.92715$$

$$= \$73,457.71652$$

You will receive $73,457.72 at the end of 2 years.

Note that there is no equivalent of general annuities for variable cash flows when compounding continuously. Since compounding is continuous, there is no difference between compounding and payment periods because all payments (regardless of frequency) are compounded at the same rate. The conversion formula, Eq. (7-14), does not contain the term c for the number of compounding periods per year. Only the frequency of payments and annual interest rate r are incorporated in the relationship for i_f.

7-4.4 Continuous Cash Flows and Continuous Compounding

Up to this point we have assumed that the variable cash flows were discrete amounts received at either the beginning or end of each period. We will now consider the situation in which the cash flows are received continuously during a period (although the amounts received each period vary). This type of cash flow—a variable continuous cash flow—would appear graphically as shown in Fig. 7-3. In this figure, CF_1 represents the continuous cash flow that occurs during period 1.

Level-payment continuous cash flows (annuities) were explained in Chap. 6, along with the concept of an *equivalent discrete payment* which occurs at the end of the period. The relationship is

$$\frac{\text{equivalent}}{\text{discrete payment}} = \frac{\text{continuous}}{\text{payment}} \times \frac{e^{r/f} - 1}{r/f} \tag{7-15}$$

With this conversion relationship we can convert each continuous variable cash flow to the equivalent discrete cash flow and then solve for PV or FV using the discrete approach previously discussed. Of course, this approach will require the conversion of each individual cash flow, which can be time-consuming where a large number of flows are involved. Fortunately, there is a simpler method. Because each cash flow is multiplied by the same constant, $(e^{r/f} - 1)/(r/f)$, we can compute the FV or PV assuming discrete flows at the end of each period and then make a single conversion to the continuous variable-cash-flow case.

Thus a generalized formula to compute PV or FV for continuous variable cash flows and compounding can be developed as follows:

$$V_K = (1 + i_f)^K \frac{e^{r/f} - 1}{r/f} \sum_{h=1}^{n} CF_h(1 + i_f)^{-h} \tag{7-16}$$

But remember that $i_f = e^{r/f} - 1$. By converting the term $e^{r/f} - 1$ to i_f, we eliminate the need to use the $\mathbf{e^x}$ key in our calculations, and thereby save some key strokes. Equation (7-16) can be restated as

$$V_K = (1 + i_f)^K \frac{i_f}{r/f} \sum_{h=1}^{n} CF_h(1 + i_f)^{-h} \tag{7-17}$$

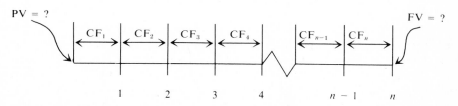

Figure 7-3 Continuous payments

where V_K = PV or FV
r = continuous decimal interest rate per year
f = number of payments per year
n = total number of payments
$i_f = e^{r/f} - 1$, the equivalent discrete compounding interest rate per period
$K = n$ for FV
$= 0$ for PV

There are only two cases for continuous variable cash flows and compounding—FV and PV— since cash flows occur continuously throughout the period rather than at the beginning or end.

We will use the same basic method as in the preceding sections, computing the equivalent discrete rate, the equivalent discrete cash flows, and the PV_E. Of course, for continuous cash, PV_E must be converted to either PV or FV. The following example demonstrates the procedure.

Example 7-10 A company is evaluating a project that earns the quarterly cash flows shown below. Because of the nature of the project—vending machines in an airport—continuous cash flows are assumed. The company requires a 12% annual rate compounded continuously on its projects. What is the present value of the project?

Period	Cash flow
1	$1500
2	3400
3	6300
4	5250

Time Diagram 7-10 is a bit different from previous diagrams because of the continuous cash flows. To solve for PV we first compute the equivalent discrete interest rate.

$$i_f = e^{.12/4} - 1$$

$$= .030454534$$

Second, we compute the factor to convert the continuous flows to discrete flows.

$$\frac{e^{r/f} - 1}{r/f} = \frac{.030454534}{.12/4} = 1.015151132$$

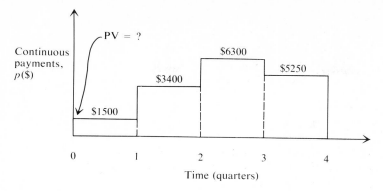

Time Diagram 7-10 Continuous payments with jumps

We can now state the problem solution as

$$PV = (1.030454534)^0 \times 1.051151132 \times \sum_{h=1}^{4} CF_h \times 1.030454534^{-h}$$

Thus we have the relationship in a familiar form and we solve it in the usual fashion. Solving for the present value we arrive at

Cash flow	Interest factor		Present value
1500	× 1.030454534^{-1}	=	$ 1,455.6683
3400	× 1.030454534^{-2}	=	3,201.99941
6300	× 1.030454534^{-3}	=	5,757.76647
5250	× 1.030454534^{-4}	=	4,656.33229
		Total	$15,071.76647

$$PV = 1.015151132 \times \$15,071.76647$$

$$= \$15,300.1208$$

The company's project has a present value of $15,300.12 based on the assumption of continuous compounding and cash flows.

Now, suppose we wished to compute the future value of the flows. Restating the formula with $K = n = 4$:

$$FV = 1.030454534^4 \times 1.015151132 \times \$15,071.76647$$

$$= \$17,250.83803$$

7-4.5 Summary: FV and PV Cases for Variable Cash Flows

The preceding sections have discussed the following four types of variable cash flows†:

1. Discrete cash flows and discrete compounding with the compounding period *equal* to the payment period.
2. Discrete cash flows and discrete compounding with the compounding period *unequal* to the payment period.
3. Discrete cash flows and continuous compounding.
4. Continuous variable cash flows and continuous compounding.

We developed a generalized formula for discrete situations that can also be applied to the various continuous situations. The basic feature of the procedure is computing the PV_E value first, with subsequent conversion to the other cases. As in previous chapters, we can develop one formula that covers all the cases in this chapter. This formula is convenient for use in programs on calculators or computers.

$$V_K = (1 + i_f)^K \left(\frac{i_f}{r/f} \right)^Q \sum_{h=1}^{n} CF_h (1 + i_f)^{-h} \qquad (7\text{-}18)$$

V_K = the case's FV_E, PV_E, FV_B, PV_B for discrete payments
  = the case's FV, PV for continuous payments
CF_h = either discrete cash flow assumed to occur at the end of period h or continuous cash flow during period h
  f = number of payments per year
  c = number of compounding periods per year
  n = total number of payments
  Q = 1 for continuous cash flows and continuous compounding and 0 for other situations
  r = annual continuous interest rate
  i_f = for discrete compounding:
    $i_f = (1 + i_c)^{c/f} - 1$
  i_f = for continuous compounding:
    $i_f = e^{r/f} - 1$
  K = for continuous cash flows and continuous compounding:
    0 for present value
    n for future value
  K = for discrete cash flows:
    n for FV_E
    0 for PV_E
    $n + 1$ for FV_B
    1 for PV_B

†We have not covered the case for continuous variable cash flows with discrete compounding. However, all the necessary background material has been developed to permit the reader to develop this case if it is needed.

Equation (7-18), with all its options, is used as the basis for a customized Level III calculator program that is described in a later section.

7-5 SOLVING FOR THE INTEREST RATES: ALL CASES

Determination of the interest rate is a problem often encountered in business practice. Using tables, it can be both difficult and time-consuming. With a calculator, however, solving for i is relatively straightforward, even with a Level I machine. The Level II and III calculators frequently have internal routines that solve the interest rate for the PV_E case. This section will demonstrate the computation of interest in various combinations of discrete and continuous cash flows and compounding.

We show two approaches. The *first* uses a generalized formula, Eq. (7-8), that requires careful manual location of each cash flow. The *second* uses Eq. (7-9) where it is possible to shift the payments and determine the case using K values. Both methods are suitable for all levels of calculators, and the second is especially useful on Level II or III calculators which have routines to compute the interest rate for the PV_E case.

7-5.1 Equivalent Interest Rates

In previous sections we used the equivalent discrete rate i_f in place of the continuous rate r/f and then the discrete formulas to compute the continuous FV and PV cases. However, the discrete iteration formula to solve for i is slow, requiring numerous iterations to determine i with accuracy. On the other hand, the continuous iteration formula, as presented in the next section, seems to require fewer iterations to determine i_f.† Therefore, in this section we will reverse the equivalence approach, solving first for the continuous interest rate j and then converting it to the equivalent i_f for discrete situations.

The equivalence relationship used is

$$i_f = e^{r/f} - 1 \qquad (7\text{-}19)$$

and

$$j = \frac{r}{f} \qquad (7\text{-}20)$$

Actually, both the i_f and j interest rates are computed at essentially the same time. As a result, discrete cash flows with either discrete or continuous compounding use the same generalized formulas, which follow.

---

†Lawrence Fisher, "An Algorithm for Finding Exact Rates of Return," *The Journal of Business,* Part II, January 1966, pp. 111–118.

7-5.2 Solving for Interest Rate Using Equation (7-8)

Once again we will resort to the Newton-Raphson iterative method to solve for an unknown interest rate when either the PV or FV is known. The basic formula used in this section is Eq. (7-8), which is applicable for both end-of-period and beginning-of-period cases, except that the payments must be placed manually to fit the appropriate case.

In order to express the iteration formulas in terms of the continuous interest rate j, Eq. (7-8) is expressed as

$$V_K = \sum_{h=0}^{n} CF_h e^{(K-h)j} \tag{7-21}$$

so

$$f(j) = \sum_{h=0}^{n} CF_h e^{(K-h)j} - V_K \tag{7-22}$$

and

$$f'(j) = \sum_{h=0}^{n} (K-h)CF_h e^{(K-h)j} \tag{7-23}$$

Calculations for estimates of j are made with

$$j_{k+1} = j_k + \frac{f(j_k)}{f'(j_k)} \tag{7-24}$$

which leads to Eq. (7-25).

The continuous interest rate j is calculated from

$$j_{k+1} = j_k + \frac{V_K - \sum_{h=0}^{n} CF_h e^{(K-h)j}}{\sum_{h=0}^{n} (K-h)CF_h e^{(K-h)j}} \tag{7-25}$$

where CF_h = cash flow for period h
j = continuous interest rate per payment period
$K = n$ for FV
$= 0$ for PV
V_K = FV if $K = n$
$= PV$ if $K = 0$
and the initial guess of $j_0 = 0$.

It is suggested that Eq. (7-25) should be used to solve for j regardless of whether you want to solve for j or i.† If a value of i is the desired end result, Eq. (7-19) is used after a value for j has been calculated.

To demonstrate, let's solve for the interest rate in Example 7-11.

†Ibid.

Example 7-11 Given the following four cash flows—$1400, $1900, $1500, $1700—compute the interest rate assuming that:

(*a*) The FV is $8263.64 and the payments occur at the *beginning* of the periods.

(*b*) The PV is $5131.070282 and the payments occur at the end of the periods.

We proceed to solve these problems as follows:

(*a*) For this FV, beginning-of-period case, substitute $K = n = 4$ and V_K = FV = $8263.64 into Eq. (7-25) to commence the iterative calculations. Using an initial guess for j_x of zero for this formula (as with all the cases for discrete variable cash flows), the first two iterations of the computational procedure would result in the following:

First iteration, $j_0 = 0$

Period, h	$n - h$	CF_h	$CF_h e^{(n-h)j}$	$(n - h)CF_h e^{(n-h)j}$
0	4	$1400	$1400	$ 5,600
1	3	1900	1900	5,700
2	2	1500	1500	3,000
3	1	1700	1700	1,700
4	0	0	0	0
		Totals	$6500	$16,000

$$j_1 = 0 + \frac{\$8263.64 - \$6500}{\$16,000}$$

$$= 0 + .1102275$$

$$j_1 = .1102275$$

Second iteration, $j_1 = .1102275$

Period, h	$n - h$	CF_h	$CF_h e^{(n-h)j}$	$(n - h)CF_h e^{(n-h)j}$
0	4	$1400	$2175.769155	$ 8,703,076621
1	3	1900	2644.643798	7,933.931393
2	2	1500	1869.965737	3,739.931474
3	1	1700	1898.104489	1,898.104489
4	0	0	0	0
		Totals	$8588.483179	$22,275.04398

$$j_2 = .1102275 + \frac{\$8263.64 - \$8588.483179}{\$22,275.04398}$$

$$= .0956442211$$

Repeating the same process without showing the calculations, the following results are obtained:

$$j_3 = .0953103493$$

$$j_4 = .0953101798$$

$$j_5 = .0953101798$$

On the fifth iteration Δj is close to zero, so the continuous interest rate j is determined to be .0953101798. A conversion to i_f results in

$$i_f = e^{.0953101798} - 1$$

$$= .10$$

(Recall that 10% was the rate originally used to compute the future values in Example 7-5.)

Next, let's go on to part (a) of Example 7-11. Note that the payments have shifted from *beginning* to *end* of period. Specifically, this means that now CF_0 is zero and $CF_4 = \$1700$. In addition, we must specify a new value for K and reuse Eq. (7-25).

(*b*) Since part (b) is a PV, end-of-period payment, substitute $K = 0$ and $V_K = PV = \$5131.070282$ into Eq. (7-25) to commence the iterative calculations. Again two iterations are shown in detail, starting with $j_0 = 0$.

First iteration, $j_0 = 0$

Period, h	$-h$	CF_h	$CF_h e^{-hj}$	$-h \times CF_h e^{-hj}$
0	0	$ 0	$ 0	$ 0
1	−1	1400	+ 1400	− 1,400
2	−2	1900	+ 1900	− 3,800
3	−3	1500	+ 1500	− 4,500
4	−4	1700	+ 1700	− 6,800
		Totals	$6500	−$16,500

$$j_1 = 0 + \frac{\$5131.070282 - \$6500}{-\$16,500}$$

$$= .0829654375$$

Second iteration, $j_1 = .0829654375$

Period, h	$-h$	CF_h	$CF_h e^{-hj}$	$-h \times CF_h e^{-hj}$
0	0	$ 0	$ 0	$ 0
1	-1	1400	1288.53614	$-$ 1,288.53614
2	-2	1900	1609.499098	$-$ 3,218.998196
3	-3	1500	1169.491216	$-$ 3,508.473647
4	-4	1700	1219.897088	$-$ 4,879.588353
		Totals	$5287.423542	$-$12,895.59634

$$j_2 = .0829654375 + \frac{\$5131.070282 - \$5287.423542423542}{-\$12,895.59634}$$

$$= .0829654375 + .0121245467$$

$$= .0950899842$$

Continuing with the iterations:

$$j_3 = .095310191$$
$$j_4 = .0953101798$$
$$j_5 = .0953101798$$

After a suitable value of j has been obtained, the solution for i is

$$i_f = e^{.0953101798} - 1$$
$$= .1$$

The annual continuous rate is 9.53101798% and the discrete interest rate is 10% for part (b) of Example 7-11.

As you can see from this example, the computation of j or i for variable cash flows is a straightforward calculation, but does require careful placement of each cash flow. The next section uses a modification of the basic iteration formula allowing payments to occur at the beginning or end, as specified.

7-5.3 Solving for Interest Rate Using Equation (7-9)

As noted in the preceding section, the formula given there requires careful manual placement of each cash flow. In this section we wish to illustrate the formula where it is possible to shift the payments automatically from end- to beginning-of-period payments. The key formula is Eq. (7-9). Following the method explained in the section above, the Newton-Raphson procedures are

$$j_{k+1} = j_k + \Delta j_k \tag{7-26}$$

$$\Delta j = \frac{V_K - \sum\limits_{h=1}^{n} CF_h e^{(K-h)j}}{\sum\limits_{h=1}^{n} (K - h) CF_h e^{(K-h)j}} \tag{7-27}$$

where V_K = FV_E, PV_E, FV_B, or PV_B

$\quad$ CF_h = discrete cash flow assumed to occur at end of period h

$\quad\quad$ j = continuous interest rate, r/f

$\quad\quad$ r = annual continuous interest rate

$\quad\quad$ f = number of payments per year

$\quad\quad$ h = 1, 2, 3, . . . , n

$\quad\quad$ n = total number of cash payments

$\quad\quad$ K = n for FV_E

$\quad\quad\quad$ = 0 for PV_E

$\quad\quad\quad$ = $n + 1$ for FV_B

$\quad\quad\quad$ = 1 for PV_B

This iteration procedure uses an initial guess for j_0 of zero, although any estimate could be used as a starting point. The continuous interest rate j is computed first and then converted to the discrete rate i_f, using

$$i_f = e^j - 1$$

This relationship can also be used for discrete compounding and cash flows where the number of payment periods per year is unequal to the number of compounding periods per year—the variable-cash-flow equivalent of general annuities. In this situation, where i_f is unequal to i_c, we solve first for i_f as described above and then convert to i_c using Eq. (7-13) in the form

$$i_c = (1 + i_f)^{f/c} - 1$$

The final variation, involving both continuous cash flows and compounding, is discussed in the next section, but also uses the generalized formula above with only a slight modification.

Because a different keystroke sequence is required for each case, FV_E, PV_E, FV_B, or PV_B, an example is given for each of the situations discussed above.

7-5.4 Four Examples for Equation (7-27)

As mentioned above, considerable emphasis is given to Eq. (7-27). It will, in fact, be the basis for a customized computer program to be discussed in a later section. A series of four examples will be presented in this section, each solving for the interest rate when either PV_E, FV_B, PV_B, or FV_E is known, respectively. Considerable detail is provided for each example for readers who may want to make similar manual calculations or debug their own program.

Example 7-12: PE_E is known The GA company is evaluating a project which requires an investment of $5900. They require a 20% return on all projects. Assuming that the following after-tax cash flows at the *end* of each 6-month period, what is the interest rate for

1. continuous compounding?
2. discrete compounding with $c = 2$ and $f = 2$?
3. discrete compounding with $c = 12$ and $f = 2$?

Period	Cash flow
1	$1000
2	− 500
3	3500
4	4000

We note from the table above that periods 1, 3, and 4 are inflows and period 2 is an outflow, as indicated by the negative sign. Frequently, negative flows, other than at period zero, can create a possible difficulty. Specifically, such negative payments may create a situation where more than one interest rate can be obtained from Eq. (7-27). The problem of multiple roots will be discussed later in this chapter, and it does not create a problem in this particular example. Now to solve Example 7-12, using Eq. (7-27).

We assume the initial interest rate is zero and proceed with the first iteration after setting $K = 0$.

First iteration, $j_0 = 0$

Period, h	$-h$	CF	CF $\times e^{-hj}$	$-h \times$ CF $\times e^{-hj}$
1	−1	$1000	$1000	−$ 1,000
2	−2	− 500	− 500	+ 1,000
3	−3	3500	3500	− 10,500
4	−4	4000	4000	− 16,000
			Totals $8000	−$26,500

$$j_1 = 0 + \frac{\$5900 - \$8000}{-\$26,500}$$

$$= 0 + .079245283$$

Second iteration, $j_1 = .079245283$

Period, h	$-h$	CF	CF $\times$ e^{-hj}	$-h \times$ CF $\times$ e^{-hj}
1	-1	1000	\$ 923.813301	$-\$$ 923.813301
2	-2	$-$ 500	$-$ 426.7155075	$+$ 853.431015
3	-3	3500	2759.438231	$-$ 8,278.314693
4	-4	4000	2913.37799	$-$ 11,653.51196
		Totals	\$6169.914015	$-\$20,002.20894$

$$j_2 = .079245283 + \frac{\$5900 - \$6169.914015}{-\$20,002.20894}$$

$$= .079245283 + .0134942104$$

$$= .0927394934$$

Continuing the iteration without the tables, we find that

$$j_3 = .0930713649$$

$$j_4 = .0930715593$$

$$j_5 = .0930715593$$

The semiannual continuous interest rate or internal rate of return is 9.30715593% and, multiplying by 2, the annual rate is 18.61431183%, which is less than the company's required rate of return. Now let's find the interest rate for part 2 of the problem, where compounding is discrete. Using the relationship

$$i_f = e^{r/f} - 1$$

$$= e^{.0930715593} - 1$$

$$= .0975402717$$

the yearly discrete rate is $2 \times i_f$ or 19.50805433%, which is still below the required 20% return.

Part 3 in the problem requires the discrete interest rate if interest is compounded monthly with semiannual payments. This third interest rate is computed using the conversion formula and the i_f just computed.

$$i_c = (1 + i_f)^{f/c} - 1$$

$$= 1.0975402717^{2/12} - 1$$

$$= .015632861$$

The annual rate is 1.5632861% $\times$ 12 or 18.75943318%, which again is less than the required return of 20%.

Next, we will determine the interest rate for the FV_B case with discrete compounding with $c = f$, $c \neq f$, and then with continuous compounding, all of which require a K value of $n + 1$ for the generalized iteration, Eq. (7-27).

Example 7-13: FV_B case You have extra money coming in from investments at the *beginning* of each quarter for the next 2 years and you need $41,500 at the end of the period. If you make the deposits and withdrawals as shown in the table below, what yield or interest rate is necessary assuming

1. continuous compounding?
2. quarterly discrete compounding?
3. weekly discrete compounding and quarterly payments?

Quarter	Deposit (or withdrawal)
1	$1000
2	7000
3	6000
4	− 3000
5	8000
6	9300
7	4200
8	6300

The first iteration using an initial interest rate of zero is shown below.

First iteration, $j_0 = 0$

Period, h	$n + 1 - h$	CF	$CF \times e^{(n+1-h)j}$	$(n + 1 - h)CF \times e^{(n+1-h)j}$
1	8	$1000	$ 1,000	$ 8,000
2	7	7000	7,000	49,000
3	6	6000	6,000	36,000
4	5	− 3000	− 3,000	− 15,000
5	4	8000	8,000	32,000
6	3	9300	9,300	27,900
7	2	4200	4,200	8,400
8	1	6300	6,300	6,300
		Totals	$38,800	$152,600

$$j_1 = 0 + \frac{\$41,500 - \$38,800}{\$152,600}$$

$$= .0176933159$$

Second iteration, $j_1 = .0176933159$

Period, h	$n + 1 - h$	CF	$CF \times e^{(n+1-h)j}$	$(n + 1 - h)CF \times e^{(n+1-h)j}$
1	8	$1000	$1,152.054105	$ 9,216.432839
2	7	7000	7,922.948012	55,460.63609
3	6	6000	6,671.997996	40,031.98797
4	5	− 3000	− 3,277.493221	− 16,387.4661
5	4	8000	8,586.702668	34,346.81067
6	3	9300	9,806.979714	29,420.93914
7	2	4200	4,351.284797	8,702.569594
8	1	6300	6,412.49585	6,412.45985
		Totals	$41,626.93392	$167,204.3701

$$j_2 = .0176933159 + \frac{\$41,500 - \$41,626.93392}{\$167,204.3701}$$

$$= .0176933159 - .0007591543$$

$$= .0169341616$$

The remaining iterations are:

$$j_3 = .0169326591$$

$$j_4 = .0169326591$$

The annual *continuous interest* rate necessary is 1.69326591% × 4 or 6.77306364%.

Computing the *quarterly discrete interest* rate for part 2 of the problem using the conversion formula gives

$$i_f = e^{.0169326591} - 1$$

$$= .0170768292$$

The *annual discrete interest* rate compounded quarterly is 4 × 1.70768292% or 6.83073168%.

Part 3 of the problem requires the discrete interest rate assuming weekly compounding. The interest rate is computed using the i_f value above and the conversion formula.

$$i_c = (1 + i_f)^{f/c} - 1$$

$$= 1.0170768292^{4/52} - 1$$

$$= .0013033609$$

The weekly discrete interest rate is .13033609 and the yearly rate is then .13033609 × 52 or 6.77747668%.

In summary, the $41,500 can be accumulated by savings accounts paying

1. 6.77306364% compounded continuously,
2. 6.83073168% compounded quarterly, *or*
3. 6.77747668% compounded weekly.

Computing the interest rate for the PV_B case with discrete compounding with $c = f$, $c \neq f$, or with continuous compounding requires a K value of 1, as shown in the next example.

Example 7-14: PV_B case A company is evaluating a lease on a machine. They have determined the following yearly after-tax flows associated with the lease. The lease agreement specifies beginning-of-year payments.

Year	Cash flow
1	$13,500
2	12,000
3	11,000
4	9,000
5	7,000

The company has the option of purchasing the machine for $38,500 or incurring the after-tax costs shown above. The company requires a return on investment of 14% annually. What is the implied cost of leasing the machine, based on the cash flows above assuming that interest is

1. compounded continuously?
2. compounded annually?
3. compounded quarterly?

The computation table for the first iteration is:

First iteration, $j_0 = 0$

Period, h	CF	$1 - h$	$CF_h e^{(1-h)j}$	$(1 - h)CF_h e^{(1-h)j}$
1	$13,500	0	$13,500	$ 0
2	12,000	−1	12,000	− 12,000
3	11,000	−2	11,000	− 22,000
4	9,000	−3	9,000	− 27,000
5	7,000	−4	7,000	− 28,000
		Totals	$52,500	−$89,000

$$j_1 = 0 + \frac{\$38,500 - \$52,500}{-\$89,000}$$

$$= 0 + .1573033708$$

Second iteration, $j_1 = .1573033708$

Period, h	CF	$1 - h$	$CF_h e^{(l-h)j}$	$(1 - h)CF_h e^{(l-h)j}$
1	$13,500	0	$13,500	$ 0
2	12,000	−1	10,253.33767	− 10,253.33767
3	11,000	−2	8,030.83519	− 16,061.67038
4	9,000	−3	5,614.286249	− 16,842.85875
5	7,000	−4	3,731.076007	− 14,924.30403
		Totals	$41,129.53512	−$58,082.17083

$$j_2 = .1573033708 + \frac{\$38,500 - \$41,129.53512}{-\$58,082.17083}$$

$$= .2025760437$$

Omitting the tables for the remaining iteration, we find

$$j_3 = .2054710773$$

$$j_4 = .2054819275$$

$$j_5 = .2054819276$$

$$j_6 = .2054819276$$

Thus the implied interest rate to the company is 20.54819276% with interest compounded continuously. The discrete interest rate compounded annually is

$$i_f = e^{.2054819276} - 1$$

$$= .2281167858$$

Now that we have the discrete interest rate i_f, we can compute the answer to part 3 of the problem. The quarterly compounding rate is

$$i_c = 1.228116786^{1/4} - 1$$

$$= .0527128321$$

The quarterly compounding rate of 5.27128321% is equivalent to a yearly rate of 4 × 5.27128321% or 21.08513284%.

In summary, the implied interest rate on the lease is

1. 20.54819276% with interest compounded continuously.
2. 22.81167858% with interest compounded annually.
3. 21.08513284% with interest compounded quarterly.

Because the implied interest rates under all the assumptions above are greater than the company's required return, the machine's purchase should be considered.

The last case of this series is for the FV_E case, where $K = n$.

Example 7-15 The AF Company must establish a sinking fund that will accumulate to $49,756.58 at the end of the fifth year. The anticipated deposits at the end of each year are:

Year	Amount
1	$10,000
2	7,500
3	6,000
4	8,500
5	4,000

What is the required annual interest return if the interest rate is

1. continuous?
2. discrete and compounded yearly?
3. discrete and compounded quarterly?

To solve for j, using zero as the initial estimate:

First iteration, $j_0 = 0$

Period, h	$n - h$	CF	$CF_h e^{(n-h)j}$	$(n - h)CF_h e^{(n-h)j}$
1	4	$10,000	$10,000	$40,000
2	3	7,500	7,500	22,500
3	2	6,000	6,000	12,000
4	1	8,500	8,500	8,500
5	0	4,000	4,000	0
		Totals	$36,000	$83,000

Now that we have the two sums, we can compute j_1.

$$j_1 = 0 + \frac{\$49,756.58 - \$36,000}{\$83,000}$$

$$= 0 + .1657419277$$

$$= .1657419277$$

The process is repeated for the second iteration:

Second iteration, $j_1 = .1657419277$

Period, h	$n - h$	CF_h	$CF_h e^{(n-h)j}$	$(n - h)CF_h e^{(n-h)j}$
1	4	$10,000	$19,405.42767	$ 77,621.71068
2	3	7,500	12,331.15274	36,993.45823
3	2	6,000	8,358.201937	16,716.40387
4	1	8,500	10,032.28198	10,032.28198
5	0	4,000	4,000.	0
		Totals	$54,127.06433	$141,363.8548

Solving for j_2:

$$j_2 = .1657419277 + \frac{\$49,756.58 - \$54,127.06433}{\$141,363.8548}$$

$$= .1657419277 - .0309165616$$

$$= .1348253661$$

The remaining iterations are shown below without the table.

$$j_3 = .13314179411$$

$$j_4 = .1331433363$$

$$j_5 = .1331433363$$

The annual continuous interest rate after five iterations is 13.31433363%. Note that each iteration requires a large number of keystrokes compared to the routines in Chaps. 4 and 5. To avoid unnecessary iterations, remember that the term Δj_k gives you the accuracy of the answer. You can generally stop after only two or three iterations if two- or three-digit accuracy is all that is required. For example, after iteration 3 above, the answer was accurate to two decimals, and five decimals after iteration 4.

Once we determine j, the continuous-rate-per-payment period, it can be converted to the annual rate:

$$r = j \times f$$

$$= .1331433363 \times 1$$

$$= .1331433363$$

Here, since $f = 1$, the rate-per-payment period is also the annual rate.

To compute i_f, the discrete rate (part 2 of the problem), we use

$$i_f = e^{r/f} - 1$$

$$= e^{.1331433363/1} - 1$$

$$= .142413736$$

The required interest rate assuming discrete annual compounding is 14.2413736% (which is, of course, larger than the continuous rate).

For part 3 of the problem, where the discrete rate is compounded quarterly, the i_c value is

$$i_c = (1 + i_f)^{f/c} - 1$$

$$= 1.142413736^{1/4} - 1$$

$$= .0338460054$$

$$r = .0338460054 \times 4 = .135840218$$

where $f = 1$
$c = 4$

Thus, if the discrete interest is compounded quarterly, an annual rate of 13.5840218% is necessary.

In *summary*, we can use the generalized formula to solve for any of three related interest rates from the same iteration procedure:

1. Continuous rate.
2. Discrete rate where $c = f$.
3. Discrete rate where $c \neq f$.

This general approach applies to the four cases: PV_E, FV_B, PV_B, and FV_E.

7-5.5 Relationships Among IRR, NPV, and NFV

Many Level II and III calculators have internal routines or external programs that compute i_f for discrete cash flows occurring at the end of each period (IRR), but not for the cases PV_B, FV_B, and FV_E. The purpose of this section is to show how to use the internal IRR routine to solve for i when any of the V_K values are given.

If the manufacturer provides an internal or library routine to solve for IRR on a Level II or Level III calculator, it probably was designed for the following conditions:

1. End-of-period payment is assumed.
2. An initial outlay, CF_0, is required.
3. Net present value, NPV, is equal to zero.
4. Both cash flows and compounding are discrete with $f = c$.

With the current state of the art, the number of cash flow entries can vary from 10 to 80. In spite of these limitations, such an IRR routine can be used effectively to solve for the four cases: PV_E, FV_E, PV_B, and FV_B.

The key to using the IRR routine for all four cases is the condition that $NPV = 0$. From the information that $NPV = 0$ and Eq. (7-1), we can assign the proper value to an initial outlay, called CF_0. Then, with a value assigned to CF_0, it becomes possible to find an i when either PV_E or PV_B is specified.

Another interesting property is that the net future value, NFV, also becomes zero for a calculated value for IRR. With this knowledge that $NFV = 0$, it becomes possible to modify the value for CF_n, the payment at end of the nth period. This knowledge of CF_n permits us to evaluate i when either FV_E or FV_B is specified. The following four examples illustrate this technique.

Example 7-16 Suppose that the following cash flow payments are specified as yearly payments: $1400, $1900, $1500, and $1700. Utilizing this cash flow sequence, solve for IRR when the following are specified:

Case 1: PV_E is given as $5131.070283.
Case 2: FV_E is given as $7512.40.
Case 3: PV_B is given as $5644.1773.
Case 4: FV_B is given as $8263.64.

Case 1: PV_E is given This is an end-of-year situation, so the following table is applicable:

End of year	Cash flow	Adjusted cash flow
0	$ 0	−$5131.070283
1	1400	1400
2	1900	1900
3	1500	1500
4	1700	1700

We also know that for NPV to be equal to zero, we have

$$NPV = CF_0 + PV_E$$

or

$$CF_0 = -PV_E = -\$5131.070283 \qquad (7\text{-}28)$$

and this value for CF_0 is shown in the column above called "adjusted cash flows."

So, if the adjusted-cash-flow stream is entered in the order shown in a Level II or Level III calculator, the answer will be IRR = 10.00%.

Case 2: FV_E is given Start with the same end-of-period payments as in case 1.

End of year	Cash flow	Adjusted cash flow
0	$ 0	$ 0
1	1400	1400
2	1900	1900
3	1500	1500
4	1700	$1700 - \$7512.40 = -\$5812.40$

In this case the adjustment will be made at end of period 4 because

$$NFV = \text{adjustment}_4 + FV = 0$$

If the adjustment is called CF'_4, then

$$NFV = CF'_4 + FV = 0$$

or

$$CF'_4 = -FV = -\$7512.40 \qquad (7\text{-}29)$$

So the adjustment to CF'_4 is made in the table above. When the adjusted cash flow payments are entered into the calculator to solve for IRR, with $\$1700 - \$7512.40 = -\$5812.40$ for the last payment, the IRR answer is 10.00%.

Case 3: PV_B is given This time we have the beginning-of-year payments, so the following table is used:

End of year	Cash flow	Adjusted cash flow
0	$1400	$\$1400 - \$5644.1773 = -\$4244.1773$
1	1900	1900
2	1500	1500
3	1700	1700
4	0	0

As expected, the first payment occurs at the end of the year zero, which is the same as the beginning of the first year. Following the same pattern, we use the relationship

$$NPV = CF_0 + PV_B$$

or

$$CF_0 = -PV_B = -\$5644.1773 \qquad (7\text{-}30)$$

Again the adjusted CF$'_0$ value is used in the adjusted-cash-flow column of the table above. The first entry into the calculator will be $1400 - $5644.1773 = -$4244.1773$, and all the other values in the adjusted column are entered in their order. The answer for IRR is again 10.00%.

Case 4: FV$_B$ is given Again we have the end-of-payment situation which is reproduced in the following table:

End of year	Cash flow	Adjusted cash flow
0	$1400	$1400
1	1900	1900
2	1500	1500
3	1700	1700
4	0	0 − $8263.64

Therefore, we use the relationship

$$\text{NFV} = \text{CF}'_4 + \text{FV}_B = 0$$

or

$$\text{CF}'_4 = -\text{FV}_B = -\$8263.64 \tag{7-31}$$

and the adjusted cash flow is constructed and used to get the answer IRR = 10.00%.

We demonstrated in this section how to use IRR capability of some Level II and Level III calculators to solve for i for the cases where one of the PV$_E$, FV$_E$, PV$_B$, or FV$_B$ is known. The method for solving these four cases can be extended for continuous interest rates and the discrete case where $c \neq f$.

The continuous interest rate j is found with this procedure by first computing i_f and then converting as follows:

$$j = \ln(1 + i_f) \tag{7-32}$$

To determine i_c when $f \neq c$, the same procedure as previously described is used:

$$i_c = (1 + i_f)^{f/c} - 1 \tag{7-33}$$

An important remaining case, solving for i where there are continuous variable cash flows, is the subject of the next section.

7-5.6 Solving for the Interest Rate with Continuous Compounding and Cash Flows

The previous sections assumed discrete cash flows. Determining the interest rate for continuous flows and compounding requires a modification to the iteration formula previously used.

As you will recall, in Sec. 7-4.4, PV and FV were computed for continuous cases by converting each period's cash flow from a continuous to a discrete payment using the relationship of Eq. (7-8):

$$\frac{e^{r/f} - 1}{r/f} \times \frac{\text{continuous}}{\text{payment}} = \frac{\text{discrete}}{\text{payment}}$$

Expressed in more precise terms, the equivalent discrete payment for time increment h becomes†

$$CF_h = p_h \frac{e^{r/f} - 1}{r/f} \qquad (7\text{-}34)$$

where CF_h = discrete payment at end of period h
$\quad\quad p_h$ = continuous payment during period h

Equation (7-34) or (7-15) was relatively easy to use in Sec. 7-4.4, where the interest rate was known in advance. Since the interest rates were known, Eq. (7-34) was used to calculate the equivalent discrete payments CF_h. Once the equivalent discrete payment was determined, the discrete FV or PV formula was used to obtain a solution. Because the conversion term is a constant, converting each payment was unnecessary. FV or PV was computed for the continuous flows by using the discrete formula, with the answer simply multiplied by the conversion term.

However, in this section, where the interest rate is unknown, the computational procedure must take into consideration that each iteration of the trial-and-error procedure must reuse Eq. (7-34) to obtain improved estimates of CF_h for every h for every iteration. Therefore, the Newton-Raphson computational formula of Eq. (7-27) is modified to give the following consolidated formula:

$$j_{k+1} = j_k + \frac{V_k - \left(\dfrac{e^{r/f} - 1}{r/f}\right)^Q \displaystyle\sum_{h=1}^{n} CF_h e^{(K-h)(r/f)}}{\left(\dfrac{e^{r/f} - 1}{r/f}\right)^Q \displaystyle\sum_{h=1}^{n}(K - h)CF_h e^{(K-h)(r/f)}} \qquad (7\text{-}35)$$

For calculations this equation is simplified to the form

$$j_{k+1} = j_k + \frac{V_k \div \left(\dfrac{e^{j_k} - 1}{j_k}\right)^Q - \displaystyle\sum_{h=1}^{n} CF_h e^{(K-h)j_k}}{\displaystyle\sum_{h=1}^{n}(K - h)CF_h e^{(K-h)j_k}} \qquad (7\text{-}36)$$

where for discrete cash flows:
K = n for FV_E
$\quad$ = 0 for PV_E
$\quad$ = $n + 1$ for FV_B
$\quad$ = 1 for PV_B

†Refer back to Chap. 6, Eq. (6-22), for the development of Eq. (7-34).

and for continuous cash flows:

$K = n$ for FV

$\quad = 0$ for PV

$Q = 1$ for continuous cash flows where $CF_h = p_n$

$\quad = 0$ for discrete cash flows in terms of CF_h

$j_k = $ continuous interest rate per period f

Note that this formula is similar to Eq. (7-27) for discrete flows, except that the V_K has been modified. The number of iterations necessary for solution, however, are increased as a result of this modification. As a result, solving for the interest rate using a Level I calculator can be quite time-consuming, unless limited accuracy is acceptable.†

As with the discrete cash flows, the interest rates for both the FV and PV cases can be computed separately. We will present an example for the PV case.

Example 7-17 A company is evaluating a project with the quarterly cash savings shown below. Because of the nature of the project, continuous variable cash flows and compounding are assumed.

The project requires an outlay of $12,000. What is the interest rate or internal rate of return?

Quarter, h	Continuous cash flow, p
1	$1500
2	3400
3	6300
4	5250

Note that for this example:

$K = 0$ for the PV case

$CF_h = p_h$ for $h = 1, 2, 3,$ and 4

$Q = 1$ for the continuous flow case

$j_0 = $ initial estimate must be a value other than zero

Next, we must make an initial interest rate guess for the first iteration. Suppose we use a small rate, say .001.

---

†The significance of Eq. (7-36) is that it consolidates so many different cases into one formula. For this reason, Eq. (7-36) is used as the basis for the computer program described at the end of this chapter.

First iteration, $j_0 = .001$

Period, h	$-h$	CF	$CF_h e^{-hj}$	$-h \times CF_h e^{-hj}$
1	-1	$1500	$ 1,498.50075	$-$ 1,498.50075
2	-2	3400	3,393.206795	$-$ 6,786.413591
3	-3	6300	6,281.128322	$-$ 18,843.38497
4	-4	5250	5,229.041944	$-$ 20,916.16778
		Totals	$16,401.87781	$-$48,044.46709

After determining the totals, the next step is to solve for j_1.

$$j_1 = .001 + \cfrac{12{,}000 \div \dfrac{e^{.001} - 1}{.001} - \$16{,}401.87781}{-\$48{,}044.46709}$$

$$= .001 + .0917457736$$

$$= .0927457736$$

While the remaining iterations are not given, j_{15} is:

$$j_{15} = .133412983$$

The interest rate or the return on this project is 13.3412983%.

Once again, many iterations were necessary to determine the interest rate with accuracy. However, this should not be a significant factor using a Level III calculator that can store a program such as the one described at the end of this chapter.

7-6 CASH FLOWS WITH SOME NEGATIVE VALUES

In some cash flow situations, it is possible to encounter a combination of both positive and negative cash flows. The most common type of application involves one negative flow, usually the initial outflow, and then the remainder are discrete, positive outflows. In such a situation, there is no difficulty in solving for IRR and getting a unique answer.

However, some special difficulties are encountered when IRR is computed for a present-value situation that involves multiple negative cash flows; specifically, there may be several answers for IRR. In this section we discuss some methods for determining whether there is a single interest rate solution or if multiple rates exist for IRR.

As stated above, generally, only one interest rate exists for any series of cash flows where the zero period cash flow is the *only* negative payment, or

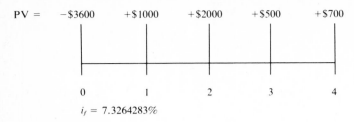

$$i_f = 7.3264283\%$$

Figure 7-4 Single negative cash flow

where the negative cash flows are in *series* beginning with period zero. (Remember that we assume the zero-period cash flow is an outlay, or negative.) Where cash flows have multiple negative payments not in series, multiple interest rates *may* exist, but such cash flows may also have a unique positive or negative interest rate. Such a situation requires the answer to two questions: (1) Is there a single unique interest rate, and (2) if not, what are the multiple interest rates?[†]

The answer to the *first question* was suggested by Mao, who used a simple *balances* test.[‡] The *second question* can be answered by systematic selection of different starting values to carry out the trial-and-error calculations.

To the first question, the first step is to calculate IRR in the usual fashion where PV is known. Next, using the iteration method previously discussed, compound the cash flows forward using the computed interest rate. If each period's balance is zero or negative, the interest rate computed is unique. But if any of the end-of-period balances are positive, multiple rates may exist.

For example, consider the situation shown in Fig. 7-4. The zero period cash flow is negative while the remaining payments are positive. Therefore, as described above, 7.33% should be the only interest rate. Furthermore, when we apply the balance test as a check, we see that all end-of-period balances are zero or negative. These end-of-period balances are computed as follows:

Period	Balance$_{h-1}$ × $(1 + i)$ + CF_h = end-of-period$_h$ balance
1	$-\$3600 \times 1.073264283 + \$1000 = -\$2863.751419$
2	$-\$2863.751419 \times 1.073264283 + \$2000 = -\$1073.562113$
3	$-\$1073.562113 \times 1.073264283 + \$500 = -\$652.2158717$
4	$-\$652.2158717 \times 1.073264283 + \$700 = 0$

[†]However, a discussion of multiple interest rates in an internal rate of return (IRR) context is beyond the scope of this book. For a more detailed discussion of the mathematics underlying this section as well as the capital budgeting implications, see James D. T. Mao, *Quantitative Analysis of Financial Decisions* (London: The Macmillan Company, 1969), pp. 181–212; Daniel Teichroew, Alexander A. Robichek, and Michael Montalbano, "Mathematical Analysis of Rates of Return Under Certainty," *Management Science,* Vol. 11, January 1965, pp. 395–403; Daniel Teichroew, Alexander A. Robichek, and Michael Montalbano, "An Analysis of Criteria for Investment and Financing Decisions Under Certainty, *Management Science,* Vol. 12, November 1965, pp. 155–179.

[‡]Mao, *Quantitative Analysis of Financial Decisions,* pp. 203–204.

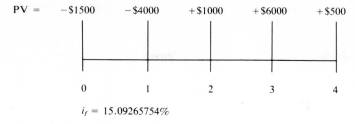

$$i_f = 15.09265754\%$$

Figure 7-5 Negative cash flow in series

Now, let's examine a cash flow pattern common in many capital budgeting situations, as shown in Fig. 7-5. Here the zero-period payment and the first-period payment are negative, with the remaining payments positive. This pattern of payments is common in capital budgeting situations where the project does not generate positive cash flows until after a number of periods. According to the previous statement, one interest rate exists. To verify this, let's compute the end-of-period balances using the balance test.

Period	Balance period$_{h-1}$ × $(1 + i)$ + CF_h = end-of-period$_n$ balance
1	$-\$1500 \times 1.1509265754 - \$4000 = -\$5726.389863$
2	$-\$5726.389863 \times 1.1509265754 + \$1000 = -\$5590.654275$
3	$-\$5590.654275 \times 1.1509265754 + \$6000 = -\$434.4325784$
4	$-\$434.4325784 \times 1.1509265754 + \$500 = 0$

The balance test agrees with the assumption that 15.09% is the only rate for this series because all end-of-period balances are zero or negative.

The situation shown in Fig. 7-6 is one where multiple interest rates may exist. But in this case there is only one interest rate.

Applying the balance test, we see that 9.75% is the unique rate because all the end-of-period balances are zero or negative.

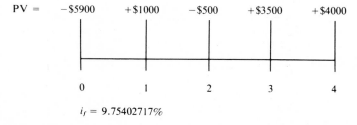

$$i_f = 9.75402717\%$$

Figure 7-6 Mixed positive and negative cash flows with single IRR

Period	Balance period$_{h-1}$ × (1 + i) + CF$_h$ = end-of-period$_n$ balance
1	−$5900 × 1.0975402717 + $1000 = −$5475.487603
2	−$5475.487603 × 1.0975402717 − $500 = −$6509.568148
3	−$6509.568148 × 1.097540217 + $3500 = −$3644.513189
4	−$3644.513189 × 1.097540217 + $4000 = 0

The situation described in Fig. 7-7 *does* have multiple rates of 7.74% and 309.54%. The balance test shows some positive balances, using the rate computed with the iteration formula, 7.74%. (We started with a zero interest rate and the lower rate was found.)

Period	Balance period$_{h-1}$ × (1 + i) + CF$_h$ = end-of-period$_n$ balance
1	−$500 × 1.0774198363 + $1000 = +$461.2900819
2	+$461.2900819 × 1.0774198363 + $6000 = +$6497.003084
3	+$6497.00384 × 1.0774198363 − $7000 = 0

In this case, the end-of-period balances for periods 1 and 2 are positive, indicating that multiple roots may exist. When this situation occurs, the following procedure can be used. First, find the general range where the net-present-value changes from positive to negative or vice versa. For this example, after computing the NPV for 200%, 300%, and 400%, we see that the change occurs between 300% and 400%.

Specified interest rate	NPV
200%	+$240.74
300%	+ 15.63
400%	− 116.00

Then because 300% is closer to the break point, we use it as our initial guess in the iteration formula and resolve for the interest rate, obtaining a value of 309.5405475%.

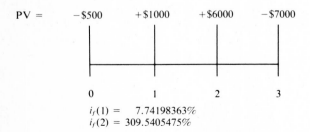

$$i_f(1) = \quad 7.74198363\%$$
$$i_f(2) = 309.5405475\%$$

Figure 7-7 Mixed positive and negative cash flows with multiple IRR's

Turning to the negative interest rates, we find that the NPV becomes increasingly negative as the rate increases, so we don't have a break point in the negative interest range or a negative rate.†

Percent rate	NPV
−25%	−$ 5,092.59
−50%	− 30,500.00
−90%	− 6,390,500.00

The cash flows shown in Fig. 7-8 also have multiple rates, one positive and the other negative. (You may want to perform the balance test to verify that some of the end-of-period balances are positive.)

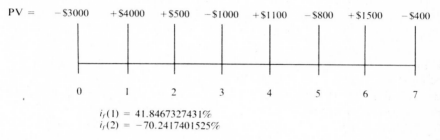

$$i_f(1) = 41.8467327431\%$$
$$i_f(2) = -70.2417401525\%$$

Figure 7-8 Discrete cash flows with multiple IRR values

The positive rate of 41.85% is found using the iteration formula with an initial guess of zero for the interest rate. The only positive break point is found at 41.85%. A negative break point is found between −50% and −90%, and an initial guess of −90% in the iteration formula produces the negative root of −70.24%.

7-7 VARIABLE-CASH-FLOW PROGRAM FOR THE TI-58/59

This program computes V_K, j, and i using Eqs. (7-18) and (7-36). For programming simplification, all interest rate calculations use the continuous compounding form, where the program automatically makes the necessary transformations for discrete compounding. The number of cash flows stored are:

	TI-58	TI-59
Without memory partitioning	20	50
With memory partitioning	N/A	80

†Beware of negative interest rates of − 100% or less.

The memory partitioning command for the TI-59 is **9, 2nd, Op, 17.**

Data entry and subsequent calculations are executed by the use of *user-defined label keys*. The functional uses of these label keys (**A, B, C, D, E, A'**, **B', C', D',** and **E'**) are indicated in Fig. 7-9. Figure 7-9 can be used as a convenient reminder as to the location and use of each label key in this program. The label keys' inputs and functions are described below in the order of execution. Note that inputs for **A, B, B', C', D',** and **E'** must be entered before pressing **C, D,** or **E**. Their use is explained below.

7-7.1 Execution of Program

7-7.1.1 Phase one—data entry

Step 1: Press **E'**.

Initialize the program. This step also initializes the interest rate with 1×10^{-10}, c/f with 1, and Q with 1.

Step 2: Enter cash flow and press **A**.

Each variable cash flow beginning with period 1 is entered. Starting with the second cash flow, **R/S** may be used in place of **A** for entering cash flows.

Step 3: Enter K value and press **B**.

The K factor for FV_E, PV_E, FV_B, or FV_B is entered.

(*Note:* Steps 4, 5, and 6 are not necessary when $c = f$, cash flows are discrete, and/or cash flows do not have a sign change.)

Step 4: Enter c/f ratio and press **B'**.

If $c = f$, omit this step, but if $c \neq f$, enter the c/f value.

Step 5: Press **C'**.

If the cash flows are discrete, omit this step, but if they are continuous, press **C'**.

Step 6: Enter decimal guess for j and press **D'**.

If solving for j and an initial guess other than 1×10^{-10} is necessary, the alternative guess is entered in this step.

7-7.1.2 Phase two—solve for unknown

Step 7a: Enter decimal value for i_c and press **C**.

Solve for V_K using discrete compounding, where the value entered is r/c in decimal form.

or

    Step 7b: Enter decimal value for *j* and press **D**.

    Solve for V_K using continuous compounding, where the value entered is r/f in decimal form.

or

    Step 7c: Enter V_K and press **E**.

    Solve for i_c and *j*. The answer in the display is i_c. Press **R/S** for *j*, the continuous rate.

7-7.1.3 Phase three—sensitivity analysis. You can change any of the values entered in step 3, 4, 5, or 6 and solve for a new unknown value in step 7a, 7b, or 7c without reentering the cash flows. After an interest rate is entered or computed, it is the initial guess for subsequent solutions of i_c and *j* unless modified as described in step 6.

    The cash flow values are stored beginning with data register 10. As a result, to correct or modify a specific cash flow already entered, simply store the replacement cash flow in memory; using STO (9 + period number for cash flow). For example, entering a new value for the third cash flow is **CF$_n$, STO, 12**.

A′	B′	C′	D′	E′
A	B	C	D	E

	c/f	Q	*j* guess	Init.
CF$_n$	K	$i_c \rightarrow V_K$	$j \rightarrow V_K$	$V_K \rightarrow i_c/j$

Figure 7-9 Use of user-defined label keys

7-7.1.4 Program listing

Lbl log	Lbl tan	RCL 05	Prt
RCL 00	(	1/x	R/S
STO 01	(	−	GTO A
−	RCL 03	1	Lbl B
9	INV ln x	=	Prt
=	−	INV EE	STO 04
STO 08	1	STO 07	R/S
0	)	Prt	Lbl C'
STO 06	÷	R/S	CLR
STO 07	RCL 03	RCL 03	1
Lbl sin	)	Prt	STO 09
(	y^x	R/S	Prt
RCL 04	RCL 09	Lbl D	R/S
−	INV SBR	Prt	Lbl B'
RCL 08	Lbl E	STO 03	STO 05
)	Prt	SBR log	Prt
×	STO 02	RCL 06	R/S
RCL 03	Lbl Prd	×	Lbl D'
=	SBR Log	SBR tan	STO 03
INV ln x	RCL 02	=	Prt
×	÷	Prt	R/S
RCL Ind 01	SBR tan	STO 02	Lbl E'
=	−	R/S	CMs
SUM 06	RCL 06	Lbl C	1
×	=	Prt	STO 05
(	÷	+	EE
RCL 04	RCL 07	1	10
−	=	=	+/−
RCL 08	Pause	y^x	STO 03
)	SUM 03	RCL 05	$x \gtreqless t$
=	$|x|$	=	INV EE
SUM 07	$x \geq t$	ln x	9
Op 31	Prd	GTO D	STO 00
Dsz 8	RCL 03	Lbl A	R/S
sin	INV ln x	Op 20	
INV SBR	y^x	STO Ind 00	

KEYSTROKE SOLUTIONS

This section contains keystroke solutions for selected examples from this chapter. These solutions are organized by *type* of calculator (Type A or Type R) and within each type by *level* (Level I, II, or III).

Type	Level	Example number	Page
A	I	7-6, 7-8, 7-10	234, 236, 240
	II	7-6, 7-8, 7-10, 7-12, 7-13, 7-14	234, 236, 240, 249, 251, 253
	III	7-6, 7-8, 7-10, 7-12, 7-13, 7-14, 7-17	234, 236, 240, 249, 251, 253, 262
R	I	7-6, 7-8, 7-10	234, 236, 240
	II	7-6, 7-8, 7-10, 7-12, 7-13, 7-14	234, 236, 240, 249, 251, 253
	III	7-6, 7-8, 7-10, 7-12, 7-14	234, 236, 240, 249, 253

Type A, Level I keystrokes for Example 7-6

TI-30/50 keystrokes	Display	Comments		TI-30/50 keystrokes	Display	Comments
C	0.			÷	57811.879	
1.09	1.09	$1 + i_f$		RCL	1.09	
STO	1.09			+	53038.421	
12000	12000.	CF_6		15800	15800.	CF_1
÷	12000.			=	68838.421	
RCL	1.09			÷	68838.421	
=	11009.174			RCL	1.09	
+	11009.174			=	63154.514	PV_E
12600	12600.	CF_5		STO	63154.514	STO PV_E
=	23609.174			×	63154.514	
÷	23609.174*			1.09	1.09	
RCL	1.09			=	68838.421	PV_B
+	21659.793			RCL	63154.514	PV_E
13400	13400.	CF_4		×	63154.514	
=	35059.793			1.09	1.09	
÷	35059.793			y^x	1.09	
RCL	1.09			6	6.	n
+	32164.948			=	105916.44	FV_E
14500	14500.	CF_3		RCL	63154.514	PV_E
=	46664.948			×	63154.514	
÷	46664.948			1.09	1.09	
RCL	1.09			y^x	1.09	
+	42811.879			7	7.	$n + 1$
15000	15000.	CF_2		=	115448.92	FV_B
=	57811.879					

272

Type A, Level I keystrokes for Example 7-8

TI-30/50 keystrokes	Display	Comments
c	0.	
.065	0.065	r
÷	0.065	
3	3.	c
+	.02166667	i_c
1	1.	
=	1.02166667	$1 + i_c$
y^x	1.02166667	
(	1.02166667	
3	3.	c
÷	3.	
4	4.	f
)	0.75	
=	1.0162064	$1 + i_f$
STO	1.0162064	
450	450.	CF_5
÷	450.	
RCL	1.0162064	
=	442.82343	
+	442.82343	
300	300.	CF_4
=	742.82343	
÷	742.82343	
RCL	1.0162064	
+	730.97694	
250	250.	CF_3
=	980.97694	
÷	980.97694	

TI-30/50 keystrokes	Display	Comments
RCL	1.0162064	
+	965.3324	
175	175.	CF_2
=	1140.3324	
÷	1140.3324	
RCL	1.0162064	
+	1122.1465	
125	125.	CF_1
=	1247.1465	
÷	1247.1465	
RCL	1.0162064	
=	1227.2571	PV_E
×	1227.2571	
RCL	1.0162064	
y^x	1.0162064	
5	5.	n
=	1329.9801	FV_E
×	1227.2571	
1227.2571	1227.2571	
RCL	1.0162064	
=	1247.1465	PV_B
×	1227.2571	
1227.2571	1227.2571	
RCL	1.0162064	
y^x	1.0162064	
6	6.	$n + 1$
=	1351.5343	FV_B

Type A, Level I keystrokes for Example 7-10

TI-30/50 keystrokes	Display	Comments		TI-30/50 keystrokes	Display	Comments
C	0.	Clear		÷	15530.77	
.12	0.12	r		RCL	1.0304545	
÷	0.12			=	15071.767	
4	4.	f		×	15071.767	
=	0.03	j		((	15071.767	
INV ln x	1.0304545	$1 + i_f$		RCL	1.0304545	
STO	1.0304545			−	1.	
5250	5250.	CF_4		1	1.	
÷	5250.			)	.03045453	
RCL	1.0304545			÷	.03045453	
+	5094.8391			(	.03045453	
6300	6300.	CF_3		.12	0.12	
=	11394.839			÷	0.12	
÷	11394.839			4	4.	
RCL	1.0304545			)	0.03	
+	11058.071			)	1.0151511	Correction factor
3400	3400.	CF_2		=	15300.12	PV
=	14458.071			×	15300.12	
÷	14458.071			RCL	1.0304545	
RCL	1.0304545			y^x	1.0304545	
+	14030.77			4	4.	n
1500	1500.	CF_1		=	17250.838	FV
=	15530.77					

274

Type A, Level II keystrokes for Example 7-6

TI-MBA keystrokes	Display	Comments	TI-MBA keystrokes	Display	Comments
CA	0	Clear	NPV	47810.17	
FIX 2	0.00	Set two-digit display	5	5	
9	9	r	x⇄y	1.41	
%i	9.00		12600	12600	CF_5
1	1		NPV	55999.31	
x⇄y	0.00		6	6	
15800	15800		x⇄y	1.54	
NPV	14495.41	CF_1	12000	12000	CF_6
2	2		NPV	63154.51	PV_E
x⇄y	1.09		PV	63154.51	
15000	15000		1	1	$K = 1$
NPV	27120.61	CF_2	N	1.00	
3	3		CPT FV	68838.42	PV_B
x⇄y	1.19		6	6	$K = n$
14500	14500		N	6.00	
NPV	38317.27	CF_3	CPT FV	105916.44	FV_E
4	4		7	7	$K = n + 1$
x⇄y	1.30		N	7.00	
13400	13400	CF_4	CPT FV	115448.92	FV_B

Type A, Level II keystrokes for Example 7-8

TI-MBA keystrokes	Display	Comments
CA	0	Clear
FIX 2	0.00	Set two-decimal display
.065	0.065	r
÷	0.07	
3	3	c
+	0.02	i_c
1	1	
=	1.02	
y^x	1.02	
(	1.02	
3	3	c
÷	3.00	
4	4	f
)	0.75	
−	1.02	$1 + i_f$
1	1	
=	0.02	i_f
STO %i	0.02	
1	1	
x⇄y	0.02	
125	125	
NPV	123.01	CF_1
2	2	
x⇄y	1.02	

TI-MBA keystrokes	Display	Comments
175	175	CF_2
NPV	292.47	
3	3	
x⇄y	1.03	
250	.250	CF_3
NPV	530.70	
4	4	
x⇄y	1.05	
300	300	CF_4
NPV	812.01	
5	5	
x⇄y	1.07	
450	450	CF_5
NPV	1227.26	PV_E
PV	1227.26	
5	5	$K = n$
N	5.00	
CPT FV	1329.98	FV_E
1	1	
N	1.00	
CPT FV	1247.15	PV_B
6	6	$K = n + 1$
N	6.00	
CPT FV	1351.53	FV_B

Type A, Level II keystrokes for Example 7-10

TI-MBA keystrokes	Display	Comments	TI-MBA keystrokes	Display	Comments
CA	0	Clear	NPV	10415.43	
FIX 2	0.00	Set two-decimal display	4	4	
.12	0.12	r	x⇄y	1.09	
÷	0.12		5250	5250	CF_4
4	4		NPV	15071.77	
=	0.03	f	PV	15071.77	
e^x	1.03	j	RCL %i	0.03	
−	1.03	$1 + i_f$	÷	0.03	
1	1		(	0.03	
=	0.03	i_f	.12	0.12	
STO %i	0.03		÷	0.12	
1	1		4	4	
x⇄y	0.03		)	0.03	
1500	1500		=	1.02	Correction factor
NPV	1455.67	CF_1	×	1.02	
2	2		RCL PV	15071.77	
x⇄y	1.03		=	15300.12	
3400	3400		PV	15300.12	PV
NPV	4657.67	CF_2	4	4	
3	3		N	4.00	$K = n$
x⇄y	1.06		CPT FV	17250.84	FV
6300	6300	CF_3			

Type A, Level II keystrokes for Example 7-12

TI-MBA keystrokes	Display	Comments
CA	0	Clear
5900	5900	CF_0; PV_E
STO 0	5900.	
1000	1000	CF_1
STO 1	1000.	
500	500	
+/−	−500	CF_2
STO 2	−500.	
3500	3500	CF_3
STO 3	3500.	
4000	4000	CF_4
STO 4	4000.	
IRR	9.75402715	i_f
%i	9.75402715	
RCL%	0.097540272	
+	0.097540272	
1	1	
=	1.097540272	$1 + i_f$
y^x	1.097540272	
(	1.097540272	
2	2	2
÷	2.	
12	12	
)	0.166666667	c
−	1.015632861	$1 + i_c$
1	1	
=	0.015632861	i_c
RCL %i	0.097540272	i_f
+	0.097540272	
1	1	
=	1.097540272	$1 + i_f$
ln x	0.093071559	j

Type A, Level II keystrokes for Example 7-13

TI-MBA keystrokes	Display	Comments
CA	0	
1000	1000	
+/-	-1000	Enter CF$_0$, but change sign because the MBA will change the sign on R$_0$
STO 0	-1000.	
7000	7000	
STO 1	7000.	CF$_1$
6000	6000	
STO 2	6000.	CF$_2$
3000	3000	
+/-	-3000	
STO 3	-3000.	CF$_3$
8000	8000	
STO 4	8000.	CF$_4$
9300	9300	
STO 5	9300.	CF$_5$
4200	4200	
STO 6	4200.	CF$_6$
6300	6300	
STO 7	6300.	CF$_7$
41500	41500	
+/-	-41500	FV$_B$

TI-MBA keystrokes	Display	Comments
STO 8	-41500.	
IRR	1.70768292	$i\%$
%i	1.70768292	i_f
RCL %i	0.01076829	i_f
+	0.01076829	
1	1	
=	1.017076829	
y^x	1.017076829	
(	1.017076829	
4	4	f
÷	4.	
52	52	c
)	0.076923077	
-	1.001303361	$1 + i_c$
1	1	
=	0.001303361	i_c
RCL %i	0.017076829	i_f
+	0.017076829	
1	1	
=	1.017076829	$1 + i_f$
ln x	0.016932659	j

Type A Level II keystrokes for Example 7-14

TI-MBA keystrokes	Display	Comments	TI-MBA keystrokes	Display	Comments
CA	0		1	1	
38500	38500	PV	=	1.228116786	
-	38500.		y^x	1.228116786	
13500	13500	CF_0	(	1.228116786	
=	25000.	CF_0	1	1	
STO 0	25000.		÷	1.	
12000	12000	CF_1	4	4	
STO 1	12000.		)	0.25	
11000	11000	CF_2	=	1.052712832	
STO 2	11000.		-	1.052712832	
9000	9000	CF_3	1	1	
STO 3	9000.		=	0.052712832	i_c
7000	7000	CF_4	RCL %i	0.228116786	
STO 4	7000.		+	0.228116786	
IRR	22.81167858	$i\%$	1	1	
%i	22.81167858	i_f	=	1.228116786	
RCL %i	0.228116786		ln x	0.205481928	j
+	0.228116786				

Type A, Level III keystrokes for Example 7-6

TI-58/59 keystrokes	Display	Comments
E′	9.	Load variable-cash-flow program Initialize
15800	15800.	CF_1
A	15800.	
15000	15000.	CF_2
A	15000.	
14500	14500.	CF_3
A	14500.	
13400	13400.	CF_4
A	13400.	
12600	12600.	CF_5
A	12600.	
12000	12000.	CF_6
A	12000.	
1	1	$K = 1$ for PV_B
B	1.	
.09	0.09	i_f
C	68838.42072	PV_B
6	6	$K = 6$ for FV_E
B	6.	
.09	0.09	i_f
C	105916.4431	FV_E
7	7	$K = 7$ for FV_B
B	7.	
.09	0.09	i_f
C	115448.923	FV_B
0	0	$K = 0$ for PV_E
B	0.	
.09	0.09	i_f
C	63154.51442	PV_E

Type A, Level III keystrokes for Example 7-8

TI-58/59 keystrokes	Display	Comments
E′	9.	Load variable-cash-flow program Initialize
125	125	CF_1
A	125.	
175	175	CF_2
A	175.	
250	250	CF_3
A	250.	
300	300	CF_4
A	300.	
450	450	CF_5
A	450.	
5	5	K
B	5.	
3	3	c
÷	3.	
4	4	f
=	0.75	c/f
B′	0.75	
.065	0.065	r
÷	0.065	
3	3	c
=	.0216666667	i_c
C	1329.980066	FV_E

Type A, Level III keystrokes for Example 7-10

TI-58/59 keystrokes	Display	Comments
E'	9.	Load variable-cash-flow program
		Initialize
1500	1500	CF$_1$
A	1500.	
3400	3400	CF$_2$
A	3400.	
6300	6300	CF$_3$
A	6300.	
5250	5250	CF$_4$
A	5250.	
0	0	K = 0 for PV
B	0.	
C'	1.	Q = 1
.12	0.12	r
÷	0.12	
4	4	f
=	0.03	r/f = j
D	15300.12079	PV
4	4	K = 4 for FV
B	4.	
.03	0.03	j
D	17250.83802	FV

Type A, Level III keystrokes for Example 7-12

TI-58/59 keystrokes	Display	Comments
E'	9.	Load variable-cash-flow program
		Initialize
1000	1000	CF$_1$
A	1000.	
500	500	CF$_2$
+/−	−500	
A	−500.	
3500	3500	CF$_3$
A	3500.	
4000	4000	CF$_4$
A	4000.	
0	0	K = 0 for PV$_E$
B	0.	
5900	5900	PV$_E$
E	.0975402715	i_c ($c = f = 2$)
R/S	.0930715591	j
12	12	c
÷	12.	
2	2	f
=	6.	c/f
B'	6.	
5900	5900	
E	.015632861	i_c ($c = 12, f = 2$)
×	.015632861	
12	12	
=	.1875943314	r ($c = 12, f = 2$)

Type A, Level III keystrokes for Example 7-13

TI-58/59 keystrokes	Display	Comments
E'		Load variable-cash-flow program
1000	1000	Initialize
A	1000.	
7000	7000	
A	7000.	
6000	6000	
A	6000.	
3000	3000	
+/−	−3000	
A	−3000.	
8000	8000	
A	8000.	
9300	9300	
A	9300.	
4200	4200	
A	4200.	
6300	6300	
A	6300.	
9	9	$K = n + 1 = 9$ for FV_B

TI-58/59 keystrokes	Display	Comments
B	9.	
41500	41500	
E	.017076292	i_c ($c = f = 4$)
×	.017076292	
4	4	c
=	.0683073167	r ($c = f = 4$)
R/S	.0169326591	j ($f = 4$)
×	.0169326591	
4	4	
=	.0677306365	r ($f = 4$)
52	52	
÷	52.	
4	4	
=	13.	
B'	13.	
41500	41500	
E	.0013033609	i_c ($c = 52, f = 4$)
×	.0013033609	
52	52	
=	.0677747656	r ($c = 52, f = 4$)

Type A, Level III keystrokes for Example 7-14

TI-58/59 keystrokes	Display	Comments
E'	9	Load variable-cash-flow program Initialize
13500	13500	CF_1
A	13500.	
12000	12000	CF_2
A	12000.	
11000	11000	CF_3
A	11000.	
9000	9000	CF_4
A	9000.	
7000	7000	CF_5
A	7000.	
1	1	$K = 1$ for PV_B
B	1.	
38500	38500	PV_B
E	.2281167858	i_c ($c = f = 1$) = r
R/S	.2054819276	$j(f = 1) = r$
4	4	c
÷	4.	
1	1	f
=	4.	c/f
B'	4.	PV_B
38500	38500	i_c ($c = 4, f = 1$)
E	.0527128321	
×	.0527128321	c
4	4	
=	.2108513284	r ($c = 4, f = 1$)

Type A, Level III keystrokes for Example 7-17

TI-58/59 keystrokes	Display	Comments
E'	9	Load variable-cash-flow program Initialize
1500	1500	CF_1
A	1500.	
3400	3400	CF_2
A	3400.	
6300	6300	CF_3
A	6300.	
5250	5250	CF_4
A	5250.	
0	0	$K = 0$ for PV
B	0.	
C'	1.	$Q = 1$
12000	12000	PV
E	.1427218256	i
R/S	.133412983	j

Type R, Level I keystrokes for Example 7-6

HP-31E/32E keystrokes	Display	Comments	HP-31E/32E keystrokes	Display	Comments
ALL	0.0000	Clear	RCL 0	1.0900	
1.09	1.09	$1 + i_f$	÷	53,038.4207	
STO 0	1.0900		15800	15,800.	CF_1
12000	12,000.	CF_6	+	68,838.4207	
RCL 0	1.0900		RCL 0	1.0900	
÷	11,009.1743		÷	63,154.5144	PV_E
12600	12,600.	CF_5	STO 1	63,154.5144	
+	23,609.1743		RCL 0	1.0900	
RCL 0	1.0900		×	68,838.4207	PV_B
÷	21,659.7929		RCL 0	1.0900	
13400	13,400.	CF_4	6	6.	n
+	35,059.7929		y^x	1.6771	
RCL 0	1.0900		RCL 1	63,154.5144	
÷	32,164.9477		×	105,916.4431	FV_E
14500	14,500.	CF_3	RCL 0	1.0900	
+	46,664.9477		7	7.	$n + 1$
RCL 0	1.0900		y^x	1.8280	
÷	42,811.8786		RCL 1	63,154.5144	
15000	15,000.	CF_2	×	115,448.9230	FV_B
+	57,811.8786				

285

Type R, Level I keystrokes for Example 7-8

HP-31E/32E keystrokes	Display	Comments
ALL	0.0000	
.065	0.065	r
ENTER↑	0.0650	
3	3.	c
÷	0.0217	i_c
1	1.	
+	1.0217	$1 + i_c$
3	3.	c
ENTER↑	3.0000	
4	4.	f
÷	0.7500	
y^x	1.0162	$1 + i_f$
STO 0	1.0162	
450	450.	CF_5
RCL 0	1.0162	
÷	442.8234	
300	300.	CF_4
+	742.8234	
RCL 0	1.0162	
÷	730.9769	
250	250.	CF_3
+	980.9769	
RCL 0	1.0162	

HP-31E/32E keystrokes	Display	Comments
÷	965.3324	CF_2
175	175.	
+	1,140.3324	
RCL 0	1.0162	
÷	1,122.1465	CF_1
125	125.	
+	1,247.1465	
RCL 0	1.0162	
÷	1,227.2571	PV_E
STO 1	1,227.2571	
RCL 0	1.0162	
5	5.	n
y^x	1.0837	
RCL 1	1,227.2571	
×	1,329.9801	FV_E
RCL 1	1,227.2571	
RCL 0	1.0162	
×	1,247.1465	PV_B
RCL 0	1.0162	
6	6.	$n + 1$
y^x	1.1013	
RCL 1	1,227.2571	
×	1,351.5342	FV_B

Type R, Level I keystrokes for Example 7-10

HP-31E/32E keystrokes	Display	Comments
ALL	0.0000	Clear
.12	0.12	r
ENTER↑	0.1200	
4	4.	f
÷	0.0300	j
e^x	1.0305	$1 + i_f$
STO 0	1.0305	
5250	5,250.	CF_4
RCL 0	1.0305	
÷	5,094.8391	
6300	6,300.	CF_3
+	11,394.8391	
RCL 0	1.0305	
÷	11,058.0707	
3400	3,400.	CF_2
+	14,458.0707	
RCL 0	1.0305	
÷	14,030.7701	
1500	1,500.	CF_1
+	15,530.7701	

HP-31E/32E keystrokes	Display	Comments
RCL 0	1.0305	
÷	15,071.7665	
STO 1	15,071.7665	
RCL 0	1.0305	
1	1.	
−	0.0305	
.12	0.12	
ENTER↑	0.1200	
4	4.	
÷	0.0300	
÷	1.0152	Correction factor
RCL 1	15,071.7665	
×	15,300.1208	PV
STO 1	15,300.1208	
RCL 0	1.0305	
4	4.	n
y^x	1.1275	
RCL 1	15,300.1208	
×	17,250.8381	FV

Type R, Level II keystrokes for Example 7-6

HP-38E keystrokes	Display	Comments
ALL	0.00	Clear
9	9.	r
i	9.00	
15800	15,800	CF_1
CF_j	15,800.00	
15000	15,000.	CF_2
CF_j	15,000.00	
14500	14,500.	CF_3
CF_j	14,500.00	
13400	13,400.	CF_4
CF_j	13,400.00	
12600	12,600.	CF_5
CF_j	12,600.00	
12000	12,000.00	CF_6
CF_j	12000.00	
NPV	63,154.51	PV_E
PV	63,154.51	
1	1.	$K = 1$
n	1.00	
FV	$-68,838.42$	PV_B
6	6.	$K = n$
n	6.00	
FV	$-105,916.44$	FV_E
7	7.	$K = n + 1$
n	7.00	
FV	$-115,448.92$	FV_B

Type R, Level II keystrokes for Example 7-8

HP-38E keystrokes	Display	Comments
ALL	0.00	
.065	0.065	r
ENTER↑	0.07	
3	3.	c
÷	0.02	i_c
1	1.	
+	1.02	$1 + i_c$
3	3.	c
ENTER↑	3.00	f
4	4.	
÷	0.75	
y^x	1.02	$1 + i_f$
1	1.	
−	0.02	i_f
100	100.	
x	1.62	$i\%$
i	1.62	
125	125.	
CF_j	125.00	CF_1

HP-38E keystrokes	Display	Comments
175	175.	CF_2
CF_j	175.00	
250	250.	CF_3
CF_j	250.00	
300	300.	CF_4
CF_j	300.00	
450	450.	CF_5
CF_j	450.00	
NPV	1,227.26	PV_E
PV	1,227.26	
5	5	$K = n$
n	5.00	
FV	−1,329.98	FV_E
1	1.	$K = 1$
n	1.00	
FV	−1,247.15	PV_B
6	6.	$K = n + 1$
n	6.00	
FV	−1,351.53	FV_B

Type R, Level II keystrokes for Example 7-10

HP-38E keystrokes	Display	Comments	HP-38E keystrokes	Display	Comments
ALL	0.00	Clear	CF_j	5,250.00	
.12	0.12	r	NPV	15,071.77	
ENTER↑	0.12		PV	15,071.77	
4	4.	f	RCL i	3.05	
÷	0.03	j	100	100.	
e^x	1.03	$1 + i_f$	÷	0.03	
1	1.		.12	0.12	
−	0.03	i_f	ENTER↑	0.12	
100	100.		4	4.	
×	3.05		÷	0.03	
i	3.05	$i\%$	÷	1.02	Correction factor
1500	1,500.	CF_1	RCL PV	15,071.77	
CF_j	1,500.00		×	15,300.12	PV
3400	3,400.	CF_2	PV	15,300.12	
CF_j	3,400.00		4	4.	
6300	6,300.	CF_3	n	4.00	$K = n$
CF_j	6,300.00		FV	−17,250.84	FV
5250	5,250.	CF_4			

Type R, Level II keystrokes for Example 7-12

HP-38E keystrokes	Display	Comments
ALL	0.00	Clear
5900	5,900	
CHS	−5,900.	CF_0; PV_E
CF_0	−5,900.00	
1000	1,000.	CF_1
CF_j	1,000.00	
500	500.	
CHS	−500.	CF_2
CF_j	−500.00	
3500	3,500.	CF_3
CF_j	3,500.00	
4000	4,000.	CF_4
CF_j	4,000.00	
IRR	9.75	i_f
100	100.	
÷	0.10	
i	0.10	
ENTER↑	0.10	
1	1.	
+	1.10	
2	2.	
ENTER↑	2.00	
12	12.	
÷	0.17	
y^x	1.02	
1	1.	
−	0.02	
(f)9	0.015632861	i_c
RCL i	0.097540271	i_c
1	1.	i_f
+	1.097540271	$1 + i_f$
LN	0.093071559	j

Type R, Level II keystrokes for Example 7-13

HP-38E keystrokes	Display	Comments	HP-38E keystrokes	Display	Comments
ALL	0.00	Clear	CF_j	-41,500.00	
1000	1,000.	CF_0	IRR	1.71	$i\%$
CF_0	1,000.00		100	100	
7000	7,000.	CF_1	÷	0.02	i_f
CF_j	7,000.00		STO 1	0.02	
6000	6,000.	CF_2	1	1.	
CF_j	6,000.00		+	1.02	
3000	3,000.	CF_3	4	4.	f
CHS	-3,000.		ENTER↑	4.00	
CF_j	-3,000.00		52	52.	c
8000	8,000.	CF_4	÷	0.08	
CF_j	8,000.00		y^x	1.00	
9300	9,300.	CF_5	1	1.	
CF_j	9,300.00		-	0.001	
4200	4,200.	CF_6	(f)9	0.001303361	
CF_j	4,200.00		RCL 1	0.017076829	i_c
6300	6,300.	CF_7	1	1.	
CF_j	6,300.00		+	1.017076829	
41,500	41,500.		LN	0.016932659	j
CHS	-41,500.	FV_B			

Type R Level II keystrokes for Example 7-14

HP-38E keystrokes	Display	Comments
ALL	0.00	
38500	38,500.	
ENTER↑	38,500.00	PV
13500	13,500.	
−	25,000.00	CF_0
CHS	−25,000.00	
CF_0	−25,000.00	CF_0
12000	12,000.	CF_1
CF_j	12,000.00	
11000	11,000.	CF_2
CF_j	11,000.00	
9000	9,000.	CF_3
CF_j	9,000.00	
7000	7,000.	CF_4
CF_j	7,000.00	
IRR	22.81	$i\%$
100	100.	
÷	0.23	i_f
1	1.	
+	1.23	
STO 1	1.23	
1	1.	
ENTER↑	1.00	
4	4.	
÷	0.25	
y^x	1.05	
1	1.	
−	0.05	
(f)9	0.052712832	i_c
RCL 1	1.228116786	
LN	0.20548192	j

Type R, Level III keystrokes for Example 7-6

HP-97/67 keystrokes	Display	Comments
9	9.	Program BD1-03A
B 0A	9.00	r
15800	15800.	
D	14495.41	NPV after CF_1
15000	15000.	
D	27120.61	NPV after CF_2
14500	14500.	
D	38317.27	NPV after CF_3
13400	13400.	
D	47810.17	NPV after CF_4
12600	12600.	
D	55999.31	NPV after CF_c
12000	12000.	
D	63154.51	PV_E
1.09	1.09	$1 + i$
x	68838.42	$PV_B = (1 + i) \times PV_E$
1.09	1.09	
ENTER↑	1.09	
5	5.	$n - 1$
y^x	1.54	$(1 + i)^{n-1}$
x	105916.44	$FV_E = (1 + i)^{n-1} \times PV_B$
1.09	1.09	$1 + i$
x	115448.92	$FV_B = (1 + i) \times FV_E$

Type R, Level III keystrokes for Example 7-8

HP-97/67 keystrokes	Display	Comments	HP-97/67 keystrokes	Display	Comments
.065	.065	Program BD1-03A	D	530.70	PV_3
ENTER↑	0.07	r	300	300.	
3	3.		D	812.01	PV_4
÷	0.02	c	450	450.	
1	1.	i_c	D	1227.26	PV_E
+	1.02		RCL B	0.02	
3	3	c	1	1.	
ENTER	3.00		+	1.02	$1 + i_f$
4	4.	f	5	5.	n
÷	0.75		y^x	1.08	
y^x	1.02	$1 + i_f$	×	1329.98	$FV_E = (1 + i)^n \times PV_E$
1	1.		RCL B	0.02	
-	0.02	i_f	1	1.	
100	100.		+	1.02	
×	1.62	$i_f\%$	×	1351.53	$FV_B = (1 + i) \times FV_E$
B 0A	1.62	$i\%$	RCL B	0.02	
125	125.		1	1.	
D	123.01	PV_1	+	1.02	
175	175.		5	5.	n
D	292.47	PV_2	CHS	-5.	$-n$
250	250		y^x	0.92	$(1 + i_f)^{-n}$
			×	1247.15	$PV_B = (1 + i_f)^{-n} \times FV_B$

Type R, Level III keystrokes for Example 7-10

HP-97/67 keystrokes	Display	Comments
.12	.12	Program BD1-03A
ENTER↑	0.12	r
4	4.	f
÷	0.03	j
e^x	1.03	$1 + i_f$
1	1.	
−	0.03	i_f
100	100.	
×	3.05	$i\%$
B 0A	3.05	
1500	1500.	CF_1
D	1455.67	NPV_1
3400	3400.	CF_2
D	4657.67	NPV_2
6300	6300.	CF_3
D	10415.43	NPV_3

HP-97/67 keystrokes	Display	Comments
5250	5250.	CF_4
D	15071.77	NPV_4
ENTER↑	15071.77	
RCL B	0.03	
.12	0.12	
ENTER↑	0.12	
4	4.	
÷	0.03	
÷	1.02	Correction factor
×	15300.12	PV
ENTER↑	15300.12	
RCL B	0.03	
1	1.	
+	1.03	
4	4.	$K = n$
y^x	1.13	
×	17250.84	FV

Type R, Level III keystrokes for Example 7-12

HP-97/67 keystrokes	Display	Comments
(f)CL REG		Program BD1-01A
5900 A	5900.00	Clear
1000 C	1.00	CF_0
500 CHS C	2.00	CF_1
3500 C	3.00	CF_2
4000 C	4.00	CF_3
D	9.75	CF_4
100	100.	i_f
÷	0.10	
ENTER↑	0.10	
ENTER↑	0.10	
1	1.	
+	1.10	
2	2.	
ENTER↑	2.00	
12	12.	
÷	0.17	
y^x	1.02	
1	1.	
−	0.02	i_c
DSP 9	0.015632861	i_c
R↓	0.097540272	i_f
1	1.	
+	1.097540272	$1 + i_f$
LN	0.093071560	j

Type R, Level III keystrokes for Example 7-14

HP-97/67 keystrokes	Display	Comments
(f) CL REG		Program BD1-01B
38500	38500.	Clear
ENTER↑	38500.00	PV
13500	13500.	
−	25000.00	
A	25000.00	
12000 C	1.00	CF_1
11000 C	2.00	CF_2
9000 C	3.00	CF_3
7000 C	4.00	CF_4
D	22.81	$i\%$
100	100.	
÷	0.23	
1	1.	
+	1.23	
STO 1	1.23	
1	1.	
ENTER↑	1.00	
4	4.	
÷	0.25	
y^x	1.05	
1 DSP9	1.000000000	
−	0.052712832	i_c
RCL 1	1.228116785	
LN	0.205481928	j

EXERCISES

Discrete Payments

7-1 Given:

Period	Discrete cash flow
1	$1000
2	1800
3	900
4	1200
5	1500

(*a*) If $i_c = .077$, find FV_E, PV_E, FV_B, and PV_B using discrete compounding.
(*b*) If $r = 9\%$, $c = 12$, and $f = 6$ using discrete compounding, find FV_E, PV_E, FV_B, and PV_B.
(*c*) If $r = 8\%$ and $f = 4$ using continuous compounding, find FV_E, PV_E, FV_B, and PV_B.
answers: (*a*) **$7430.41, $5127.84, $8002.55, $5522.68**; (*b*) **$6589.51, $6115.08, $6688.72, $6207.15**; (*c*) **$6655.56, $6022.20, $6790.02, $6143.86**

7-2 Given:

Period	Discrete cash flow
1	$11,500
2	9,800
3	9,400
4	8,650
5	7,325
6	6,450

(*a*) If $r = 5.85\%$ and $c = f = 2$, find FV_E, PV_E, FV_B, and PV_B using discrete compounding.
(*b*) If $r = 5.74\%$, $c = 12$, and $f = 3$, find FV_E, PV_E, FV_B, and PV_B using discrete compounding.
(*c*) If $r = 6.25\%$ and $f = 5$, find FV_E, PV_E, FV_B, and PV_B using continuous compounding.

7-3 Given:

Period	Discrete cash flow
1	−$1000
2	− 3000
3	250
4	1000
5	4500
6	5200
7	6000
8	6400

(a) If $i_c = .09$ and $f = c = 1$, find FV_E, PV_E, FV_B, and PV_B using discrete compounding.
(b) If $r = 8.35\%$, $c = 4$, and $f = 6$, find FV_E, PV_E, FV_B, and PV_B using discrete compounding.
(c) If $r = 11\%$ and $f = 2$, find FV_E, PV_E, FV_B, and PV_B using continuous compounding.
   answers: (a) **$19,882.65, $9978.43, $21,672.09, $10,876.49**; (b) **$19,483.08, $17,450.34, $19,753.28, $17,692.35**; (c) **$19,783.85, $12,741.52, $20,902.44, $13,461.93**

7-4 Given:

Period	Discrete cash flow
1	−$ 6,000
2	− 400
3	600
4	1,000
5	3,000
6	6,000
7	8,000
8	− 4,000
9	7,000
10	8,000
11	7,500
12	8,000
13	− 3,000
14	4,500
15	5,550
16	9,300
17	− 2,500
18	6,500
19	74,750

(a) If $r = 11.65\%$ and $c = f = 4$, find FV_E, PV_E, FV_B, and PV_B using discrete compounding.
(b) If $r = 10.78\%$, $c = 3$, and $f = 4$, find FV_E, PV_E, FV_B, and PV_B using discrete compounding.
(c) If $r = 12.47\%$ and $f = 4$, find FV_E, PV_E, FV_B, and PV_B using continuous compounding.

7-5 Given:

Period	Discrete cash flow
1	$1000
2	3000
3	2000
4	5000
5	4000

(a) If $f = 1$, find j and r using continuous compounding if $FV_E = \$16,655.98$.
answer: **6.8812%**

(b) If $c = f = 1$, find i_c and r using discrete compounding if $FV_E = \$16,655.98$.
answer: **7.1235%**

(c) If $f = 1$ and $c = 2$, find i_c and r using discrete compounding if $FV_E = \$16,655.98$.
answers: **3.5005%, 7.0009%**

(d) If $f = 1$, find j and r using continuous compounding for $PV_E = \$8668.53$.
answer: **16.1177%**

(e) If $c = f = 1$, find i_c and r using discrete compounding for $PV_E = \$8668.53$.
answer: **17.4892%**

(f) If $f = 1$ and $c = 3$, find i_c and r using discrete compounding for $PV_E = \$8668.53$.
answers: **5.5195%, 16.5585%**

(g) If $f = 1$, find j and r using continuous compounding for $FV_B = \$17,011.77$.
answer: **5.0206%**

(h) If $c = f = 1$, find i_c and r using discrete compounding for $FV_B = \$17,011.77$.
answer: **5.1488%**

(i) If $f = 1$ and $c = 4$, find i_c and r using discrete compounding for $FV_B = \$17,011.77$.
answers: **1.2631%, 5.0523%**

(j) If $f = 1$, find j and r using continuous compounding for $PV_B = \$9711.42$.
answer: **18.2322%**

(k) If $c = f = 1$, find i_c and r using discrete compounding for $PV_B = \$9711.42$.
answer: **20%**

(l) If $f = 1$ and $c = 6$, find i_c and r using discrete compounding for $PV_B = \$9711.42$.
answers: **3.0853%, 18.5120%**

7-6 Given:

Period	Discrete cash flow
1	$ 850
2	900
3	1200
4	1450
5	1125
6	1060

    (*a*) If $f = 2$ and $FV_E = \$7450.42$, find j and r using continuous compounding.

    (*b*) If $f = c = 2$ and $FV_E = \$7450.42$, find i_c and r using discrete compounding.

    (*c*) If $f = 2$, $c = 1$, and $FV_E = \$7450.42$, find i_c and r using discrete compounding.

    (*d*) If $f = 2$ and $PV_E = \$5441.86$, find j and r using continuous compounding.

    (*e*) If $f = 2$, $c = 2$, and $PV_E = \$5441.86$, find i_c and r using discrete compounding.

    (*f*) If $f = 2$, $c = 3$, and $PV_E = \$5441.86$, find i_c and r using discrete compounding.

    (*g*) If $f = 2$ and $FV_B = \$7087.83$, find j and r using continuous compounding.

    (*h*) If $f = 2$, $c = 2$, and $FV_B = \$7087.83$, find i_c and r using discrete compounding.

    (*i*) If $f = 2$, $c = 1$, and $FV_B = \$7087.83$, find i_c and r using discrete compounding.

    (*j*) If $f = 2$ and $PV_B = \$4994.63$, find j and r using continuous compounding.

    (*k*) If $f = 2$, $c = 2$, and $PV_B = \$4994.63$, find i_c and r using discrete compounding.

    (*l*) If $f = 2$, $c = 1$, and $PV_B = \$4994.63$, find i_c and r using discrete compounding.

7-7 Given:

Period	Discrete cash flow
1	$3500
2	− 2500
3	3800
4	3300

    (*a*) If $f = 1$ and $FV_E = \$8674.70$, find j and r using continuous compounding.
answer: **5.7089%**

    (*b*) If $f = 2$, $c = 2$, and $FV_E = \$8431.50$, find i_c and r using discrete compounding.
answers: **3.45998%, 6.91995%**

    (*c*) If $f = 1$, $c = 2$, and $FV_E = \$8361.87$, find i_c and r using discrete compounding.
answers: **1.3657%, 2.7313%**

    (*d*) If $f = 2$ and $PV_E = \$6291.14$, find j and r using continuous compounding.
answers: **9.1339%, 18.2677%**

    (*e*) If $f = 1$, $c = 1$, and $PV_E = \$4833.33$, find i_c and r using discrete compounding.
answer: **21.3650%**

    (*f*) If $f = 2$, $c = 3$, and $PV_E = \$6795.15$, find i_c and r using discrete compounding.
answers: **4.2805%, 12.8415%**

    (*g*) If $f = 1$ and $FV_B = \$9255.28$, find j and r using continuous compounding.
answer: **6.0498%**

(h) If $f = 2$, $c = 2$, and $FV_B = \$8658.22$, find i_c and r using discrete compounding.
answers: **3.11%, 6.22%**

(i) If $f = 1$, $c = 2$, and $FV_B = \$8591.09$, find i_c and r using discrete compounding.
answers: **1.3637%, 2.7274%**

(j) If $f = 2$ and $PV_B = \$7354.78$, find j and r using continuous compounding.
answers: **5.3540%, 10.7081%**

(k) If $f = 1$, $c = 1$, and $PV_B = \$6486.66$, find i_c and r using discrete compounding.
answer: **13.69%**

(l) If $f = 2$, $c = 1$, and $PV_B = \$6220.21$, find i_c and r using discrete compounding.
answer: **36.3057%**

7-8 For Exercises 7-7(e) and 7-7(k), is there a unique root, or positive interest rate?

7-9 The series of cash flows below have a PV_E of $3871.43. The cash flows are:

Period	Discrete cash flow
1	$1000
2	− 2000
3	5000
4	− 2000
5	− 1000
6	7000

(a) What is the interest rate (IRR)?
answer: **16%**

(b) Is there only one positive interest rate? (*Hint:* Apply balances test.)
answer: **yes**

7-10 For Exercise 7-3, if the PV_E is $19,363.69, what is the interest rate, and is there a unique answer?

7-11 For Exercise 7-4, if the PV_E is $16,748.95, what is the discrete interest rate i_c, and is there a unique answer? (Assume that $c = f = 1$.)
answers: **14.5000%, yes**

7-12 The series of cash flows below have a PV_E of $5000, what is the interest rate and is there one unique interest rate? (*Hint:* Try the balances test.)

Period	Cash flow
1	$7000
2	− 2500
3	3000
4	− 1000

Continuous Payments and Compounding

7-13 Given:

Period	Continuous cash flow
1	$8000
2	1500
3	2000
4	3000

    (*a*) Find the PV if $f = 1$ and $r = 18\%$.
answer: **$11,344.85**
    (*b*) Find the FV if $f = 1$ and $r = 8\%$.
answer: **$17,799.31**
    (*c*) If PV = $9000 and $f = 1$, what is the interest rate?
answer: **38.9507%**
    (*d*) If FV = $17,300 and $f = 1$, what is the interest rate?
answer: **6.9122%**

7-14 Given:

Period	Continuous cash flow
1	$8500
2	4800
3	6500
4	2100
5	3800

    (*a*) Find the PV if $f = 2$ and $r = 13.8\%$.
    (*b*) Find the FV if $f = 3$ and $r = 6.5\%$.
    (*c*) If PV = $20,500, find the interest rate.
    (*d*) If FV = $31,800, find the interest rate.

Applications

7-15 A company is evaluating a project which has the quarterly after-tax cash inflows shown below. The project requires a cash outlay after taxes of $9975. The machine has a salvage value of $2000 at the end of the ninth quarter. Assume that cash flows occur at the end of each period.

Quarter	Cash flow
1	$ 800
2	1200
3	1250
4	1300
5	1400
6	1400
7	1350
8	1200
9	1000
9—salvage	2000

(*a*) Assuming that the company requires a 20% return compounded quarterly, what is the present value of the cash inflows and the difference between the present value and the cash outlay required?

answers: **$9846.74, −$128.26**

(*b*) Answer part (*a*) but assume that compounding is semiannual while the cash flows occur quarterly.

answers: **$9906.93, −$68.07**

(*c*) Answer part (*a*) but assume continuous compounding.

answers: **$9783.09, −$191.91**

(*d*) What is the internal rate of return for the project if discrete compounding occurs quarterly?

answer: **18.9897%**

(*e*) What is the internal rate of return for the project if compounding occurs semiannually?

answer: **19.4404%**

(*f*) What is the internal rate of return for the project if compounding is continuous?

answer: **18.5527%**

(*g*) If the cash inflows and the salvage value are overestimated by 5%, what impact occurs with respect to the present value and internal rate of return for parts (*a*) and (*d*)?

answers: **$9354.40, 15.03965%**

(*h*) If the cash flows are estimated correctly but the salvage value is actually $500, what are the answers for parts (*a*) and (*d*)?

answers: **$8879.83, 10.4206%**

7-16 This is an exercise in sensitivity analysis which illustrates an interesting technique. The present value of the cash flows compounded at 15% annual is $7695.33, rounded to two places.

Year	Estimated cash flow
1	$2500
2	3200
3	− 500
4	6000

(a) What is the present value if the actual cash flows are 90% of the estimated value? Compute using the formula in the chapter.

(b) Does .9 × $7695.33 = $6925.80 give the same answer as part (a)?

(c) Now compute the present value if the actual cash flows are 110% of that estimated using (1) the variable-cash-flow approach in part (a), and (2) the formula approach in part (b). Do you get the same answer?

(d) In general, is the formula below valid?

$$\text{adjusted present value} = \text{estimated present value} \times 1 \pm \text{decimal \% error between actual and estimated cash flows}$$

The estimated present value is based on the estimated cash flows.

(e) Is the relationship in part (d) valid if the interest rate changes?

(f) Is the relationship in part (d) valid if the error is expressed as a dollar amount, say $100 per year, instead of a percent?

7-17 The two projects shown below have been proposed by different division managers:

	Project	
Year	X: cash inflow	Y: cash inflow
1	$1800	$ 700
2	1400	1200
3	1375	1800
4	1350	1900
5	1200	2000
6	1355	1950
7	750	1840
Cost of project	$5924	$5705

Assume that the cash flows occur at the end of each year. The company requires a 17% annual return on such projects.

(a) Which project would you select based on the excess or net present value (present value less cost of project)?

answers: **X's NPV = $−458.42, Y's NPV = $193.20**

(*b*) Which project would you select based on the internal rate of return interest rate?

answers: **X's IRR = 13.9993%, Y's IRR = 17.9987%**

(*c*) Which project would you select if interest is compounded monthly based on
    (1) net present value?
    (2) internal rate of return?

answers: (1) **X's NPV = −$650.72, Y's NPV = −$73.01**; (2) **X's IRR = 13.1740%, Y's IRR = 16.6650%**

(*d*) Which project would you select if interest is compounded continuously based on
    (1) net present value?
    (2) internal rate of return?

answers: (1) **X's NPV = −$669.64, Y's NPV = −$99.09**; (2) **X's IRR = 13.1022%, Y's IRR = 16.5504%**

(*e*) Assuming that the cash flows occur continuously, what is your answer to part (*d*)?

answers: (1) **X's NPV = −$196.60, Y's NPV = $405.60**; (2) **X's IRR = 15.6605%, Y's IRR = 19.0560%**

7-18 The annual cash savings for two projects are shown below. Assume that the cash flows occur at the end of each year and yearly discrete compounding.

Year	Project X	Project Y
1	$1000	$2000
2	1850	2500
3	2500	2200
4	3000	1900
5	4000	3000

(*a*) If the company requires a 10% return, which project has the greatest net present value if both projects require an outlay cost each of $8500? What is the internal rate of return for each project?

(*b*) If the company requires a 20% return, which project has the greatest net present value if both projects require an outlay of $6500 each? What is the internal rate of return for each project?

(*c*) If you select X in one part and Y in another part above, explain why.

7-19 A real estate project has the following end-of-year cash flows over its 10-year life. The initial investment required is $36,000. All cash flows are after taxes. Assume that the investor wants to earn 9% compounded annually.

  (*a*) What is the net present value?
  (*b*) What is the internal rate of return?
  (*c*) Is there a unique positive rate of return?

Year	Cash flow
1	−$ 6,500
2	− 1,200
3	2,300
4	2,900
5	3,500
6	− 1,500
7	3,800
8	4,000
9	3,700
10	85,000

answers: (*a*) **$3932.19**; (*b*) **10.0842%**; (*c*) **yes**

7-20 Assume monthly compounding and answer Exercise 7-19.

7-21 Assume continuous compounding and answer Exercise 7-19.

answers: (*a*) **$2368.99**; (*b*) **9.6075%**; (*c*) **yes**

7-22 A company is planning to lease a machine for 6 years. Twelve beginning-of-period payments will be made. The after-tax cash flows are shown below. What is the present value of the lease using a discount rate (interest rate) of 9% annual compounded semiannually?

Period	Cash flow
1	$6500
2	6200
3	5900
4	5600
5	5300
6	5000
7	4700
8	4400
9	4100
10	3800
11	3500
12	3200

7-23 If the 9% annual interest is compounded yearly, what is the present value of the cash flows in Exercise 7-22?

answer: **$47,897.56**

7-24 If the 9% annual interest is compounded continuously, what is the present value of the lease in Exercise 7-22?

7-25 Repeat Exercise 7-22, but assume that the payments occur at the end of each semiannual period.

   answer: **$45,653.35**

7-26 Answer Exercise 7-22, but assume that the payments occur at the end of each semiannual period and that interest is compounded quarterly.

7-27 Answer Exercise 7-22, but assume that payments occur at the end of each semiannual period and that interest is compounded continuously.

   answer: **$45,417.50**

7-28 You are planning on either purchasing a car for cash or leasing a car for 3 years. You can purchase the car for $10,850 and you estimate its salvage value at the end of 3 years to be $3870. If you lease the car, the end-of-period semiannual payments are:

Period	Payment
1	$1300
2	1200
3	1100
4	1000
5	900
6	900

   (*a*) Assuming that you can invest money at 6.5% compounded monthly, which is greatest, the net cost of the car or the present value of the lease payments? (*Hint:* Net the present value of the car's salvage and cost together and compare to the present value of the lease payments.)

   (*b*) Would your answer to part (*a*) be different if the lease payments were made at the end of each period?

7-29 Assume that you deposit the following amounts each month in a savings account.

Month	Deposit
1	$25
2	50
3	75
4	50
5	80
6	65
7	90
8	40
9	55
10	65
11	85
12	70

   (*a*) If interest is 5⅞% annual compounded monthly, what is the amount in the account at the end of the twelfth period assuming that payments are made at the beginning of the period?

   (*b*) If payments are made at the end of each month, what is the balance?

   (*c*) If interest is compounded continuously at 5⅞% annual, what is the future value assuming beginning-of-month deposits?

(*d*) What is the future value if end-of-month deposits are made assuming continuous compounding?

answers: (*a*) **$772.60**; (*b*) **$768.84**; (*c*) **$772.66**; (*d*) **$768.89**

7-30 A company expects to generate excess cash for the next 6 months which they plan to use for inventory purchases at the end of 6 months. They will deposit the money in an account paying 6.2% annual.

Month	Deposit
1	$15,000
2	16,500
3	20,000
4	25,000
5	23,000
6	22,000

(*a*) If interest is compounded monthly, what is the balance at the end of 6 months if deposits are made at the beginning of the month? End of month?

(*b*) Assuming that interest is compounded daily, what is the future value if deposits are made at the beginning of each month? End of each month?

(*c*) Assuming that interest is compounded continuously, what is the future value if deposits are made at the beginning of each month? End of each month?

(*d*) What interest rate is required to have a future value of $123,350 if interest is

(1) compounded monthly?

(2) compounded quarterly?

(3) compounded daily?

(4) compounded continuously?

Assume beginning-of-month deposits.

(*e*) Answer part (*d*) but assume end-of-month deposits.

7-31 You have just received notice that you were the $500,000 winner of the state lottery. You have the option of receiving $500,000 now, which means you will keep $237,000 after taxes, or receiving $100,000 a year for 5 years but because of your regular income and taxes, the amount of each $100,000 payment after taxes you keep is:

Year	After-tax proceeds
1	$60,000
2	60,000
3	55,000
4	55,000
5	50,000

You plan to invest your after-tax winnings in an account paying $5\frac{7}{8}$% annual.

(*a*) Which alternative would you select if interest is compounded monthly and if payments are received at the end of each year?

answers: **PV_E = $236,886.88; take the $237,000**

(b) Which alternative would you select if interest is compounded continuously and if payments are received at the end of each year?

answers: **PV$_E$ = $236,791.98; take the $237,000**

(c) Answer part (a), but assume that payments are received at the beginning of each year.

answers: **PV$_B$ = $251,184.92; take the payments**

(d) Answer part (b), but assume that payments are received at the beginning of each year.

answers: **PV$_B$ = $251,120.28; take the payments**

(e) What interest rate would be required to make the yearly payments grow to $360,000, assuming end-of-year deposits and monthly compounding?

answer: **r% = 11.4717%**

(f) Answer part (e), but assume end-of-year deposits and yearly compounding.

answer: **r% = 12.0945%**

(g) Answer part (e), but assume beginning-of-year deposits and monthly compounding.

answer: **r% = 7.9610%**

(h) Answer part (e), but assume beginning-of-year deposits and yearly compounding.

answer: **r% = 8.2580%**

(i) Answer part (e), but assume beginning-of-year deposits and continuous compounding.

answer: **r% = 7.9347%**

(j) Answer part (e), but assume end-of-year deposits and continuous compounding.

answer: **r% = 11.4172%**

7-32 You have been considering a real estate investment, which requires additional investments over time with cash returns occurring only at the end of year 5 and at the time the real estate investment is sold for $350,000 at the end of year 9.

Year	Cash investment	Cash return
Initial investment	−$50,000	
1	− 25,000	
2	− 15,000	
3	0	
4	0	
5		$30,000
6	0	
7	− 10,000	
8	0	
9		350,000

(a) What is your return on the investment, and does a unique positive interest rate exist?

(b) Assuming monthly compounding, what is the return rate?

(c) Assuming continuous compounding, what is the return rate?

7-33 Your old buddie from college has proposed to your company a sure-fire investment. He claims that your return is 31.24%, based on the cash flows below. What is your opinion of the returns on the project? (Assume end-of-year payments and yearly compounding.)

Year	Cash flow
0	−$ 7,000
1	6,000
2	10,000
3	− 5,000
4	3,000
5	− 10,000
6	2,000

answer: **other two roots are −78.92% and 11.58%**

7-34 What is the interest rate for Exercise 7-33 if the initial outlay is $6000?

7-35 What is the interest rate for Exercise 7-33 if the initial outlay is $5000?

answers: **−78.91%, −5.19%, 92.30%**

7-36 The Gusher Oil Company has world-wide operations. Because of a recent multinational computer network for banks, money is deposited in Gusher Oil's account almost continuously 24 hours a day through electronic fund transfers. They plan to retire $5,000,000 in bonds in 3 years using a sinking fund where 5% of each day's receipts are deposited in their savings account at the Big City Bank. The bank can automatically transfer 5% of the receipts as they are received to a savings account paying 5⅞% annual compounded continuously. Gusher's estimated deposits for the next 3 years are shown below. Assume a 365-day year.

Year	Average daily deposit in savings account during year
1	$3500
2	4100
3	4200

(*Hint:* Convert the daily flows to a yearly amount.)

    (*a*) How much will be in the savings account at the end of the third year?

    (*b*) What is the present value of the deposits?

    (*c*) What interest rate is necessary to make the projected savings equal $5,000,000?

7-37 The SPAD Airline Company is evaluating a new computer system modification for verifying customer credit. Since reservations and tickets are made and purchased 24 hours a day, the savings resulting from the machine are continuous for all practical purposes. The airline estimates that at least $5000 a week can be saved over the system's 5-year life, but the savings per week will increase over the 5-year period owing to increased efficiency. The system requires an initial outlay of $205,000 with the following projected savings for the next 5 years.

Year	Estimated savings per year
1	$60,000
2	66,000
3	75,600
4	76,800
5	79,200

The company requires a return of 16% on computer system investments.

(*a*) Assuming continuous cash flows and compounding, what is the present value of the savings? Comparing the present value of the savings to the outlay, would you accept the project based on these estimates?

answers: **$240,656.76, yes**

(*b*) What is the internal rate of return for the project? (Solve for r.)

answer: **23.1543%**

(*c*) If the monthly savings are overestimated by 10%, would your answer to parts (*a*) and (*b*) change? (Use $CF_i \times .9$ for adjusted cash flows.)

answers: **$216,591.08, 18.4029%**

EIGHT

BALLOON ANNUITIES: APPLICATIONS USING PRESENT VALUES

IN THIS CHAPTER

In this chapter present-value annuities are broadened to include *balloon* payments. This is a particularly useful combination because of its numerous practical applications:

Remaining balance on a mortgage.
Yield on a mortgage.
Payment amount for a mortgage with a balloon.
Payment amount for a lease with residual values.
Yield on a lease with residual values.
Bond price and yield.
Net present value and internal rate of return for capital budgeting projects with
    level payments and salvage values.

● ● ● ● ●

Balloon annuities consist of n equal payments plus a *balloon* payment. Because loan and mortgage terms vary among lenders, it is difficult to give a precise definition or description of balloon payments for all possible situations. In this book we will simply define a balloon payment as one made at the end of time period L which is *separate* from (or in addition to) the n regular level payments. Typically, in practice, balloon payments will occur at the *end* of the last payment period. (In some cases this will mean that the final payment is actually the sum of the regular final payment and the balloon.) Later sections of this chapter will also consider the less common situation in which one or more balloon payments are made during or after the term of the annuity (instead of at the end).

The typical situation, as shown in Fig. 8-1, is a single balloon payment, of amount BAL, occurring at the end of the nth period. The addition of this single, irregular payment to an annuity adds considerable flexibility in formulating problems but does not add excessive complexity to the annuity formulas. To illustrate, suppose that we wish to solve for the present value of the ordinary balloon annuity of Fig. 8-1. The present value of this series of level payments with a balloon can be expressed as

$$\begin{array}{c} \text{present} \\ \text{value} \end{array} = \begin{array}{c} \text{PV of annuity} \\ \text{component} \end{array} + \begin{array}{c} \text{PV of balloon} \\ \text{payment} \end{array}$$

This chapter will concentrate on balloon annuity applications that involve present value. In some of the applications discussed, the present value is the unkown to be calculated. In other applications the present value is specified and the unknown may be any of the other terms, such as the number of payments, the amount of the regular payment, or the amount of the balloon payment.

We'll begin with an ordinary annuity with a balloon at the end of the final period ($L = n$).

8-1 PRESENT VALUE OF A SIMPLE BALLOON ANNUITY

Let's return to the ordinary annuity illustrated in Fig. 8-1, with a balloon payment located at the end of the nth payment. As we know from Chap. 4, an ordinary annuity can be expressed as n payments of the amount PMT, where all payments are made at the end of the periods. Also, in this simple situation, the payment and compounding periods coincide ($c = f$).

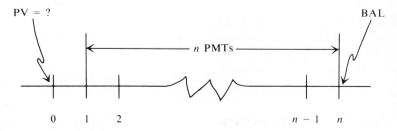

Figure 8-1 Ordinary annuity with balloon.

The present value for an ordinary annuity without a balloon can be obtained from Eq. (4-5):

$$\text{PV of ordinary annuity} = \text{PMT} \times A(n,i_f) \qquad (8\text{-}1)$$

where i_f = the compounding rate per payment period

The present value of the balloon compounded at the end of the nth payment must be

$$\text{PV of balloon payment} = \text{BAL} \times (1 + i_f)^{-n} \qquad (8\text{-}2)$$

Therefore, the present value for the simple balloon annuity becomes

$$\text{PV} = \text{PMT} \times A(n,i_f) + \text{BAL} \times (1 + i_f)^{-n} \qquad (8\text{-}3)$$

Equation (8-3) has practical value in its given form, which will be demonstrated later with numerous examples. Since Eq. (8-3) contains only one more term than Eq. (8-1), the calculations are only slightly more difficult to execute. In fact, several of the Level II and Level III calculators have a BAL function key (or a library program) which is used either to solve for BAL or to specify a value for BAL in Eq. (8-3).

8-1.1 Annuity Due with a Balloon

Not all the applications described later in this chapter fit the condition of ordinary annuity with the balloon occurring at the end of the nth period. Some involve the annuity-due situation, where the payments are located at the beginning of the periods but the balloon is still at the end of the nth period. For this case the present-value formula can be developed from Eq. (4-18), to give

$$\text{PV} = (1 + i_f) \times \text{PMT} \times A(n,i_f) + \text{BAL} \times (1 + i_f)^{-n} \qquad (8\text{-}4)$$

Note that a shifting of the level payments took place in going from the ordinary annuity formula of Eq. (8-3) to the annuity-due formula of Eq. (8-4). Specifically, the n level payments of amount PMT *shifted backward* one payment period, but the balloon payment *did not shift*. The proper positioning is indicated in Fig. 8-2.

Use of Eq. (8-4), with the balloon term, is straightforward.

8-1.2 General Annuities with Balloon

It would be desirable to develop an approach to balloon payments that provides for one or more additional payments and allows us to build on the formulas already developed for annuities in Chaps. 4, 5, and 6. This includes a variety of general cases:

Discrete payments of amount PMT may be either at the beginning or end of period.

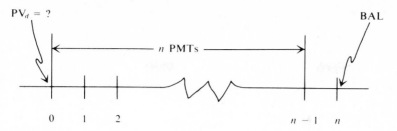

Figure 8-2 Annuity due with balloon.

Discrete compounding may or may not coincide with the payment periods.
The balloon payment (or payments) may be located almost anywhere on the
    time scale.
The regular payments may be continuous rather than discrete.
The compounding may be continuous rather than discrete.
The present value or future value may be involved.

   This chapter will (1) develop a generalized formula to handle most of the
situations described above, and (2) use the generalized formula to solve practical applications. Remember, however, that formulas will be developed only
for the cases involving present value. This is not a serious limitation, since:

1. The present-value cases cover the bulk of the application situations.
2. The future-value formulas with balloons would be very similar to those
   presented for the present value.

   The next two sections will present, in a terse, summary form, the generalized formulas for all the cases mentioned above.

PRESENT VALUE

8-2 GENERALIZED EQUATION FOR ANNUITIES WITH BALLOON PAYMENTS

The generalized formula for PV annuities can be expanded to include balloon
payments by simply adding the term for the compound interest component as
follows:

$$V_K = (1 + I)^K \times \text{PMT} \times A(n,I) + \text{BAL}(1 + I)^{-L}$$

$$= (1 + I)^K \times \text{PMT} \times \frac{1 - (1 + I)^{-n}}{I} + \text{BAL}(1 + I)^{-L} \qquad (8\text{-}5)$$

where V_K = PV or PV$_d$ case
$\quad K$ = 0 for PV case
$\qquad$ = 1 for PV$_d$ case
$\quad L$ = end of time period when balloon payment is made
$\quad T$ = time coinciding with end of nth period, years
$\quad c$ = number of compounding periods per year
$\quad f$ = number of payments per year
$\quad r$ = nominal annual interest rate as a decimal
$\quad$ BAL = balloon payment
$\quad$ PMT = regular discrete annuity payment
$\quad n$ = number of regular payments ($T \times f$)
$\quad I$ = i_f if $c = f$ where $i_f = r/f$
$\qquad$ = $(1 + i_c)^{c/f} - 1$ if $c \neq f$ where $i_c = r/c$
$\qquad$ = $e^{r/f} - 1$ for continuous compounding

Note that a new term, I, is incorporated in this formula, generalizing it to include areas where payment periods and compounding periods per year are either equal or unequal or where continuous compounding is assumed. Note also that the equation assumes discrete payments and covers *only* the two present-value cases (for ordinary annuities and annuities due). The time when the balloon occurs, t_{BAL}, is expressed in terms of payment periods, L, where $L = t_{BAL} \times f$. As a result, $L = n$ means that the balloon is paid at the end of the last payment period.

Now let's examine the procedures necessary to solve for the various unknown values—BAL, PMT, n, L, and I—in Eq. (8-5).

8-2.1 Solving for the Balloon

$$\text{BAL} = [V_K - (1 + I)^K \times \text{PMT} \times A(n,I)] \times (1 + I)^L \qquad (8\text{-}6)$$

8-2.2 Solving for the Regular Payment

$$\text{PMT} = \frac{V_K - \text{BAL} \times (1 + I)^{-L}}{(1 + I)^K \times A(n,I)} \qquad (8\text{-}7)$$

Solving for either the balloon or the payment is straightforward on a Level II or III calculator, as later examples will demonstrate.

8-2.3 Solving for n and L

Solving for the number of payments requires an assumption concerning the relationship of L to n.

8-2.3.1 Solving for *n* and *L* when *n* = *L*. Assuming that *n* = *L* (which means the balloon is made at the end of the last period), a formula for *n* can be derived from Eq. (8-5), to give

$$n = -\ln\left[\frac{I \times V_K - (1 + I)^K \times \text{PMT}}{I \times \text{BAL} - (1 + I)^K \times \text{PMT}}\right] \Big/ \ln(1 + I) \qquad (8\text{-}8)$$

Solving for *n* in Eq. (8-8) is straightforward, except where *n* is computed to be a fractional value. Fractional values for *n* are discussed in Sec. 8-2.4.

8-2.3.2 Solving for *n* when *n* ≠ *L*. The more general case where *L* ≠ *n* can also be obtained from Eq. (8-6), to give

$$n = -\ln\left[\frac{I \times [\text{BAL}(1 + I)^{-L} - V_K]}{(1 + I)^K \times \text{PMT}} + 1\right] \Big/ \ln(1 + I) \qquad (8\text{-}9)$$

Some of the examples given in this chapter utilize Eq. (8-9) in a slightly different form. Recall that the present value for the balloon payment is

$$\text{PV}_{\text{BAL}} = \text{BAL} \times (1 + I)^{-L}$$

Then introducing PV_{BAL} into Eq. (8-9), we obtain

$$n = -\ln\left[\frac{I \times (\text{PV}_{\text{BAL}} - V_K)}{(1 + I)^K \times \text{PMT}} + 1\right] \Big/ \ln(1 + I) \qquad (8\text{-}10)$$

8-2.3.3 Solving for *L* when *n* ≠ *L*. The general formula for *L*, obtained from Eq. (8-6), becomes

$$L = \ln\left\{\frac{\text{BAL} \times I}{I \times V_K - (1 + I)^K \times \text{PMT}[1 - (1 + I)^{-n}]}\right\} \Big/ \ln(1 + I) \qquad (8\text{-}11)$$

Equation (8-11) can be simplified by introducing a term for the present value without a balloon, that is:

$$V_K^a = (1 + I)^K \times \text{PMT} \times A(n,I) \qquad (8\text{-}12)$$

Using the relationship for V_K^a from Eq. (8-12) in Eq. (8-5), we obtain

$$V_K = V_K^a + \text{BAL} \times (1 + I)^{-L} \qquad (8\text{-}13)$$

which leads to

$$L = \frac{\ln[\text{BAL}/(V_K - V_K^a)]}{\ln(1 + I)} \qquad (8\text{-}14)$$

It is quite possible that solutions for *L* will lead to computed values that are fractional. In such situations the user must decide if the location of the balloon should be shifted to an integral time value (with proper adjustment of the amount of the balloon).

8-2.4 Solving for Amount of Final Regular Payment

The computed value of n is usually not an integer, which means that we must compute a different value for the final payment, as in Chap. 4. To review the procedure:

1. Compute the value for n from Eq. (8-8), (8-9), or (8-10). If the answer is not an integer, as represented by $M.X$, truncate to obtain the integral value of M. Generally, this means that M regular payments are required plus a final payment that will be smaller in amount than PMT.
2. Compute the present value of the final payment by subtracting the present value of M regular payments and the balloon from the V_K.
3. Compound forward the present value of the final payment determined in step 2 to obtain the final payment at $M + 1 - K$.

The general equation to carry out these steps is as follows:

final partial payment

$$= (1 + I)^{M+1-K}[V_K - \text{BAL}(1 + I)^{-L} - \text{PMT}(1 + I)^K A(M,I)] \quad (8\text{-}15)$$

where $K = 0$ for the PV case and $K = 1$ for the PV_d case.

8-2.5 Solving for the Interest Rate

The iteration formula introduced in Chap. 4 and used in Chaps. 5, 6, and 7 is also applicable here. By extending Eq. (4-36) to include the balloon term of Eq. (8-5), we get

$$f(i) = (1 + i)^K[1 - (1 + i)^{-n}] + \frac{i}{\text{PMT}}[\text{BAL}(1 + i)^{-L} - V_K] \quad (8\text{-}16)$$

and

$$f'(i) = K + (1 + i)^K \frac{(1 + i)^{-n} - 1}{i} + (n - K)(1 + i)^{-n+K-1}$$

$$- \frac{i \times L \times \text{BAL}(1 + i)^{-L-1}}{\text{PMT}} \quad (8\text{-}17)$$

The iteration calculations are made by using†

$$i_{k+1} = i_k - \frac{f(i_k)}{f'(i_k)} \quad (8\text{-}18)$$

---

†The iteration technique described in Eqs. (8-16), (8-17), and (8-18), as well as (8-5), for PV can be used with slight modifications to solve deferred annuities, as described in Chap. 9.

where $V_K = $ PV or PV_d

$\qquad K \ = 0$ for PV

$\qquad\quad = 1$ for PV_d

$\quad$ BAL $=$ balloon payment at end of period L

$\quad$ PMT $=$ regular payments made for n periods

$\qquad i \ =$ discrete compounding interest rate per payment period, i_f

$\qquad n \ =$ number of regular payments

$\qquad L \ =$ end of period when balloon is paid

The initial value for i_0 is†

$$i_0 = \frac{\text{BAL} - V_K + n(\text{PMT})}{V_K(n + 1)} \qquad (8\text{-}19)$$

The interest rate computed by this formula is i_f, the interest rate per payment period. The interest rate per compounding period, i_c (for the general annuity cases), is computed by converting i_f as follows:

$$i_c = (1 + i_f)^{f/c} - 1 \qquad (8\text{-}20)$$

For continuous compounding the interest rate j is determined by

$$j = r/f = \ln(i + i_f) \qquad (8\text{-}21)$$

Note that while the general formulas used to compute PV, BAL, PMT, and n use the interest rates i_f, i_c, or j directly, the iteration routine described above computes i_f; i_c and j must then be derived.

8-3 MULTIPLE BALLOON PAYMENTS

When a loan is set up with multiple balloon payments, the present value, regular payment, number of regular payments, and value of one specific balloon payment can be computed using the procedure established for single balloon payments. However, since the timing of the multiple balloons can vary, the variable-cash-flow approach should be used to compute the interest rate.

$\quad$ The present value with multiple balloon payments is

$$V_K = (1 + I)^K \times \text{PMT} \times A(n,I) + \text{PV}_{\text{BALS}} \qquad (8\text{-}22)$$

Let

$\qquad PV_{\text{BALS}} =$ present value of balloon payments

$$= \text{BAL}_1(1 + I)^{-L_1} + \text{BAL}_2(1 + I)^{-L_2}$$

$$+ \cdots + \text{BAL}_h(1 + I)^{-L_h} + \cdots \qquad (8\text{-}23)$$

---

†*Program Manual FLI: Finance Library (SR-52)*, Texas Instruments, Inc., Dallas, Tex., 1976, p. 56.

where BAL_h is the specific balloon payment at period h.

The regular level payments are computed as

$$\text{PMT} = \frac{(V_K - \text{PV}_{\text{BALS}})}{(1 + I)^K \times A(n,I)} \qquad (8\text{-}24)$$

To solve for one specific balloon payment at time period h,

$$\text{BAL}_h = [V_K - (1 + I)^K \times \text{PMT} \times A(n,I) - \text{PV}_y](1 + I)^{L_h} \qquad (8\text{-}25)$$

where BAL_h = amount of unknown balloon
$\quad\quad L_h$ = end of period when unknown balloon is paid
$\quad\quad \text{PV}_y$ = present value of known balloons

To solve for the number of regular payments when all the balloons are known:

$$n = -\ln\left[\frac{I \times (\text{PV}_{\text{BALS}} - V_K)}{(1 + I)^K \times \text{PMT}} + 1 \right] \Big/ \ln(1 + I) \qquad (8\text{-}26)$$

8-4 USING LEVEL II AND III CALCULATORS TO SOLVE BALLOON ANNUITIES

Many of the Level III calculators have library programs that solve for the balloon annuity values when $L = n$. But even if library programs are not available, the equations in this chapter are easily programmed.

The Level II calculators vary in their treatment of balloon annuities, but several shortcuts can be taken which simplify solving balloon annuities for these calculators when $L = n$.

The *present value* V_K is computed by adding the present values of the regular payments to the present value of the balloon.

The *regular payment amount* PMT is computed by subtracting the present value of the balloon from the total present value V_K. The net amount is entered using the **PV** key and the payment is solved using the calculator annuity routine. This same procedure will allow *n to be computed* when the payment is known.

The *balloon amount* can be computed for the ordinary annuity—PV case on several Level II calculators using what is called the "Accumulated Interest and Loan Balance" key, or the "Amortization" key. These function keys calculate the remaining balance on a loan, which is the same as the balloon.

The more advanced Level II calculators can *solve directly for* i_f, the *interest rate*, when the balloon occurs at the end of the period, $L = n$. A simple modification allows solving for i_f when $L = n + 1$ for the PV case. Simply enter the value L for the number of periods in **N** and enter $(\text{BAL} - \text{PMT})$ using the **FV** or balloon key; then enter the payment and solve for i_f.

For the other situations where $L \neq n$, or for multiple balloon payments, a trial-and-error approach or the general iterative equation should be used.

The keystroke examples at the end of the chapter illustrate several of these techniques for Level II and III calculators.

APPLICATIONS

The practical problems involving balloon payments are too numerous to list or describe exhaustively. However, this section will consider some of the more important balloon applications, including mortgages and loans, leases, capital budgeting, and bonds. Because they are so similar to previous examples, the following examples do not show all intermediate calculations; however, selected keystroke examples are given at the end of the chapter.

8-5 MORTGAGE AND LOAN APPLICATIONS

8-5.1 Balloons at the End of the Last Period

Many mortgages and loans have the first payment due at the end of the first payment period, categorizing them as an ordinary annuity. The examples below show the solutions for various values that are commonly required in mortgage and loan applications, with an additional balloon payment at the end of the last regular payment period.

Example 8-1 Suppose that you are considering investing in a mortgage held by a local bank. The mortgage has a current balance of $110,000 with 10 years of $1061.30 monthly payments remaining, plus a $50,000 balloon payment due with the last regular payment. The next payment is due in 1 month. Assuming that you would be satisfied with an annual yield of 9.5% compounded monthly, what price should you offer for the mortgage?

The problem, which is described in Time Diagram 8-1, requires a PV calculation—the present value of an ordinary annuity with a balloon payment. Using $K = 0$, $L = n$, and $i_f = I$ in Eq. (8-5):

$$PV = (1 + i_f)^0 \times PMT \times A(n,i_f) + BAL(1 + i_f)^{-n}$$

$$= (1 + i_f)^0 \times PMT \times \frac{1 - (1 + i_f)^{-n}}{i_f} + BAL(1 + i_f)^{-n}$$

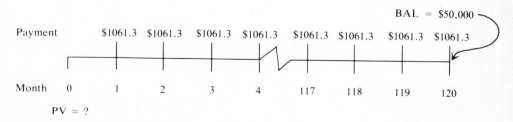

Time Diagram 8-1

Entering the following values from the problem and solving for PV:

$$i_f = \frac{.095}{12}$$

$$PMT = \$1061.30$$

$$BAL = \$50,000$$

$$n = 120$$

$$PV = 1061.30 \frac{1 - (1 + .095/12)^{-120}}{.095/12} + 50,000\left(1 + \frac{.095}{12}\right)^{-120}$$

$$= \$101,428.0701$$

To achieve the yield of 9.5%, a price of $101,428.07 is the most that could be offered for the mortgage.

Example 8-2 Suppose that you are considering an investment in a land development outside the city. The bank has agreed to make a loan for $150,000 on a 30-year monthly amortization schedule at a 9.75% annual rate of interest (compounded monthly), but they insist that the loan be repaid by a balloon payment at the end of 15 years. Assuming that payments occur at the end of each month, what is the required monthly payment and the balloon?

This problem can be solved in two steps. First, the monthly payment must be computed for a 30-year mortgage at 9.75% annual interest compounded monthly—a simple ordinary annuity situation (solving for the payment). If $BAL = 0$, $I = i_f$, and $K = 0$ (for PV), Eq. 8-7 becomes

$$PMT = \frac{PV - 0(1 + i_f)^{-L}}{(1 + i_f)^0 A(n,i_f)}$$

Substituting the appropriate values for PV, i_f, and n gives

$$PMT = \frac{150,000}{A(360,.0975/12)}$$

$$= 150,000 \Bigg/ \frac{1 - (1 + .0975/12)^{-360}}{.0975/12}$$

$$= \$1288.731618$$

Rounding to two places gives a monthly payment of $1288.73.

Now, we can proceed to determine the amount of the balloon. The cash flows are shown in Time Diagram 8-2. Substituting 0 for K, n for L, and i_f for I in the balloon payment formula equation (8-6),

$$BAL = [PV - (1 + i_f)^0 \times PMT \times A(n,i_f)](1 + i_f)^L$$

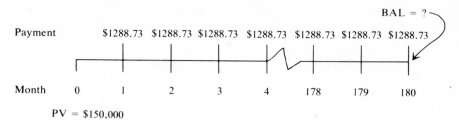

Time Diagram 8-2

Inserting the appropriate values from the problem (including $n = 15 \times 12 = 180$, the date of the balloon payment):

$$\text{BAL} = \left[\, 150{,}000 - 1288.73 \times \frac{1 - (1 + .0975/12)^{-180}}{.0975/12} \right]\left(1 + \frac{.0975}{12}\right)^{180}$$

$$= \$121{,}652.2543$$

Note that the balloon payment of \$121,562.25 is also the loan balance after the 180th payment. Therefore, the formula for computing the balloon will also compute the *remaining balance* on a mortgage or loan, as demonstrated by some later examples.

Example 8-3 Suppose that you wish to borrow \$85,000, paying off the loan in 10 years with a final balloon of \$30,000. Assuming that the current interest rate is 8% annual compounded monthly, what is the amount of the payment due at the end of each month?

Because the payment is unknown and the other values are given (Time Diagram 8-3), Eq. (8-7) can be used to solve the problem. With $K = 0$ (for the PV case), $L = n$, and $I = i_f$:

$$\text{PMT} = \frac{\text{PV} - \text{BAL}(1 + i_f)^{-n}}{(1 + i_f)^0 A(n, i_f)}$$

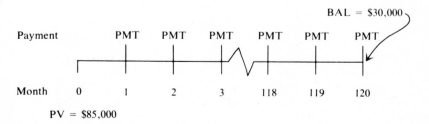

Time Diagram 8-3

Entering the values from the problem into the formula:

$$PMT = \left[85,000 - 30,000 \left(1 + \frac{.08}{12} \right)^{-120} \right] \bigg/ \frac{1 - (1 + .08/12)^{-120}}{.08/12}$$

$$= \$867.301769$$

Example 8-4 Suppose that you wish to borrow $225,000, making monthly payments of $2300 and a balloon of $50,000 with the last payment. Assuming a 9.5% annual rate compounded monthly, how many payments are necessary?

As Time Diagram 8-4a shows, the unknown in this problem is the number of payments. Recall that in mortgage and loan situations where the payment is specified and the number of payments is to be computed, the number computed is usually not an integer, so that the final payment must be either smaller or larger than the regular payments. However, with the final payment made at the same time as the balloon, it is customary to add the final payment to the balloon.

Determining the number of payments requires the use of Eq. (8-8). Because this is a PV case, $K = 0$, $L = n$, and $I = i_f$, which gives the following formula:

$$n = -\ln\left[\frac{i_f \times PV - PMT}{i_f \times BAL - PMT} \right] \bigg/ \ln(1 + i_f)$$

Now entering the problem values, to solve for n:

$$n = -\ln\left[\frac{(.095/12) \times 225,000 - 2300}{(.095/12) \times 50,000 - 2300} \right] \bigg/ \ln\left(1 + \frac{.095}{12} \right)$$

$$= 164.907567$$

This means that 164 payments of $2300 are necessary plus a final payment, along with the balloon of $50,000 at the end of period 165. Alternatively, 165 payments of $2300 can be made, with a smaller balloon payment at the end of the last period, which is identical to Example 8-2 as to solution. For the first approach, we can compute the final payment using Eq. (8-15), with $K = 0$, $L = M + 1$, $M = 164$, and $I = i_f$.

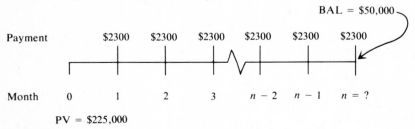

Time Diagram 8-4a

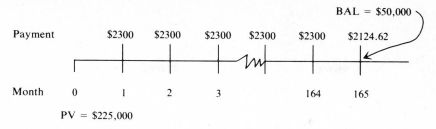

Time Diagram 8-4b

Final payment $= (1 + i_f)^{M+1-0}[PV - BAL(1 + i_f)^{-(M+1)} - PMT(1 + i_f)^0 A(M,i_f)]$

Entering the values for Example 8-4 into the equation,

$$\text{final payment} = \left(1 + \frac{.095}{12}\right)^{165}$$

$$\times \left[225,000 - 50,000\left(1 + \frac{.095}{12}\right)^{-165} - 2300\, A\left(164, \frac{.095}{12}\right)\right]$$

$$= \$2124.621248$$

    The final payment (in addition to the balloon) at the end of period 165 is $2124.62, as shown in Time Diagram 8-4b. As a check, let's compute the present value of 164 payments of $2300, plus the present value of the final payment and balloon received at the end of the 165th period; the sum of these present values should be $225,000.

PV of annuity of $2300 received for 164 periods	= $210,810.0941
PV of final payment of $2124.62 =	578.3861
PV of balloon of $50,000 =	13,611.5194
Total PV	$224,999.9996

The slight discrepancy resulted from rounding the final payment to the nearest penny.

    The final example in this section involves computing the interest rate or the yield of a mortgage with a balloon payment.

Example 8-5 A bank is selling a mortgage for $100,000. It has 120 monthly payments of $1061.30 remaining and a $50,000 balloon due at the end of the 120th period. Assuming the payments are made at the end of each period, what is the yield if interest is:

(*a*) Compounded monthly?
(*b*) Compounded semiannually?
(*c*) Compounded continuously with $f = 12$?
We proceed to solve these problems as follows.

(*a*) Equation (8-18) can be used to solve for the interest rates. First, we compute the initial guess for i_f by use of Eq. (8-19):

$$i_0 = \frac{50,000 - 100,000 + 120(1061.30)}{100,000(120 + 1)}$$

$$= .0063930579$$

Next, we solve the interation formula (8-18) until the answer stabilizes, using $K = 0$, $L = n$.

$$i_{k+1} = i_k - \frac{1 - (1 + i_k)^{-120} + \dfrac{i_k}{1061.30}[50,000(1 + i_k)^{-120} - 100,000]}{\dfrac{(1 + i_k)^{-120} - 1}{i_k} + 120(1 + i_k)^{-121} - \dfrac{i_k(120)(50,000)(1 + i_k)^{-121}}{1061.30}}$$

The iteration values are

$$i_1 = .0080070231$$

$$i_2 = .008138647$$

$$i_3 = .0081394354$$

$$i_4 = .0081394354$$

The answer stabilizes on the fourth iteration, so the monthly compounding rate is .81394354%. This rate, when multiplied by 12, gives the annual rate of 9.767322538%.

(*b*) If interest is compounded semiannually—as it is in Canadian mortgages—it is necessary to convert the i_f value to i_c as follows, using Eq. (8-20):

$$i_c = (1.0081394354)^{12/2} - 1$$

$$= .0498412169$$

The equivalent semiannual compounding rate with monthly payments is 4.98412169%, or 9.96824338% annually.

(*c*) To determine the equivalent continuous rate with $f = 12$, we solve for the equivalent continuous rate using Eq. (8-21).

$$j = r/f = \ln(1.0081394354)$$

$$= .0081064889$$

The monthly continuous rate j is .81064885%, and the annual continuous rate r is 9.727786147%.

While determination of the interest rate is not particularly complex, it is rather time consuming on a Level I calculator. Remember, however, that one or two iterations will generally give one- or two-digit accuracy, which is adequate for many situations. Many Level II and III calculators will solve for i when a balloon payment is present, making them extremely efficient for this type of analysis. Now we turn our attention to applications where the balloon payment occurs after the final regular payment.

8-5.2 Balloons Not at the End of the Last Payment Period

This section will present some applications in which the balloon payment occurs at a time other than the last payment period. For various reasons, a loan may have a series of regular payments, with the balloon being paid some number of periods after the final regular payment. The general balloon equations given earlier will still enable us to compute any of the possible unknown values. Because the basic computational technique has been shown previously, the following examples are given without additional explanation.

Example 8-6: Solving for PMT A company is borrowing \$55,000 and wants to make 120 monthly payments and a \$10,000 balloon payment at the end of the *twelfth* year (month 144). If interest is compounded monthly at a 10% annual rate and the payments are made at the end of each month, what is the regular monthly payment?

From Time Diagram 8-6 we identify the annuity component as an ordinary annuity PV with 120 payments. Next, we substitute .1/12 for I, 0 for K, 120 for n, and 144 for L into Eq. (8-7), and solve for the payment amount.

$$\text{PMT} = \frac{55,000 - 10,000(1 + .10/12)^{-144}}{A(120,.10/12)}$$

$$= \$686.8276065$$

Rounding to the nearest penny gives a monthly payment of \$686.83.

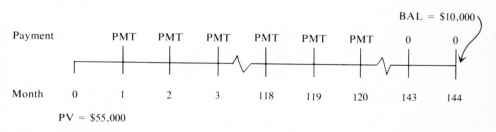

Time Diagram 8-6

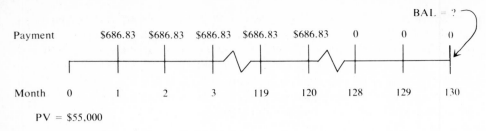

PV = $55,000

Time Diagram 8-7a Payoff at end of period 130.

Example 8-7: Solving for BAL Suppose that the company in Example 8-6 wishes to pay off the loan earlier. Using the monthly payments of $686.83, what is the balloon payment necessary to pay off the loan:

(*a*) At the end of the 130th month?

(*b*) At the end of the 108th month?

Remember, when you compute the balloon payment required to pay off the loan, you are really computing the remaining balance of the loan at that point in time, as indicated in Time Diagrams 8-7a and 8-7b.

(*a*) The balloon at the end of period 130 is computed by using the values from Example 8-6, with PMT = $686.83 and *L* = 130 substituted in Eq. (8-6).

$$BAL = [55,000 - (686.83)\, A(120,.10/12)]\left(1 + \frac{.10}{12}\right)^{130}$$

$$= \$8902.587964$$

The balloon payment necessary is $8902.59.

(*b*) Notice that in part (*a*), where the balloon occurred after the last regular payment, the values for *n* and *L* were 120 and 130, respectively. But if the loan is paid off at period 108, the last regular payment of $686.83 also occurs at *n* = 108. As Time Diagram 8-7b shows, this becomes an ordinary annuity— PV case, where *L* = *n*, solved as follows:

$$BAL = [55,000 - (686.83)A(108,.10/12)]\left(1 + \frac{.10}{12}\right)^{108}$$

$$= \$15,229.30684$$

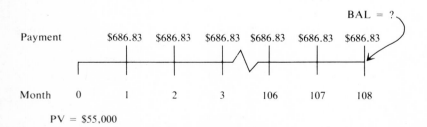

PV = $55,000

Time Diagram 8-7b Payoff at end of period 108.

A regular payment of 686.83 plus a balloon payment of $15,229.31 (for a total of $15,916.14) is necessary to pay off the loan at the end of period 108. Note that this approach, which was followed previously, considers the balloon as a separate payment with a regular payment due at the same time. Alternatively, it is possible to compute the *total* payment due at the end of period 108, but the value used for n must be $L - 1$. Resolving the problem with $L = 108$ and $n = 107$, we obtain a balloon of $15,916.14 (which is equal to the total payment computed above).

$$\text{BAL} = \left[55,000 - 686.83 \times \frac{1 - (1 + .10/12)^{-107}}{.10/12} \right]\left(1 + \frac{.10}{12}\right)^{108}$$

$$= \$15,916.13684$$

Example 8-8: Solving for n and L An investor is buying some land which costs $85,000, and can afford monthly payments of $650. The current loan rate is 8% annual compounded monthly.

(*a*) If he makes a balloon payment of $20,000 at the end of 30 years, how many payments (made at the end of each month) are necessary?

(*b*) If he makes monthly payments for 20 years, when is the balloon payment due?

We proceed to solve these problems as follows.

(*a*) Since this is a PV case annuity, the value for K is 0, and $L = 360$ and $I = i_f = .08/12$. Substituting these values into Eq. (8-9):

$$n = -\ln\left[\frac{(.08/12)(20,000(1 + .08/12)^{-360} - 85,000)}{650} + 1 \right] \bigg/ \ln\left(1 + \frac{.08}{12}\right)$$

$$= 288.5941523$$

Therefore, 288 payments of $650 are required, plus a partial payment at period 289, which can be computed using Eq. (8-15). (Or, instead of the partial payment, a somewhat higher balloon payment could be made at period 360.)

(*b*) To compute L, the balloon payment period, where $n = 240$, we use Eq. (8-11):

$$L = \frac{\ln\{20,000(.08/12)/[(.08/12)85,000 - 650(1 - (1 + .08/12)^{-240})]\}}{\ln(1 + .08/12)}$$

$$= 151.8943436$$

The balloon is due at period 151.8943436. In practice, the amount of the necessary balloon at period 151 or 152 would probably be computed and paid at the end of one of these two periods.

We do not show an example here in which the interest rate is computed because the procedure is identical to Example 8-5.

8-5.3 Solving for Multiple Balloon Payments

Loans and mortgages are occasionally set up where in addition to the regular level payments, *multiple* balloon payments are made. The following example describes such a loan for which the regular payment must be determined.

Example 8-9 A $250,000 loan is being set up to allow for balloon payments of $20,000, $25,000, and $30,000 at the end of periods 60, 144, and 180, respectively. Interest is 11% compounded monthly. If regular payments are made at the end of each month for 180 months, what is the amount of the regular payment?

Because the balloons are known, Eq. (8-23) can be used to compute the payment amounts shown in Time Diagram 8-9. Setting K equal to 0, n equal to 180, and $I = i_f = .011/12$ and substituting in the equation:

$$PV_{BALS} = 20,000\left(1 + \frac{.11}{12}\right)^{-60} + 25,000\left(1 + \frac{.11}{12}\right)^{-144} + 30,000\left(1 + \frac{.11}{12}\right)^{-180}$$

$$= \$24,091.57362$$

Using Eq. (8-24), we get

$$PMT = \frac{250,000 - 24,091.57362}{(1 + .11/12)^0 A(180,.11/12)}$$

$$= \$2567.668249$$

The regular monthly payment is $2567.67, rounded up to the nearest cent. As a result of this rounding, the final balloon payment will be slightly different than $30,000. The exact amount of the final payment can easily be computed.

First, we compute the present value of the known balloon payments PV_y.

$$PV_y = 20,000\left(1 + \frac{.11}{12}\right)^{-60} + 25,000\left(1 + \frac{.11}{12}\right)^{-144}$$

$$= \$18,286.60632$$

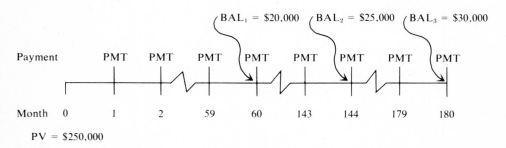

Time Diagram 8-9

Next, we compute the balloon payment due at the end of period 180 using Eq. (8-25).

$$BAL_{180} = \left[250,000 - \left(1 + \frac{.11}{12} \right)^0 (2567.67) A \left(180, \frac{.11}{12} \right) - 18,286.60632 \right]$$

$$\times \left(1 + \frac{.11}{12} \right)^{+180}$$

$$= \$29,999.20394$$

The final balloon payment is \$29,999.20 if the regular payments are \$2567.67.

8-6 LEASE APPLICATIONS

Conceptually, a lease with level payments is really an annuity with a final balloon. The balloon can represent either (1) the residual value of the leased asset at the end of the term of the lease, or (2) a large final payment. If the lease payments are made at the *end* of each period, the various unknown values are computed using the PV case in exactly the same manner as was used to solve the problems in the previous section. If the payments are made at the *beginning* of each period, as they frequently are in lease applications, the annuity-due case or PV_d is used. The following examples show a solution for the lease payment and the interest rate, or yield, on a lease.

Example 8-10 A company is leasing a building for 10 years. They estimate that the value of the building as \$280,000 today and \$150,000 at the end of 10 years. They wish to earn a return of 18% from the lease. Assuming beginning-of-month payments, what is the payment amount if:

(*a*) Interest is compounded monthly?
(*b*) Interest is compounded semiannually?
We proceed to solve these problems as follows.

(*a*) Since, as shown in Time Diagram 8-10, the payments occur at the start of each month, the annuity due—PV case applies. The annuity has 120 payments with a balloon value at the end of period 120. Here the balloon represents a residual value rather than a cash payment, but it can be treated in an identical manner.

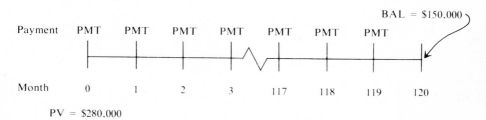

Time Diagram 8-10

The payment amount is computed using Eq. (8-7) with K equal to 1, n equal to 120, L equal to 120, and for part (a), $i = .18/12$. Solving for the payment:

$$PMT = \frac{280,000 - 150,000(1 + .18/12)^{-120}}{(1 + .18/12)^1 A(120,.18/12)}$$

$$= \$4524.539495$$

The monthly lease payment rounded to the nearest cent is \$4524.54 if interest is compounded monthly.

(b) If interest is compounded semiannually, the value for I is $[(1 + .18/2)^{2/12} - 1]$, or .0144665921. Using the equation with $I = .0144665921$, the resulting payment is \$4395.504655, or \$4395.50 rounded to the nearest cent.

Example 8-11 Assume that the lease in Example 8-10 was finally negotiated to have a monthly payment of \$4550. What is the yield to the lessor assuming:

(a) Monthly compounding?

(b) Semiannual compounding?

(c) Continuous compounding?

We proceed to solve these problems as follows.

(a) As the problem statement indicates, all values except the interest rate are known in this annuity-due balloon situation. First, we solve for the initial value of i using Eq. (8-19).

$$i_0 = \frac{150,000 - 280,000 + 120(4550)}{280,000(120 + 1)}$$

$$= .0122786305$$

Next, using the i_0 value, we solve the iteration equation (8-18) until the values stabilize. Placing i_0 or .0122786305 in Equation (8-18) we have, for the first iteration,

$$i_1 = i_0 - \frac{(1 + i_0)[1 - (1 + i_0)^{-120}] + \dfrac{i_0}{4550}[150,000(1 + i_0)^{-120} - 280,000]}{1 + (1 + i_0)\dfrac{(1 + i_0)^{-120} - 1}{i_0} + (119)(1 + i_0)^{-120} - \dfrac{120 i_0\, 150,000(1 + i_0)^{-121}}{4550}}$$

The values for each iteration are

$$i_1 = .014807153$$

$$i_2 = .015106145$$

$$i_3 = .0151050588$$

$$i_4 = .01510505925$$

$$i_5 = .01510505925$$

After five iterations, the answer stabilizes and we have the monthly compounding rate of 1.51050925%, which is an annual rate of 18.126111%.

Because the company negotiated a least payment larger than the previously computed payment of \$4,525.54, they increased the return on the project from 18% to 18.126% (assuming monthly compounding.)

(*b*) To determine the interest rate with semiannual compounding, we use Eq. (8-20):

$$i_c = (1.0151050925)^{12/2} - 1$$

$$= .094122512$$

The annual rate for semiannual compounding is 18.8245024%.

(*c*) The continuous rate is computed using Eq. (8-21), where $f = 12$:

$$j = \ln(1.0151050925)$$

$$= .0149921465$$

The annual continuous rate is 17.99057585, with monthly payments.

8-7 CAPITAL BUDGETING APPLICATIONS

Capital budgeting may be defined as the process of evaluating long-term investment projects. While the topic of capital budgeting is too extensive to be covered here in depth, we will explain the techniques necessary to answer two questions that provide the keys to investment analysis.

1. What is the present value of the after-tax cash flows associated with an investment project using an assumed interest rate?
2. Given the projects cost (or PV) and the cash inflows, what is the resulting interest return or yield? (This is often called the *internal rate of return.*)

In this section we assume that the periodic cash inflows from the investment project are constant, with a final balloon cash flow. (For variable cash flows, the techniques discussed in Chap. 7 can be used to compute the present value or the interest rate.)

The three major cash flow components are (1) the cost of the project at time zero, which is the present value PV; (2) the periodic level savings or revenues, which represent PMT; and (3) the final residual or salvage value of the investment, which is BAL. Note that this describes the capital budgeting model in the form of an annuity with a balloon, which can be solved in the same fashion as the previous examples for mortgages and leases. To compute the present value of a project for a given discount (interest) rate, we simply solve for PV or PV$_a$, depending on the timing of the payments. To obtain the internal rate of return, or the interest rate yield, we use the cost of the project as the present value, which makes the net present value equal to zero, and solve for i. Both computations are demonstrated in the following example.

Example 8-12 A company is considering the purchase of a $250,000 machine, which is expected to have a market value of $50,000 at the end of 8 years. The machine should generate after-tax savings of $5025 per month. Assume that all savings occur at the end of each month. The company requires all projects of this type to earn 17%.

(*a*) What is the present value of the monthly savings and residual?

(*b*) What is the internal rate of return?

We proceed to solve these problems as follows.

(*a*) As Time Diagram 8-12 shows, this capital budgeting problem can be expressed as an ordinary annuity with balloon. To find the *present value* of the savings, we use Eq. (8-5), with the following values: $K = 0$, $n = 8 \times 12 = 96$, $L = 96$, and PMT = $5025, and $I = i_f = .17/12$:

$$PV = 5025A\left(96, \frac{.17}{12}\right) + 50,000\left(1 + \frac{.17}{12}\right)^{-96}$$

$$= 5025\frac{1 - (1 + .17/12)^{-96}}{.17/12} + 50,000\left(1 + \frac{.17}{12}\right)^{-96}$$

$$= \$275,749.9168$$

The present value, $275,749.92, exceeds the cost of the project, $250,000, by *$25,749.92*. This amount is called the *net present value*. The positive net present value implies that the internal rate of return (IRR) is *higher* than the discount rate of 17% used to compute PV. A negative net present value would indicate that the IRR is less than the discount rate. In this problem the machine

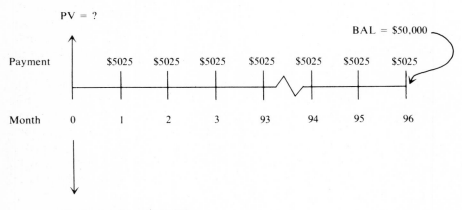

Time Diagram 8-12

investment will earn more than 17%, but how much more? This, of course, is part (*b*) of the example.

(*b*) To determine the *internal rate of return,* we must solve for I with the net present value equal to zero. Thus PV is equal to $250,000. Using Eq. (8-18) with the values

$$K = 0$$

$$PV = 250,000$$

$$n = 96$$

$$L = 96$$

$$PMT = 5025$$

$$BAL = 50,000$$

we solve for i.

The result of the iteration procedure (not shown because the process is the same as in Example 8-5), is 1.667180807%, or 20.00616968% annually. The machine earns about 20%, or 3% above the minimum required rate.

8-8 BOND APPLICATIONS

Bonds are normally issued with a fixed number of interest payment periods, which are usually semiannual or annual. The amount of each interest payment is computed by first multiplying the par value of the bond by the nominal interest rate† to get the annual interest, and then simply dividing by the number of payments per year. At the end of the last payment period the bond is redeemed for its *par* or *face value* (also called the *redemption value*).

In this section we will assume that the bonds have equal coupon payments, a redemption value at the end of period n, and more than one coupon payment remaining. For bonds that do not have equal coupon payments the variable-cash-flow procedures described in Chaps. 7 and 9 can be used to compute the bond yield and price.

Because the periodic interest payment is fixed in amount, bonds will actually sell at a premium or discount from face or par value to meet current market yield requirements. For example, a bond with an 8% face value would sell for a premium above par if the yield required is 7%, but would sell for a discount if the market yield is 9%. Note that bonds paying a fixed number of level payments, and with a redemption value, represent an ordinary annuity with a balloon at the end of the period, with one of two values unknown: (1) the *price* or present value, or (2) the required yield.

---

†The nominal interest rate is the value printed on the bond.

8-8.1 Bonds Sold on Interest Date

Example 8-13 A $1000 bond has 20 semiannual coupon payments of 4%, or $40 per payment, remaining with the face value redeemed at the end of the last period.

(*a*) Assuming that the buyer wants to earn a yield or return of 9%, how much should she pay for the bond?

(*b*) What is the yield if she buys the bond for $941.25?

We proceed to solve these problems as follows.

(*a*) From Time Diagram 8-13 we see that the bond is the same as an ordinary annuity with a balloon at the end of the last payment period. The present value, or price, is determined using Eq. (8-5), with the values $K = 0$, $n = 20$, $L = 20$, PMT $= \$40$, BAL $= \$1000$, and $I = .09 \div 2 = .045$:

$$PV = 40\left(\frac{1 - 1.045^{-20}}{.045}\right) + 1000(1.045)^{-20}$$

$$= \$934.9603177$$

The price of the bond on the interest date should be $934.96. A price lower than this amount yields more than 9% and a higher price yields less than 9%.

(*b*) To find the yield if the bond is sold for $941.25, we can use the iteration equation (8-18) to compute the yield or interest rate. Since this procedure has been demonstrated previously, the detailed solution is not given. With $K = 0$, PV $= 941.25$, $n = L = 20$, PMT $= \$40$, and BAL $= \$1000$, the yield is computed to be 4.449680189% per semiannual payment, or 8.899360378% annually.

Most Level II and III calculators have routines to solve for *i* in an ordinary annuity—PV and balloon situation, so that computing the yield on the bond price for a sale on an interest date is not difficult. However, somewhat more complex methods are required when bonds are sold *between* interest dates.

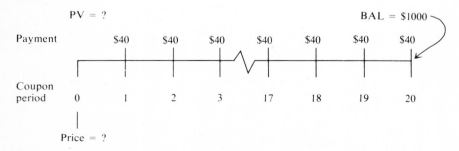

Time Diagram 8-13

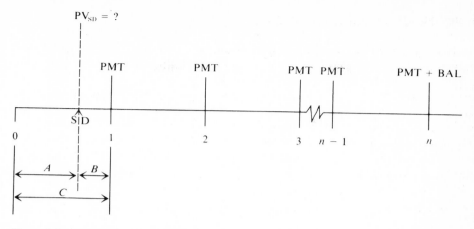

Figure 8-3 Bond sold at settlement date, SD.

8-8.2 Bonds Sold Between Interest Payment Dates

In the previous section the bonds were sold on an interest or coupon payment date, which means there was no accrued interest payable to the seller. When a bond is sold between coupon dates, however, the normal practice is to pay the seller her share of the accrued interest up to the settlement date (the date the bond is actually sold). This interest amount is computed using a "day-basis allocation" rather than compound interest.† For example, if a bond is sold after two-thirds of the coupon period has passed, the seller would receive two-thirds of the next coupon payment. This means that the purchaser of the bond pays to the seller the price of the bond plus two-thirds of the next coupon payment. Of course, the purchaser will receive the full coupon payment at the end of the coupon period during which the purchase occurs.

Because the accrued interest is allocated on a day basis (rather than on a compound interest basis), a problem occurs in calculating either the price or yield for a bond sold between interest dates. Consider Fig. 8-3, which shows all the remaining interest payments to be made. Specifically, Fig. 8-3 indicates the time of the settlement date, SD. The seller received a full interest payment at time t_0, the end of the period zero, so that particular payment is not shown on the time diagram. The symbols used are defined as

C = number of days in coupon period

A = number of days from last coupon period to settlement date

B = number of days from settlement date to next coupon period

†There are two common methods in use for counting days: (1) The 360-day/year method, which assumes that each month has 30 days; (2) the actual-day method, which counts the actual days in each month and year. In our examples we will give the number of actual days in each coupon period and the days to the next coupon period from the settlement date. Some of the advanced Level II, and the Level III calculators have day count routines.

Note that $C = A + B$.

The bond is sold on the settlement date, SD, which falls between the beginning and end of the coupon period C. Computing the price of a bond sold between interest dates requires a two-step procedure.

Step 1: Compute the present value at the time of the settlement date; that is, determine PV_{SD} at time t_{SD}. The payments involved in calculating PV_{SD} include all the future coupon payments as well as the redemption value at time t_n. Specifically, as shown in Fig. 8-3, the buyer will receive n payments of amount PMT and a balloon payment BAL. One method of determining PV_{SD} is to first calculate PV_1 at t_1 and then discount PV_1 back to time t_{SD}. This is shown in two parts.

(a) *Determine* PV_1. Use the ordinary annuity formula, Eq. (8-5), to compute V_K for $K = 0$ for the $(n - 1)$th payment and a balloon occurring also after the $(n - 1)$th payment. Then add on the PMT payment made at time t_1. So we get

$$PV_1 = V_K + PMT \tag{8-27a}$$

or

$$PV_1 = [PMT \times A(n - 1, i) + BAL(1 + i)^{-n+1}] + PMT \tag{8-27b}$$

(b) *Discount to* t_{SD}. Now discount PV_1 from time t_1 to time t_{SD}. From Fig. 8-3 we see that the fractional discounting period is the ratio B/C. So we get

$$PV_{SD} = PV_1 \times (1 + i)^{-B/C} \tag{8-28}$$

Substituting PV_1 from Eq. (8-27b) in (8-28) leads to

$$PV_{SD} = [PMT \times A(n - 1, i) + BAL(1 + i)^{-n+1} + PMT](1 + i)^{-B/C} \tag{8-29}$$

The quantity PV_{SD} represents the present value of the future cash flows that the buyer will receive, based on the settlement date t_{SD}. Thus it represents the value to the buyer of the future n coupon payments and the redemption value balloon. It also represents the value that the seller is transferring to the buyer on the settlement date.

However, industry practice subdivides this value into a bond price and an accrued interest due to seller. This subdivision is indicated in step 2.

Step 2: Accrued interest and bond price. First, let us determine the amount of the accrued interest and then subtract it from the PV_{SD}. Since more than one method will be used to calculate the accrued interest, this particular method is identified by the symbols

ACP = accrued interest calculation as used in industry practice

BPP = bond price based on industry practice used to calculate ACP

As stated earlier in this section, the accrued interest, ACP, is calculated on a prorated "day basis" rather than on a "compound interest" basis. That is,

$$ACP = PMT \times \frac{A}{C} \qquad (8\text{-}30)$$

where A/C is the fraction of the last period where the bond was still owned by the seller and for which interest has accrued. Now that ACP is known, it is possible to determine the bond price, or

$$BPP = PV_{SD} - ACP \qquad (8\text{-}31)$$

Substituting PV_{SD} from Eq. (8-29) into (8-31), we obtain

$$BPP = [PMT \times A(n - 1, i) + BAL(1 + i)^{-n+1} + PMT]$$

$$(1 + i)^{-B/C} - PMT\left(\frac{A}{C}\right) \qquad (8\text{-}32)$$

Equation (8-32) is now arranged in a form similar to that appearing in industry reference sources.† Perhaps it is useful to summarize all the symbols before solving a specific example.

n = number of coupon payments remaining after the settlement date $(n > 1)$

ACP = accrued interest calculated by industry practice

BPP = bond price when ACP is used

PMT = dollar amount of coupon payment

BAL = redemption value of bond

i = periodic yield

C = number of days in coupon period

A = number of accrued interest days from *last* coupon payment to settlement date

B = number of days from settlement date to *next* coupon payment period

Now let's consider an example using this procedure.

Example 8-14 A $1000 bond paying interest semiannually is sold on the twenty-fifth day of a 182-day coupon period. Including the current period, 17 coupon payments remain, with the bond being redeemed at the end of the last period. The bond pays 8.5% annually and was sold to yield 9% annual. What is the selling price of the bond?

The period A is 24 days, because interest is generally not accrued for the settlement date (which was day 25). As a result, period B has 158 days. In terms of payment periods, A/C is 24/182 periods and B/C is 158/182 periods.

† See, for example, Bruce M. Spence et al., *Standard Securities Calculation Methods,* Securities Industry Association, New York, 1973.

While Time Diagram 8-14 shows 17 periods ($n = 17$), remember that the formula uses the annuity relationship with $n - 1$ periods.

We use the yield, .09, divided by the number of payment periods per year, 2, to compute $i(.09 \div 2 = .045)$. The payment is computed by multiplying the bond nominal interest rate (8.5%) times the face value ($1000) and dividing by the number of payments per year (2):

$$\frac{\$.085 \times 1000}{2} = \$42.5$$

Then, using Eq. (8-32) for the bond price:

$$BPP = [42.5 + 42.5 \times A(17 - 1,.045)$$

$$+ 1000(1.045)^{-17+1}](1.045)^{-158/182} - 42.5\left(\frac{24}{182}\right)$$

$$= 1014.414962(1.045)^{-158/182} - 42.5\left(\frac{24}{182}\right)$$

$$= 976.3829464 - 5.604395604$$

$$= \$970.7785508$$

The price of the bond BPP is $970.77855 and the accrued interest ACP is $5.6044. The seller, of course, would receive both the bond price and the accrued interest on the settlement date, which amounts to $976.3829464.

The calculations given above are based upon the industry or professional practice for calculating the accrued interest ACP, using Eq. (8-30). The next section discusses the theoretical approach to the subdivision between bond price and accrued interest.

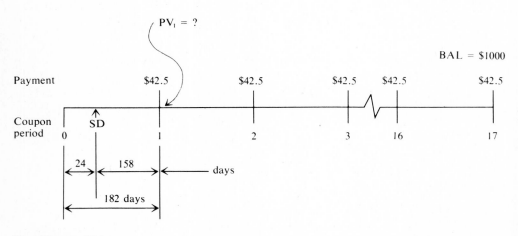

Time Diagram 8-14

8-8.3 Theoretical Treatment of Bonds Between Interest Dates

A more theoretically correct formula could be used as a substitute for the industry practice calculations, under which the buyer and seller would divide the next interest payment in a manner that is consistent with the rules of compound interest. Of course, when fractional periods are involved, the more theoretically correct method will lead to different results than the method used in practice.

The approach for evaluating the seller's accrued interest can be developed by using the concepts of compounding.† The key equation becomes

$$ACT = PMT \times S(A/C,i) \qquad (8\text{-}33)$$

where ACT = accrued interest calculated from Eq. (8-33)

$S(A/C,i)$ = ordinary annuity S factor for the fractional period A/C and interest i

Equation (8-33) can be developed from concepts described in Sec. 5-5.1. Having defined ACT, we can proceed to evaluate the theoretical bond price, BPT. To obtain BPT, we must subtract the accrued interest ACT from the present value:

$$BPT = PV_{SD} - ACT \qquad (8\text{-}34)$$

where PV_{SD} is the present value at time t_{SD}, as illustrated in Eq. (8-29).

It is useful to develop an expanded formula for BPT for computational purposes. By using Eqs. (8-33), (8-29), and (8-34), it is possible to express BPT in the following form:

$$BPT = PMT \times A(n - 1 + B/C,i) + BAL \times (1 + i)^{-(n-1+B/C)} \qquad (8\text{-}35)$$

Note, however, that it is simply Eq. (8-5) for V_K, where $K = 0$ and the periods are $n - 1 + B/C = n - A/C$; $n - A/C$ represents the elapsed time from settlement date t_{SD} to the redemption time t_n. Equation (8-35) can now be used to solve for BPT. The calculation is demonstrated below using data from Example (8-14):

$$n - 1 + \frac{B}{C} = 17 - 1 + \frac{158}{182}$$

$$i = .045$$

$$BAL = \$1000$$

$$PMT = 42.5$$

so

$$BPT = 42.5 \times A\left(17 - 1 + \frac{158}{182}, .045\right) + 1000 \times (1.045)^{-(17-1+158/182)}$$

$$= \$970.8850494 \qquad (8\text{-}36)$$

†This formula has been developed by P. M. Hummel and C. L. Seeback, *Mathematics of Finance*, McGraw-Hill Book Company, New York, 1971, p. 130.

Comparing the theoretical value of BPT with the industry practice value BPP, we note that

$$BPT = \$970.8850494$$

$$BPP = \underline{970.7785508}$$

$$\text{difference} = .1064986$$

Although the differences were expressed by subtracting the two bond prices, the source of error is due to the two methods for calculating accrued interest.

$$ACP = PMT \times (A/C) = 42.5 \times (24/182) \qquad = 5.6043956$$

$$ACT = PMT \times S(A/C,i) = 42.5 \times S(24/182,.045) = \underline{5.4978970}$$

$$\text{difference} = .1064986$$

Note that the difference in accrued interest is the same as the difference in bond price. While the differences may appear minor, remember that large dollar values are involved in many bond transactions.

An important side benefit from the theoretical analysis is a simple method for calculating the bond price in practice, BPP, with Level II or III calculators. We can use the expression

$$BPP = BPT + ACT - ACP \tag{8-37}$$

where BPT comes from Eq. (8-35)
 ACT comes from Eq. (8-33)
 ACP comes from Eq. (8-30)

By using Eq. (8-37), we can easily compute the bond price with Level II and III calculators that have financial function keys. The bond price in Example 8-14 can be computed using Eq. (8-19) as follows:

$$BPP = PMT \times A\left(n - 1 + \frac{B}{C}, i\right) + BAL(1 + i)^{-1-n-B/C}$$

$$+ PMT \times S\left(\frac{A}{C}, i\right) - PMT\left(\frac{A}{C}\right) \tag{8-38}$$

$$= 42.5 \times A\left(17 - 1 + \frac{158}{182}, .045\right) + 1000(1.045)^{1-17-158/182}$$

$$+ 42.5 \times S\left(\frac{24}{182}, .045\right) - 42.5\left(\frac{24}{182}\right)$$

$$= 494.954160914 + 475.930888428 + 5.497897052052 - 5.604395604395$$

$$= 970.885049342 + 5.497897052052 - 5.604395604395$$

$$= \$970.7785507897$$

If you are using a calculator that has financial function keys, this method will prove more efficient to program and use.

In summary, the annuity formula, when used with n plus a fraction, allocates the accrued interest differently than is done in practice, where accrued interest is allocated on a per day basis. You can use the fractional-period annuity concept as an approximation or as part of a shortcut calculation technique. We will also use this technique as part of the bond-yield solution procedure discussed next.

8-8.4 Computing Bond Yield

As you may suspect, solving for the yield or interest rate of a bond sold between interest dates is more complicated than computing the interest rate for an annuity with balloon, where n is an integer. Fortunately, most Level II and III calculators have routines that make the procedure fairly straightforward. We will discuss two methods of computing the yield for a bond sold between interest dates with more than one coupon period remaining: (1) a Newton-Raphson iteration procedure, and (2) a combination of an iteration and an equivalence approach.

The iteration procedure uses the same general approach employed in the applications earlier in this chapter.

8-8.4.1 Newton-Raphson procedure

$$i_{k+1} = i_k - \Delta i_k$$

$$\Delta i = \frac{f(i)}{f'(i)}$$

Arranging Eq. (8-33) in the proper form, we get

$$f(i) = 1 + \frac{1}{i} + (1 + i)^{1-n}\left(\frac{BAL}{PMT} - \frac{1}{i}\right) - \left(\frac{A}{C} + \frac{PV}{PMT}\right)(1 + i)^{B/C} \quad (8\text{-}39)$$

$$f^1(i) = \frac{BAL}{PMT}(1 + i)^{-n}\left[1 - n - \frac{B}{C}(1 + i)\right] - \left(\frac{B}{C} + \frac{1}{i}\right)\frac{1 - (1 + i)^{1-n}}{i}$$

$$- \frac{B}{C} + \frac{(n - 1)(1 + i)^{-n}}{i} \quad (8\text{-}40)$$

$$i_0 = \frac{BAL - PV + n(PMT)}{PV(n + 1)}$$

where $n > 1$

n = number of coupon periods including the period of sale
PMT = dollar amount of periodic coupon payment
BAL = redemption value of bond
n = periodic decimal yield
C = total number of days in coupon period

A = number of accrued interest days from last coupon payment to settlement date

B = number of days from settlement date to next coupon payment period

This iteration procedure is too complex for practical solution using a Level I calculator because of the large number of keystrokes required for each iteration. It is feasible only on calculators that are Level III programmables. (A complete program for this method is given at the end of the chapter.)

8-8.4.2 Combination iterative and equivalence approach. Now let's look at the second method for computing the yield, which is feasible on any Level II (or Level III) calculator that computes the interest rate for an annuity with a balloon.

As you recall, we pointed out that Eq. (8-37) and the annuity with balloon equation (8-5) used with n plus a fractional period each compute the same present value before accrued interest is deducted. We can restate Eq. (8-37) in terms of BPT as follows:

$$BPT = BPP + ACP - ACT \qquad (8-41)$$

This equation is the key to computing the yield for a bond sold between interest dates, because when the true interest rate is found, Eq. (8-41) balances.

Rewrite Eq. (8-41) to show which terms are dependent upon the trial value of i, called i_k. $BPT(i_k)$ represents the bond price computed using Eq. (8-35) with i_k, and $ACT(i_k)$ the theoretical accrued interest using Eq. (8-33) with i_k.

$$BPT(i_k) = (BPP + ACP) - ACT(i_k) \qquad (8-41)$$

At this point the quantity (BPP + ACP) is known. For the iterative relationship we will modify Eq. (8-41) to read

$$BPT(i_{k+1}) = BPP + ACP - ACT(i_k) \qquad (8-42)$$

The iterative procedure is as follows.

Step 0: For the initial estimate, i_0, let ACP = ACT, so

$$BPT(i_1) = BPP$$

Step 1: Solve for i_1, knowing that BPT is known. This is easily done on a Level II or III calculator.

Step 2: Solve for $ACT(i_1)$, knowing that i_1 is known.

Step 3: Solve for i_2 from the value of BPT, using

$$BPT(i_2) = (BPP + ACP) - ACT(i_1)$$

Steps 1 to 3 are repeated until a satisfactory interest rate is obtained.

This iterative process is even easier to deal with when talking in terms of the keystroke sequence. The computation requires four basic steps.

Step 0: Enter the bond price BPP in **PV**. This is our initial estimate of

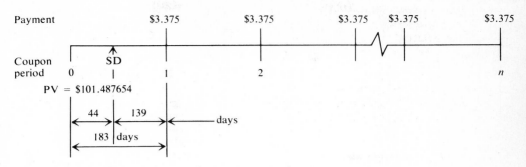

Time Diagram 8-15

BPT. Enter $n - 1 + B/C$ in **N**, coupon payment in **PMT**, and redemption value in **BAL** or **FV**.

Step 1: Solve for i using your calculator's keystroke sequence.

Step 2: Using the i just calculated, calculate the annuity accrued interest (ACT) using $PMT \times S(A/C,i)$, and subtract this amount from the total of the *original* bond price BPP plus day-basis accrued interest ACP. This new total is the new estimate for BPT and is entered in **PV**. The adjustment is always made to the original bond price BPP and ACP in this step.

Step 3: Repeat steps 1 and 2 until the interest rate stabilizes [which means that Eq. (8-42) balances]. This interest rate is the true bond yield.

A program which is particularly convenient for Level II financial calculators with program steps is available.† Both this method and the iteration approach described earlier are illustrated in the next example.

Example 8-15 A price of $101.487654 is quoted for a bond with 26 semiannual coupon payments remaining. The coupon rate is 6.75%. The current coupon period contains 183 days, and the settlement date is 45 days into the period. Assuming that the bond is redeemed at par, what is the yield?

The values for the problem are (see Time Diagram 8-15):

$$BPP = 101.487654$$

$$n = 26$$

$$PMT = .0675 \times \frac{100}{2} = \$3.375$$

$$BAL = \$100$$

$$C = 183$$

$$A = 44$$

$$B = 139$$

†For the MBA calculator, programs are found in R. F. Farish and E. B. Greynolds, *Calculator Analysis for Business and Finance*, Texas Instruments, Inc., Dallas, Tex., 1977, Chap. 5.

We will first compute the yield using the iteration equation (8-41), the first method. The initial guess for i is found as follows:

$$i_0 = \frac{100 - 101.487654 + 26(3.375)}{101.487654(27)}$$

$$= .0314806932$$

Solving the iteration equation (8-20), we find:

$$i_1 = .0328555002$$

$$i_2 = .0328790768$$

$$i_3 = .0328791166$$

$$i_4 = .0328791166$$

After four iterations the interest rate stabilizes at 3.28791166%, which is an annual yield of 6.57582333%.

Now, let's solve for the yield using the *second method*, assuming that a Level II financial calculator is used.

Step 0: Compute the interest rate of an ordinary annuity with the following values.

$$\text{BPP} = \text{PV} = \$101.487654$$

$$\text{BAL} = \$100$$

$$\text{PMT} = \$3.375$$

$$n = 26 - 1 + \frac{139}{183} = 25.75956284$$

Step 1: Compute i_0, which is .03288484227.
Step 2: Compute adjusted value of BPT.

$$\text{BPT}_1 = 101.487654 + \frac{44}{183} \times 3.375 - 3.375 \times S\left(\frac{44}{183}, .03288484227\right)$$

$$= 101.487654 + .81147541 - .801531994$$

$$= 102.2991294 - .801531994$$

$$= 101.4975974$$

Enter 101.4975974 in **PV**, but remember to reenter 100 in **FV** or **BAL** and 25 + 139/183 in **N** before computing i_1. Also, remember to use the original PV when computing BPT each time.

Step 3: Repeat steps 1 and 2, to obtain:

$$i_1 = .03287911566$$

$$i_2 = .03287911665$$

$$i_3 = .03287911665$$

We repeat steps 1 and 2 until the interest rate stabilizes, which it does here on the fourth iteration. The result is in close agreement with the answer obtained using the first iteration method. As a check, let's compute the price of the bond using the interest rate computed above using a Level II calculator. It is $101.487654, which is identical to the stated bond price.

It has been shown that some Level II calculators can be used very effectively in the bond calculations made above. Because many of the financial calculators have extra memories available, the values for PV, n, and FV can be stored, thereby avoiding the need to reenter these constant values. The computation procedure becomes simpler on a Level II calculator that has some programmable features, and also on Level III's.

8-9 BOND PRICE AND YIELD PROGRAM FOR THE TI-58/59

This program computes the bond price and the bond yield using Eqs. (8-33) and (8-41), respectively.

Data entry and subsequent calculations are executed by the use of "user-defined label keys." The functional use of these label keys (**A, B, C, D, E, A', B', C', D'**, and **E'**) is indicated in Fig. 8-4, which can be used as a convenient reminder of the location and use of each label key in this program. The label keys' inputs and functions are described below in the order of execution. Note that inputs for **A, B, C, D, E, A'**, and **E'** must be entered before pressing **B'** or **C'**. Their use is explained below.

C	Enter price; solve for yield	Enter yield; solve for price		Init.
Coupon $ payment	Redemption value	n	A	B

Figure 8-4 Data entry for bond program.

8-9.1 Execution of Program

8-9.1.1 Phase one—data entry

Step 1: Press **E'**.   Initialize the program.
Step 2: Enter $ coupon payment and press **A**.
Step 3: Enter redemption value of bond and press **B**.
Step 4: Enter number of remaining coupon payments and press **C**.

> *Step 5:* Enter *A* and press **D**.

> *A* is the last number of accrued interest days from last coupon payment to settlement date.

> *Step 6:* Enter *B* and press **E**.

> *B* is the number of days from the settlement date to the next coupon payment period.

> *Step 7:* Enter *C* and press **A'**.

> *C* is the number of days in the current coupon period.

8-9.1.2 Phase two—solve for unknown

> *Step 8a:* Enter bond price and solve for the yield by pressing **B'**.

or

> *Step 8b:* Enter decimal yield rate and solve for bond price by pressing **C'**.

LBL B'	−	×	RCL 04
STO 01	RCL 04	RCL 09	)
RCL 03	)	y^x	)
−	×	RCL 04	÷
RCL 01	(	+/−	RCL 08
+	RCL 03	×	−
RCL 04	÷	(	RCL 06
×	RCL 02	1	÷
RCL 02	−	−	RCL 07
=	RCL 08	RCL 04	+
÷	1/x	−	(
(	)	RCL 06	RCL 04
RCL 01	−	÷	−
×	(	RCL 07	1
(	RCL 05	×	)
RCL 04	÷	RCL 09	×
+	RCL 07	)	RCL 09
1	+	−	y^x
)	RCL 01	(	RCL 04
=	÷	RCL 06	+/−
STO 08	RCL 02	÷	÷
+	)	RCL 07	RCL 08
1	×	+	=
=	RCL 09	RCL 08	STO 11
STO 09	y^x	1/x	RCL 10
Lbl sin	(	)	÷
1	RCL 06	×	RCL 11
+	÷	(	=
RCL 08	RCL 07	1	PAUSE
1/x	)	−	+/−
+	=	RCL 09	SUM 08
RCL 09	STO 10	y^x	SUM 09
y^x	RCL 03	(	|x|
(	÷	1	x ≥ t
1	RCL 02	−	

sin	×	RCL 07	Lbl D
RCL 08	RCL 02	+/−	STO 05
R/S	+	)	R/S
	RCL 02	−	
Lbl C′	=	RCL 02	Lbl E
STO 08	+	×	STO 06
+	RCL 03	RCL 05	R/S
1	×	÷	
=	RCL 09	RCL 07	Lbl A′
STO 09	y^x	=	STO 07
y^x	(	R/S	R/S
(	RCL 04		
RCL 04	−	Lbl A	Lbl E′
−	1	STO 02	CMs
1	)	R/S	1
)	+/−		EE
+/−	=	Lbl B	10
−	×	STO 03	+/−
1	RCL 09	R/S	$x \geqslant t$
=	y^x		INV
+/−	(	Lbl C	EE
÷	RCL 06	STO 04	R/S
RCL 08	÷	R/S	

8-10 PROGRAM FOR COMPUTING THE INTEREST RATE FOR A PV BALLOON ANNUITY WHEN $n \neq L$ FOR THE TI-58/59

This program computes the interest rate for a PV balloon annuity using Eq. (8-18), and allows L to be unequal to n.

Data entry and subsequent calculations are executed by the use of "user-defined label keys." The functional use of these label keys (**A, B, C, D, E, A′, B′, C′, D′,** and **E′**) is indicated in Fig. 8-5, which can be used as a convenient reminder of the location and use of each label key in this program. The label keys' inputs and functions are described below in the order of execution. Note that inputs for **A, B, C, D, E, A′, B′, C′,** and **E′** must be entered before pressing **D′**. Their use is explained below.

BAL	c	f	Solve for i_f and i_c	Init.
V_k	K	n	L	PMT

Figure 8-5 Data entry for generalized annuity-balloon program.

8-10.1 Execution of Program

8-10.1.1 Phase one—data entry

Step 1: Press **E'**.   Initialize the program. This step also initializes c and f with 1.

Step 2: Enter V_K and press **A**. V_K is either PV or PV_d.

Step 3: Enter K value and press **B**.   The K factor for PV or PV_B is entered.

Step 4: Enter n and press **C**.

Step 5: Enter L and press **D**.

Step 6: Enter PMT and press **E**.

Step 7: Enter BAL and press **A'**.

Step 8: Enter c and press **B'**.   If c is equal to 1, this step can be omitted.

Step 9: Enter f and press **C'**.   If f is equal to 1, this step can be omitted.

8-10.1.2 Phase two—solve for unknown

Step 10: Press **D'**.   The interest rate i_f is shown as a decimal interest rate.

Press **R/S**.   The interest rate i_c is shown as a decimal interest rate.

Lbl D'	=	RCL 10	÷
RCL 06	STO 10	y^x	RCL 09
−	Lbl sin	RCL 04	+
RCL 01	1	+/−	(
+	−	−	RCL 03
RCL 03	RCL 10	RCL 01	−
×	y^x	=	RCL 02
RCL 05	RCL 03	STO 11	)
=	+/−	RCL 02	×
÷	=	+	RCL 10
(	×	RCL 10	y^x
RCL 01	RCL 10	y^x	(
×	y^x	RCL 02	RCL 03
(	RCL 02	×	+/−
RCL 03	+	(	+
+	RCL 09	RCL 10	RCL 02
1	÷	y^x	−
)	RCL 05	RCL 03	1
=	×	+/−	)
STO 09	(	−	−
+	RCL 06	1	RCL 04
1	×	)	×

RCL 09	PAUSE	STO 01	R/S
×	+/−	R/S	
RCL 06	SUM 09		Lbl B′
×	SUM 10	Lbl B	STO 07
RCL 10	|x|	STO 02	R/S
y^x	$x \geq t$	R/S	Lbl C′
(	sin		STO 08
RCL 04	RCL 09	Lbl C	R/S
+	R/S	STO 03	
1	RCL 10	R/S	Lbl E′
)	y^x		CMs
+/−	(	Lbl D	1
÷	RCL 08	STO 04	STO 07
RCL 05	÷	R/S	STO 08
=	RCL 07		EE
STO 12	)	Lbl E	10
RCL 11	−	STO 05	+/−
÷	1	R/S	$x \gtrless t$
RCL 12	=		INV
=	R/S	Lbl A′	EE
PAUSE	Lbl A	STO 06	R/S

KEYSTROKE SOLUTIONS

This section contains keystroke solutions for selected examples from this chapter. These solutions are organized by *type* of calculator (Type A or Type R) and within each type by *level* (Level II or III).

Type	Level	Example number	Page
A	II and III	8-1, 8-3, 8-5, 8-6, 8-7, 8-11, 8-14, 8-15	321, 323, 325, 327, 328 332, 339, 345
R	II and III	8-1, 8-3, 8-5, 8-6, 8-7, 8-11, 8-14, 8-15	321, 323, 325, 327, 328 332, 339, 345

Type A, Level II keystrokes for Example 8-1

TI-MBA/BA-II keystrokes	Display	Comments
CA	0	Clear
120	120.	n
N	120.	
9.5	9.5	$r\%$
÷	9.5	
12	12	c
=	0.7916666667	$i_c\%$
%i	0.7916666667	
1061.3	1061.3	PMT
PMT	1061.3	
50000	50000	BAL
FV	50000.	
CPT	50000.	
PV	82018.54995	
STO 0	82018.54995	
0	0	
PMT	0.	
CPT	0.	
PV	19409.52038	
SUM 0	19409.52038	
RCL 0	101428.0703	PV

Type A, Level II keystrokes for Example 8-3

TI-MBA/BA-II keystrokes	Display	Comments
Fix 2	0.00	Set display
CLR	0	Clear
120	120	n
N	120.00	
8	8	$r\%$
÷	8.00	
12	12	c
=	0.67	$i_c\%$
%i	0.67	
30000	30000	BAL
FV	30000.00	
CPT	30000.00	
PV	13515.70	PV of BAL
+/-	-13515.70	
+	-13515.70	
85000	85000	
=	71484.30	PV − PV of BAL
PV	71484.30	
CPT	71484.30	
PMT	867.30	PMT

Type A, Level II keystrokes for Example 8-5

TI-MBA keystrokes	Display	Comments
CA	0	Clear
FIX 2	0.00	Set display
120	120	n
N	120.00	
100000	100000	PV
PV	100000.00	
1061.3	1061.3	PMT
PMT	1061.30	
50000	50000	BAL
FV	50000.00	
CPT	50000.00	
%i	0.81	$i_c\%$
×	0.81	
12	12	c
=	9.77	$r\%$
FIX 9	9.767322528	

Type A, Level II keystrokes for Example 8-6

TI-MBA/BA-II keystrokes	Display	Comments
CA	0	Clear
FIX 2	0.00	Set display
10	10	$r\%$
÷	10.00	
12	12	c
=	0.83	$i_c\%$
%i	0.83	
144	144	n for BAL
N	144.00	
10000	10000	BAL
FV	10000.00	
CPT	10000.00	
PV	3026.96	PV of BAL
+/−	−3026.96	
+	−3026.96	
55000	55000	PV
=	51973.04	PV − PV of BAL
PV	51973.04	
120	120	n for annuity
N	120.00	
CPT	120.00	
PMT	686.83	PMT

Type A, Level II keystrokes for Example 8-7

TI-BA-II keystrokes	Display	Comments
FIX 2	0.00	Set display
CMR	0.00	Clear
686.83	686.83	PMT
PMT	686.83	
10	10	$r\%$
÷	10.00	
12	12	c
=	0.83	$i_c\%$
%i	0.83	
120	120	n for payments
N	120.00	
CPT	120.00	
PV	51973.22	PV of payments
+/-	-51973.22	
+	-51973.22	
55000	55000	
=	3026.78	PV of BAL
PV	3026.78	PV
130	130	n for BAL
N	130.00	
0	0	
PMT	0.00	
CPT FV	8902.59	BAL at period 130
55000	55000	PV
PV	55000.00	
686.83	686.83	PMT
PMT	686.83	
CPT	686.83	
N	132.62	Period for BAL
108	108	
Acc/Bal	34406.95	
x⇌y	15229.31	BAL at period 108

Type A, Level II keystrokes for Example 8-7

TI-MBA keystrokes	Display	Comments
CA	0	Clear
FIX 2	0.00	Set display
686.83	686.83	PMT
PMT	686.83	
10	10	$r\%$
÷	10.00	
12	12	c
=	0.83	$i_c\%$
%i	0.83	
120	120	n
N	120.00	
CPT	120.00	
PV	51973.23	PV of payments
+/-	-51973.23	
+	-51973.23	
55000	55000	
=	3026.77	PV of BAL
PV	3026.77	PV
130	130	n for BAL
N	130.00	
0	0	
PMT	0.00	
CPT	0.00	
FV	8902.59	BAL at period 130
55000	55000	PV
PV	55000.00	
686.83	686.83	PMT
PMT	686.83	
108	108	n for BAL
BAL	15229.31	BAL at period 108

Type A, Level II keystrokes for Example 8-11

TI-MBA keystrokes	Display	Comments
CA	0	Clear
120	120	n
N	120.	
4550	4550	PMT
PMT	4550.	
280000	280000	PV
PV	280000.	
150000	150000	BAL
FV	150000.	
DUE	150000.	
%i	1.510505924	$i_c\%$

Type A, Level II keystrokes for Example 8-14

TI-MBA/BA-II keystrokes	Display	Comments
CA	0	Clear
16	16	n
N	16.	
4.5	4.5	$i_c\%$
%i	4.5	
42.5	42.5	PMT
PMT	42.5	
STO 0	42.5	
1000	1000	
FV	1000.	
CPT PV	477.4456397	
SUM 0	477.4456397	
0	0	
PMT	0.	
CPT PV	494.4693227	$PMT + PMT(n-1,i) + BAL(1+i)^{-n+1}$
SUM 0	494.4693227	
RCL 0	1014.414962	
FV	1014.414962	
158	158	B
÷	158.	
182	182	C
=	0.868131868	B/C
N	0.868131868	
CPT PV	976.3829463	
STO 0	976.3829463	
42.5	42.5	PMT
×	42.5	
24	24	A
÷	1020	
182	182	C
=	5.604395604	$PMT(A/C)$
+/−	−5.604395604	
SUM 0	−5.604395604	
RCL 0	970.7785507	Bond price (BPP)

Type A, Level II keystrokes for Example 8-15

TI-MBA keystrokes	Display	Comments
CA	0	Clear
25	25	
+	25.	$n - 1$
139	139	0I
÷	139.	
183	183	CP
=	25.75956284	$n - 1 + B/C$
N	25.75956284	
STO 0	25.75956284	
44	44	A
÷	44.	
183	183	
=	0.240437158	
STO 1	0.240437158	
×	0.240437158	
3.375	3.375	
PMT	3.375	PMT
=	0.81147541	
STO 2	0.81147541	
101.487654	101.487654	PV
PV	101.487654	
SUM 2	101.487654	
100	100	
FV	100.	FV
STO 9	100.	
CPT %i	3.288484227	i_c
RCL 1	0.240437158	Iteration 1
N	0.240437158	
CPT FV	0.801531994	
+/−	−0.801531994	
+	−0.801531994	
RCL 2	102.291294	
=	101.4975974	

TI-MBA keystrokes	Display	Comments
PV	101.4975974	
RCL 9	100.	
FV	100.	
RCL 0	25.75956284	
N	25.75956284	
CPT %i	3.287911566	i_1
RCL 1	0.240437158	Iteration 2
N	0.240437158	
CPT FV	0.8015337	
+/−	−0.8015337	
+	−0.8015337	
RCL 2	102.2991294	
=	101.4975957	
PV	101.4975957	
RCL 9	100.	
FV	100.	
RCL 0	25.75956284	
N	25.75956284	
CPT %i	3.287911665	i_2
RCL 1	0.240437158	Iteration 3
N	0.240437158	
CPT FV	0.801533696	
+/−	−0.801533696	
+	−0.801533696	
RCL 2	102.2991294	
=	101.4975957	
PV	101.4975957	
RCL 9	100.	
FV	100.	
RCL 0	25.75956284	
N	25.75956284	
CPT %i	3.287911665	i_3

Type A, Level III keystrokes for Example 8-3

TI-58/59 keystrokes	Display	Comments
CMs	0.	Clear memories
Pgm 19	0.	Call pgm 19
E'	0.	Initialize
C'	0.	Select PV case
120	120	n
A	120.	
8	8	$r\%$
÷	8.	
12	12	c
=	.6666666667	$i_c\%$
B	0.6667	
85000	85000	PV
D	85000.00	
30000	30000	BAL
E	30000.00	
0	0	
C	867.30	PMT

Type A, Level III keystrokes for Example 8-1

TI-58/59 keystrokes	Display	Comments
CMs	0.	Clear memories
Pgm 19	0.	Call pgm 19
E'	0.	Initialize
C'	0.	Select PV case
120	120	n
A	120.	
9.5	9.5	$r\%$
÷	9.5	
12	12	c
=	.7916666667	$i_c\%$
B	0.7917	
1061.3	1061.3	PMT
C	1061.3	
50000	50000	BAL
E	50000.00	
0	0	
D	101428.07	PV

TI-58/59 keystrokes	Display	Comments
CMs	0.	Clear memories
Pgm 19	0.	Call pgm 19
E'	0.	Initialize
C'	0.	Select PV case
10	10	$r\%$
÷	10.	
12	12	c
=	.8333333333	$i_c\%$
B	0.8333	
÷	0.8333	
100	100	
+	0.0083	
1	1	
=	1.0083	
y^x	1.0083	
144	144	n for BAL
+/-	-144	
×	0.3027	
10000	10000	BAL
+/-	-10000	
+	-3026.9560	PV of BAL
55000	55000	PV
=	51973.0440	PV - PV of BAL
D	51973.04	
120	120	n for annuity
A	120.	
0	0	
C	686.83	PMT

Type A, Level III keystrokes for Example 8-5

TI-58/59 keystrokes	Display	Comments
CMs	0.	Clear memories
Pgm 19	0.	Call pgm 19
E'	0.	Initialize
C'	0.	Select PV case
120	120	n
A	120.	
1061.3	1061.3	PMT
C	1061.30	
100000	100000	PV
D	100000.00	
50000	50000	BAL
E	50000.00	
0	0	
B	0.8139	$i_c\%$
×	0.8139	
12	12	c
=	9.7673	$r\%$

Type A, Level III keystrokes for Example 8-7

TI-58/59 keystrokes	Display	Comments
CMs	0.	Clear memories
Pgm 19	0.	Call pgm 19
E'	0.	Initialize
C'	0.	Select PV case
686.83	686.83	PMT
C	686.83	
120	120.	n for payments
A	120.	
10	10	$r\%$
÷	10.	
12	12	
=	.8333333333	c
B	0.8333	$i_c\%$
0	0	
D	51973.23	PV of payments
+/-	-51973.23	
+	-51973.23	
55000	55000	PV

TI-58/59 keystrokes	Display	Comments
=	3026.77	PV of BAL
×	3026.77	
(	3026.77	
1	1	
+	1.00	
.1	0.1	
÷	0.10	
12	12	
)	1.01	
y^x	1.01	
130	130	n for BAL
=	8902.59	BAL at period 130
55000	55000	PV
D	55000.00	
108	108	n
A	108.	
0	0	
E	15229.31	BAL at period 108

Type A, Level III keystrokes for Example 8-11

TI-58/59 keystrokes	Display	Comments
CMs	0.	Clear memories
Pgm 19	0.	Call pgm 19
E'	0.	Initialize
D'	0.	Select PV_d case
120	120.	n
A	120.	
4550	4550	PMT
C	4550.00	
280000	280000	PV
D	280000.00	
150000	150000	BAL
E	150000.00	
0	0	
B	1.5105	$i_c\%$
Fix 9	1.510505891	

Type A, Level III keystrokes for Example 8-14

TI-58/59 keystrokes	Display	Comments
		Bond price and yield program
E'	0.	Initialize
42.5	42.5	Coupon payment
A	42.5	
1000	1000	Redemption value
B	1000.	
17	17	n
C	17.	
24	24	A
D	24.	
158	158	B
E	158.	
182	182	C
A'	182.	
.045	.045	Yield
C'	970.7785508	Price (BPP)

Type A, Level III keystrokes for Example 8-15

TI-58/59 keystrokes	Display	Comments
E'		Bond price and yield program
3.375	0.	Initialize
A	3.375	coupon payment
100	3.375	
B	100.	Redemption value
26	26.	
C	26.	n
44	44.	A
D	44.	B
139	139.	
E	139.	C
183	183.	
A'	183.	BPP
101.487654	101.487654	
B'	.0328791166	Yield per coupon period
×	.0328791166	
2	2	
=	.0657582333	Annual yield

Type R, Level II keystrokes for Example 8-1

HP-37E/38E keystrokes	Display	Comments
ALL	0.00	Clear
END	0.00	Set payment switch
120	120.	
n	120.00	n
9.5	9.5	
12 ÷	0.79	$r\%$
1061.3	1,061.3	
PMT	1,061.30	PMT
50000	50,000.	
FV	50,000.00	BAL
PV	−101,428.07	PV

Type R, Level II keystrokes for Example 8-3

HP-37E/38E keystrokes	Display	Comments
ALL	0.00	Clear
END	0.00	Set payment switch
120	120	n
n	120.00	
8	8.	$r\%$
12 ÷	0.67	$i_c\%$
85000	85,000	PV
CHS	-85,000	
PV	-85,000.00	
30000	30,000	FV
FV	30,000.00	
PMT	867.30	PMT

Type R, Level II keystrokes for Example 8-5

HP-37E/38E keystrokes	Display	Comments
ALL	0.00	Clear
END	0.00	Set payment switch
120	120.	n
n	120.00	
100000	100,000.	PV
CHS	-100,000.	
PV	-100,000.00	
1061.30	1,061.30	PMT
PMT	1,061.30	
50000	50,000.	FV
FV	50,000.00	
i	0.81	$i_c\%$
12	12.	
×	9.77	$r\%$
(f)9	9.767322538	

Type R, Level II keystrokes for Example 8-6

HP-37E/38E keystrokes	Display	Comments
ALL	0.00	Clear
END	0.00	Set payment switch
10	10.	$r\%$
12 ÷	0.83	$i_c\%$
144	144.	n
n	144.00	
10000	10,000.	
FV	10,000.00	FV
PV	−3,026.96	PV of BAL
55000	55,000	PV
+	51,973.04	PV − PV of BAL
PV	51,973.04	
120	120.	n
n	120.00	
0	0.	
FV	0.00	
PMT	−686.83	PMT

Type R, Level II keystrokes for Example 8-7

HP-38E keystrokes	Display	Comments
ALL	0.00	Clear
END	0.00	Set payment switch
686.83	686.83	PMT
PMT	686.83	
10	10.	$r\%$
12 ÷	0.83	$i_c\%$
120	120.	n
n	120.00	
PV	−51,973.23	
55000	55,000.	
+	3,026.77	
PV	3,026.77	
130	130.	
n	130.00	
0	0.	
PMT	0.00	
FV	−8,902.59	BAL at period 130
55000	55,000.	
CHS	−55,000.	
PV	−55,000.	
686.83	686.83	
PMT	686.83	
108	108.	
(f)9	108.0000000	
AMORT	34,406.94684	
RCL	34,406.94684	
PV	−15,229.30682	BAL at period 108

Note: The **(f)9** was used so that the answer will agree with the text because the **38E** computes the remaining balance by rounding all values to the number of places set in the display.

Type R, Level II keystrokes for Example 8-11

HP-37E/38E keystrokes	Display	Comments
ALL	0.00	Clear
BEGIN	0.00	Set payment switch
120	120.	n
n	120.00	
4550	4,550.	PMT
PMT	4,550.00	
280000	280,000.	PV
CHS	−280,000.	
PV	−280,000.00	
150000	150,000.	FV
FV	150,000.00	
i	1.51	$i_c\%$
(f)9	1.510505925	

Type R, Level II keystrokes for Example 8-14

HP-37E/38E keystrokes	Display	Comments
ALL	0.00	Clear
END	0.00	Set payment switch
16	16.	n
n	16.00	
4.5	4.5	$i_c\%$
i	4.50	
42.5	42.5	PMT
CHS	−42.5	
PMT	−42.50	
1000	1,000.	BAL
CHS	−1,000.	
FV	−1,000.00	
PV	971.91	$\mathrm{PMT}(n-1,i)+\mathrm{BAL}(1+i)^{-n+1}$
42.5	42.5	PMT
+	1,014.41	$\mathrm{PMT}+\mathrm{PMT}(n-1,i)+\mathrm{BAL}(1+i)^{-n+1}$
FV	1,014.41	
0	0.	
PMT	0.00	
158	158.	B
ENTER↑	158.00	
182	182.	C
÷	0.87	B/C
n	0.87	
PV	−976.38	
42.5	42.5	PMT
ENTER↑	42.5	
24	24.	A
×	1,020.00	
182	182.	C
÷	5.60	$\mathrm{PMT}(A/C)$
+	−970.78	
(f)9	−970.7785504	Bond price (BPP)

Type R, Level II keystrokes for Example 8-15

HP-37E/38E keystrokes	Display	Comments
ALL	0.00	
END	0.00	
44	44.	
ENTER↑	44.00	A
183	183	C
÷	0.24	A/C
STO 5	0.24	
3.375	3.375	PMT
×	0.81	
STO 6	0.81	
3.375	3.375	
CHS	-3.375	
PMT	-3.38	
100	100.	
CHS	-100.	
FV	-100.00	FV
STO 4	-100.00	
101.487654	101.487654	PV
PV	101.49	
STO 1	101.49	
139	139.	B
ENTER↑	139.00	C
183	183.	B/C
÷	0.76	
25	25.	$n - 1$
+	25.76	$n - 1 + B/C$
n	25.76	
STO 2	25.76	

HP-37E/38E keystrokes	Display	Comments
i	3.29	i_c
(f)9	3.28484226	Iteration 1
(f)2	3.29	
0	0.	
PV	0.00	
RCL 5	0.24	
n	0.24	
FV	0.80	
CHS	-0.80	
RCL 6	0.81	
+	0.01	
RCL 1	101.49	
+	101.50	
PV	101.50	
RCL 4	-100.00	
FV	-100.00	
RCL 2	25.76	
n	25.76	
i	3.29	i_1
0	0.	Iteration 2
PV	0.00	
RCL 5	0.24	
n	0.24	
FV	0.80	
CHS	-0.80	
RCL 6	0.81	
+	0.01	

HP-37E/38E keystrokes	Display	Comments
RCL 1	101.49	
+	101.50	
PV	101.50	
RCL 4	-100.00	
FV	-100.00	
RCL 2	25.76	
n	25.76	
i	3.29	i_2
(f)9	3.287911665	
(f)2	3.29	Iteration 3
0	0.	
PV	0.00	
RCL 5	0.24	
n	0.24	
FV	0.80	
CHS	-0.80	
RCL 6	0.81	
+	0.01	
RCL 1	101.49	
+	101.50	
PV	101.50	
RCL 4	-100.00	
FV	-100.00	
RCL 2	25.76	
n	25.76	
i	3.29	i_3
(f)9	3.287911665	

Type R, Level III keystrokes for Example 8-1

HP-97/67 keystrokes	Display	Comments
(f)A	0.00	Program SD-05A Initialize
120	120.	n
STO A	120.00	
9.5	9.5	$r\%$
ENTER↑	9.50	
12	12.	f
÷	0.79	$i_c\%$
STO B	0.79	
1061.30	1061.3	PMT
STO C	1061.30	
50000	50000.	BAL
STO E	50000.00	
D	101428.07	PV

Type R, Level III keystrokes for Example 8-3

HP-97/67 keystrokes	Display	Comments
(f)A	0.00	Program SD-05A Initialize
120	120.	n
STO A	120.00	
8	8.	$r\%$
ENTER↑	8.00	
12	12.	f
÷	0.67	$i_c\%$
STO B	0.67	
85000	85000.	PV
STO D	85000.00	
30000	30000.	BAL
STO E	30000.00	
C	867.30	PMT

Type R, Level III keystrokes for Example 8-5

HP-97/67 keystrokes	Display	Comments
		Program SD-05A
DSP 9	0.000000000	Set display to nine places
(f)A	0.000000000	Initialize
120	120.	n
STO A	120.0000000	
1061.3	1061.3	PMT
STO C	1061.300000	
100000	100000.	PV
STO D	100000.0000	
50000	50000.	BAL
STO E	50000.00000	
B	0.813943528	$i_f\%$
12	12.000000000	f
×	9.767322341	$r\%$

Type R, Level III keystrokes for Example 8-6

HP-97/67 keystrokes	Display	Comments
		Program SD-05A
(f)A	0.00	Initialize
144	144.	L
STO A	144.00	
10	10.	$r\%$
ENTER↑	10.00	
12	12.	f
÷	0.83	$i_f\%$
STO B	0.83	
10000	10000.	BAL
STO E	10000.00	
D	3026.96	PV of BAL
CHS	−3026.96	
55000	55000.	PV
+	51973.04	
STO D	51973.04	$PV - PV_{BAL}$
120	120.	n
STO A	120.00	
0	0.	
STO E	0.00	
C	686.83	PMT

Type R, Level III keystrokes for Example 8-7

HP-97/67 keystrokes	Display	Comments
(f)A	0.00	Program SD-05A
120	120.	n
STO A	120.00	
10	10.	r%
ENTER↑	10.00	
12	12.	f
÷	0.83	i_f%
STO B	0.83	
686.83	686.83	PMT
STO C	686.83	
D	51973.22	A(120..10/12)
CHS	−51973.22	
55000	55000.	PV
+	3026.78	
STO D	3026.78	
130	130.	L
STO A	130.00	
0	0.	
STO C	0.00	
E	8902.59	BAL
108	108.	n
STO A	108.00	
686.83	686.83	PMT
STO C	686.83	
55000	55000.	PV
STO D	55000.00	
E	15229.31	BAL

Type R, Level III keystrokes for Example 8-11

HP-97/67 keystrokes	Display	Comments
(f)A	0.00	Program SD-05A
(f)B	1.00	Initialize
120	120.	Select PV_d case
STO A	120.00	n
4550	4550.	PMT
STO C	4550.00	
280000	280000.	PV_d
STO D	280000.00	
150000	150000.	BAL
STO E	150000.	
B	1.51	i_c%
12	12.	
×	18.13	r%
DSP 4	18.1261	

Type R, Level III keystrokes for Example 8-14

HP-97/67 keystrokes	Display	Comments
16	16.	BD1-15A
ENTER↑	16.00	$n-1$
158	158.	
ENTER↑	158.00	B
182	182.	
÷	0.87	C
+	16.87	B/C
A	16.87	$(n-1) + B/C$
8.5	8.5	Coupon rate
B	8.50	
9	9.	
C	9.00	Yield
E	97.08	Price per $100 (BPP)
DSP 9	97.07785511	
10	10.	
×	970.7785511	Price for $1000 bond

Type R, Level III keystrokes for Example 8-15

HP-97/67 keystrokes	Display	Comments
25	25.	Program BD1-15A
ENTER↑	25.00	$n-1$
139	139.	
ENTER↑	139.00	B
183	183.	
÷	0.76	C
+	25.76	B/C
A	25.76	$n-1 + B/C$
6.75	6.75	Coupon rate
B	6.75	
101.487654	101.487654	
E	101.49	Price (BPP)
C	6.58	Yield
DSP 9	6.575801142	

EXERCISES

Note: $n = T \times f$.

8-1 Given PMT = \$500, BAL = \$5000, $T = 30$, and $r = 8\%$, find PV for:
(*a*) $I = i_c$, $c = f = 12$, $L = n$.
(*b*) $I = i_f$, $c = 2$, $f = 12$, $L = n$.
(*c*) $I = r/f$, $f = 12$, $L = n$.
answers: (*a*) **\$68,598.96**; (*b*) **\$69,468.32**; (*c*) **\$68,422.68**

8-2 Given PMT = \$800, BAL = \$6500, $T = 25$, and $r = 9\frac{1}{2}\%$, find PV for:
(*a*) $I = i_c$, $c = f = 12$, $L = n$.
(*b*) $I = i_f$, $c = 6$, $f = 12$, $L = n$.
(*c*) $I = r/f$, $f = 12$, $L = n$.

8-3 Given PMT = \$1250; BAL = \$25,000; $T = 6$, and $r = 11.5\%$, find PV_d for:
$c = f = 4$, $L = n$.
(*b*) $I = i_f$, $c = 12$, $f = 4$, $L = n$.
(*c*) $I = r/f$, $f = 4$, $L = n$.
answers: (*a*) **\$34,736.26**; (*b*) **\$34,594.80**; (*c*) **\$34,523.02**

8-4 Given PMT = \$975, BAL = \$6500, $T = 8$, and $r = 12.5\%$, find PV_d for:
(*a*) $I = i_c$, $c = f = 12$, $L = n$.
(*b*) $I = i_f$, $c = 2$, $f = 12$, $L = n$.
(*c*) $I = r/f$, $f = 12$, $L = $ n.

8-5 Given PV = \$50,000, BAL = \$15,000, $T = 15$, and $r = 8\frac{3}{4}\%$, find PMT for:
(*a*) $I = i_c$, $c = f = 12$, $L = n$.
(*b*) $I = i_f$, $c = 2$, $f = 12$, $L = $ n.
(*c*) $I = r/f$, $f = 12$, $L = n$.
answers:!A* (*a*) **\$459.18**; (*b*) **\$454.04**; (*c*) **\$460.24**

8-6 Given PV = \$100,000, BAL = \$25,000, $T = 8$, and $r = 11.65\%$, find PMT for:
(*a*) $I = i_c$, $c = f = 6$, $L = n$.
(*b*) $I = i_f$, $c = 12$, $f = 6$, $L = n$.
(*c*) $I = r/f$, $f = 6$, $L = n$.

8-7 Given $PV_d = \$19,250$, BAL = \$2000, $T = 5$, and $r = 12.55\%$, find PMT for:
(*a*) $I = i_c$, $c = f = 4$, $L = n$.
(*b*) $I = i_f$, $c = 6$, $f = 4$, $L = n$.
(*c*) $I = r/f$, $f = 4$, $L = n$.
answers: (*a*) **\$1199.38**; (*b*) **\$1201.22**; (*c*) **\$1204.97**

8-8 Given $PV_d = \$65,000$, BAL = \$5500, $T = 5$, and $r = 9.8\%$, find PMT for:
(*a*) $I = i_c$, $c = f = 12$, $L = n$.
(*b*) $I = i_c$, $c = 4$, $f = 12$, $L = n$.
(*c*) $I = r/f$, $f = 12$, $L = $ n.

8-9 Given PV = \$75,420, PMT = \$556.85, $T = 15$, and $r = 7.75\%$, find BAL for:
(*a*) $I = i_c$, $c = f = 12$, $L = n$.
(*b*) $I = i_f$, $c = 2$, $f = 12$, $L = n$.
(*c*) $I = r/f$, $f = 12$, $L = n$.
answers: (*a*) **\$51,807.11**; (*b*) **\$49,487.30**; (*c*) **\$52,289.52**

8-10 Given PV = \$75,500, PMT = \$1259.58, $T = 21$, and $r = 13.7\%$, find BAL for:
(*a*) $I = i_c$, $c = f = 4$, $L = n$.
(*b*) $I = i_f$, $c = 12$, $f = 4$, $L = n$.
(*c*) $I = r/f$, $f = 4$, $L = n$.

8-11 Given $PV_d = \$25,000$, PMT = \$465.47, $T = 9$, and $r = 10.5\%$, find BAL for:
(*a*) $I = i_c$, $c = f = 6$, $L = n$.
(*b*) $I = i_f$, $c = 2$, $f = 6$, $L = n$.

    (c) $I = r/f, f = 6, L = n$.

    answers: (a) **\$21,797.32**; (b) **\$21,184.13**; (c) **\$22,119.08**

8-12 Given $PV_d = \$1250$, PMT $= \$25.50$, $T = 3$, and $r = 14.75\%$, find BAL for:

    (a) $I = i_c$, $c = f = 12$, $L = n$.

    (b) $I = i_f$, $c = 52$, $f = 12$, $L = n$.

    (c) $I = r/f, f = 12, L = n$.

8-13 Given PV $= \$35,628.03$, PMT $= \$295.76$, BAL $= \$8500$, and $r = 8.75\%$, find n and final payment for:

    (a) $I = i_c$, $c = f = 12$, $L = n$.

    (b) $I = i_f$, $c = 2$, $f = 12$, $L = n$.

    (c) $I = r/f, f = 12, L = n$.

    answers: (a) **n = 257.62; 257 regular payments with \$206.21 at period 258 in addition to balloon**; (b) **n = 246.008, 246 regular payments with \$62.79 at period 247 in addition to balloon**; (c) **n = 260.22, 260 regular payments with \$112.99 at period 261 in addition to balloon.**

8-14 Given PV $= \$66,092.47$, PMT $= \$1874.58$, BAL $= \$18,350$, and $r = 6.875\%$, find n and final payment for:

    (a) $I = i_c$, $c = f = 4$, $L = n$.

    (b) $I = i_f$, $c = 12$, $f = 4$, $L = n$.

    (c) $I = r/f, f = 4, L = n$.

8-15 Given $PV_d = \$12,264.16$, PMT $= \$355.75$, BAL $= \$3500$, and $r = 11.375\%$, find n and final payment for:

    (a) $I = i_c$, $c = f = 6$, $L = n$.

    (b) $I = i_f$, $c = 360$, $f = 6$, $L = n$.

    (c) $I = r/f, f = 6, L = n$.

    answers: (a) **n = 43.84, 43 regular payments with \$310.39 at start of period 44 in addition to balloon at end of period 44**; (b) **n = 44.21, 44 regular payments with \$125.87 at start of period 45 in addition to balloon at end of period 45**; (c) **n = 44.21, 44 regular payments with \$127.71 at start of period 45 in addition to balloon at end of period 45**

8-16 Given $PV_d = \$14,521.54$, PMT $= \$169.13$, BAL $= \$10,000$, and $r = 13.845\%$, find n and final payment for:

    (a) $I = i_c$, $c = f = 12$, $L = n$.

    (b) $I = i_f$, $c = 2$, $f = 12$, $L = n$.

    (c) $I = r/f, f = 12, L = n$.

8-17 Given PV $= \$50,000$, PMT $= \$426.12$, BAL $= \$44,214.48$, and $T = 12.5$, find r for:

    (a) $I = i_c$, $c = f = 12$, $L = n$.

    (b) $I = i_f$, $c = 6$, $f = 12$, $L = n$.

    (c) $I = r/f, f = 12, L = n$.

    answers: (a) **r = 9.7501%, i_c = .8125%**; (b) **r = 9.7897%, i_c = 1.6316%, i_f = .8125%**; (c) **r = 9.7107%, j = .8092%, i_f = .8125%**

8-18 Given PV $= \$6000$, PMT $= \$101.25$, BAL $= \$3400$, and $T = 1.5$, find r for:

    (a) $I = i_c$, $c = f = 26$, $L = n$.

    (b) $I = i_f$, $c = 12$, $f = 26$, $L = n$.

    (c) $I = r/f, f = 26, L = n$.

8-19 Given $PV_d = \$17,500$, PMT $= \$333.29$, BAL $= \$8741.68$, and $T = 9$, find r for:

    (a) $I = i_c$, $c = f = 6$, $L = n$.

    (b) $I = i_f$, $c = 12$, $f = 6$, $L = n$.

    (c) $I = r/f, f = 6, L = n$.

    answers: (a) **r = 7.6807%, i_c = 1.2801%**; (b) **r = 7.6563%, i_c = .6380%, i_f = 1.2801%**; (c) **r = 7.6319%, j = 1.2720%, i_f = 1.2801%**

8-20 Given $PV_d = \$77,650$, PMT $= \$613.28$, BAL $= \$7000$, and $T = 29$, find r for:

    (a) $I = i_c$, $c = f = 12$, $L = n$.

(b) $I = i_f$, $c = 2$, $f = 12$, $L = n$.

(c) $I = r/f$, $f = 12$, $L = n$.

8-21 Given PMT = \$456.85, BAL = \$15,000, and $r = 10\%$, find PV for:

(a) $I = i_c$, $c = f = 12$, $L = 201$, $n = 200$.

(b) $I = i_f$, $c = 2$, $f = 12$, $L = 201$, $n = 200$.

(c) $I = r/f$, $f = 12$, $L = 201$, $n = 200$.

answers: (a) **\$47,224.90**; (b) **\$47,876.01**; (c) **\$47,092.06**

8-22 Given PMT = \$1562.45, BAL = \$50,000, and $r = 9.4\%$, find PV for:

(a) $I = i_c$, $c = f = 4$, $L = 74$, $n = 65$.

(b) $I = i_f$, $c = 12$, $f = 4$, $L = 74$, $n = 65$.

(c) $I = r/f$, $f = 4$, $L = 74$, $n = 65$.

8-23 Given PMT = \$456.75, BAL = \$12,500, and $r = 8.75\%$, find PV for:

(a) $I = i_c$, $c = f = 12$, $L = 84$, $n = 120$.

(b) $I = i_f$, $c = 4$, $f = 12$, $L = 84$, $n = 120$.

(c) $I = r/f$, $f = 12$, $L = 84$, $n = 120$.

answers: (a) **\$43,234.73**; (b) **\$43,363.36**; (c) **\$43,169.68**

8-24 Given PMT = \$975.27, BAL = \$5000, and $r = 7.78\%$, find PV for:

(a) $I = i_c$, $c = f = 6$, $L = 24$, $n = 60$.

(b) $I = i_f$, $c = 12$, $f = 6$, $L = 24$, $n = 60$.

(c) $I = r/f$, $f = 6$, $L = 24$, $n = 60$.

8-25 Given PMT = \$2500, BAL = \$25,000, and $r = 12.7\%$, find PV_d for:

(a) $I = i_c$, $c = f = 12$, $L = 181$, $n = 180$.

(b) $I = i_f$, $c = 2$, $f = 12$, $L = 181$, $n = 180$.

(c) $I = r/f$, $f = 12$, $L = 181$, $n = 180$.

answers: (a) **\$206,554.69**; (b) **\$210,174.39**; (c) **\$205,812.76**

8-26 Given PMT = \$1475, BAL = \$4000, and $r = 15.7\%$, find PV_d for:

(a) $I = i_c$, $c = f = 4$, $L = 25$, $n = 24$.

(b) $I = i_f$, $c = 12$, $f = 4$, $L = 25$, $n = 24$.

(c) $I = r/f$, $f = 4$, $L = 25$, $n = 24$.

8-27 Given PMT = \$645.63, BAL = \$15,000, and $r = 14.32\%$, find PV_d for:

(a) $I = i_c$, $c = f = 6$, $L = 42$, $n = 30$.

(b) $I = i_f$, $c = 12$, $f = 6$, $L = 42$, $n = 30$.

(c) $I = r/f$, $f = 6$, $L = 42$, $n = 30$.

answers: (a) **\$19,617.32**; (b) **\$19,560.00**; (c) **\$19,502.04**

8-28 Given PMT = \$1943.25, BAL = \$3500, and $r = 10.585\%$, find PV_d for:

(a) $I = i_c$, $c = f = 3$, $L = 10$, $n = 21$.

(b) $I = i_f$, $c = 6$, $f = 3$, $L = 10$, $n = 21$.

(c) $I = r/f$, $f = 3$, $L = 10$, $n = 21$.

8-29 Given PV = \$75,000, BAL = \$20,000, and $r = 9.95\%$, find PMT for:

(a) $I = i_c$, $c = f = 26$, $L = 312$, $n = 311$.

(b) $I = i_f$, $c = 4$, $f = 26$, $L = 312$, $n = 311$.

(c) $I = r/f$, $f = 26$, $L = 312$, $n = 311$.

answers: (a) **\$379.46**; (b) **\$377.16**; (c) **\$379.88**

8-30 Given PV = \$184,675, BAL = \$50,000, and $r = 7.43\%$, find PMT for:

(a) $I = i_c$, $c = f = 6$, $L = 120$, $n = 119$.

(b) $I = i_f$, $c = 12$, $f = 6$, $L = 120$, $n = 119$.

(c) $I = r/f$, $f = 6$, $L = 120$, $n = 119$.

8-31 Given PV = \$95,000, BAL = \$50,000, and $r = 11.57\%$, find PMT for:

(a) $I = i_c$, $c = f = 12$, $L = 180$, $n = 144$.

(b) $I = i_f$, $c = 3$, $f = 12$, $L = 180$, $n = 144$.

(c) $I = r/f$, $f = 12$, $L = 180$, $n = 144$.

answers: (a) **\$1108.69**; (b) **\$1097.46**; (c) **\$1112.53**

8-32 Given PV = \$128,700, BAL = \$80,000, and r = 4.78%, find PMT for:
(*a*) $I = i_c$, $c = f = 4$, $L = 18$, $n = 28$.
(*b*) $I = i_f$, $c = 6$, $f = 4$, $L = 18$, $n = 28$.
(*c*) $I = r/f$, $f = 4$, $L = 18$, $n = 28$.

8-33 Given PV_d = \$65,700, BAL = \$39,755, and r = 7.78%, find PMT for:
(*a*) $I = i_c$, $c = f = 12$, $L = 240$, $n = 239$.
(*b*) $I = i_f$, $c = 2$, $f = 12$, $L = 240$, $n = 239$.
(*c*) $I = r/f$, $f = 12$, $L = 240$, $n = 239$.
answers: (*a*) **\$469.00**; (*b*) **\$463.04**; (*c*) **\$470.23**

8-34 Given PV_d = \$25,000, BAL = \$7000, and r = 11.75%, find PMT for:
(*a*) $I = i_c$, $c = f = 4$, $L = 21$, $n = 20$.
(*b*) $I = i_f$, $c = 12$, $f = 4$, $L = 21$, $n = 20$.
(*c*) $I = r/f$, $f = 4$, $L = 21$, $n = 20$.

8-35 Given PV_d = \$38,750, BAL = \$25,000, and r = 7.76%, find PMT for:
(*a*) $I = i_c$, $c = f = 6$, $L = 48$, $n = 42$.
(*b*) $I = i_f$, $c = 3$, $f = 6$, $L = 48$, $n = 42$.
(*c*) $I = r/f$, $f = 6$, $L = 48$, $n = 42$.
answers: (*a*) **\$773.23**; (*b*) **\$770.44**; (*c*) **\$776.07**

8-36 Given PV_d = \$24,500, BAL = \$6000, and r = 14.6%, find PMT for:
(*a*) $I = i_c$, $c = f = 12$, $L = 108$, $n = 120$.
(*b*) $I = i_f$, $c = 4$, $f = 12$, $L = 108$, $n = 120$.
(*c*) $I = r/f$, $f = 12$, $L = 108$, $n = 120$.

8-37 Given PV = \$48,000, PMT = \$364.54, and r = 8.45%, find BAL for:
(*a*) $I = i_c$, $c = f = 12$, $L = 360$, $n = 359$.
(*b*) $I = i_f$, $c = 4$, $f = 12$, $L = 360$, $n = 359$.
(*c*) $I = r/f$, $f = 12$, $L = 360$, $n = 359$.
answers: (*a*) **\$5002.84**; (*b*) **\$1725.71**; (*c*) **\$6697.09**

8-38 Given PV = \$25,000, PMT = \$293.28, and r = 7.4%, find BAL for:
(*a*) $I = i_c$, $c = f = 6$, $L = 180$, $n = 179$.
(*b*) $I = i_f$, $c = 12$, $f = 6$, $L = 180$, $n = 179$.
(*c*) $I = r/f$, $f = 6$, $L = 180$, $n = 179$.

8-39 Given PV = \$30,000, PMT = \$1343.33, and r = 12.78%, find BAL for:
(*a*) $I = i_c$, $c = f = 4$, $L = 10$, $n = 28$.
(*b*) $I = i_f$, $c = 12$, $f = 4$, $L = 10$, $n = 28$.
(*c*) $I = r/f$, $f = 4$, $L = 10$, $n = 28$.
answers: (*a*) **\$7373.97**; (*b*) **\$7537.60**; (*c*) **\$7621.23**

8-40 Given PV = \$100,000, PMT = \$964.71, and r = 11.13%, find BAL for:
(*a*) $I = i_c$, $c = f = 12$, $L = 60$, $n = 180$.
(*b*) $I = i_f$, $c = 6$, $f = 12$, $L = 60$, $n = 180$.
(*c*) $I = r/f$, $f = 12$, $L = 60$, $n = 180$.

8-41 Given PV = \$51,885.05, PMT = \$1500, BAL = \$10,000, and r = 9.35%, find n for:
(*a*) $I = i_c$, $c = f = 4$, $L = 40$.
(*b*) $I = i_f$, $c = 12$, $f = 4$, $L = 40$.
(*c*) $I = r/f$, $f = 4$, $L = 40$.
answers: (*a*) n = **59.43**; (*b*) n = **60.05**; (*c*) n = **60.38**

8-42 Given PV = \$57,100, PMT = \$419.15, BAL = \$25,000, and r = 10.4%, find n for:
(*a*) $I = i_c$, $c = f = 12$, $L = 96$.
(*b*) $I = i_f$, $c = 3$, $f = 12$, $L = 96$.
(*c*) $I = r/f$, $f = 12$, $L = 96$.

8-43 Given PV = \$53,320, PMT = \$925, BAL = \$15,000, and r = 9%, find L for:
(*a*) $I = i_c$, $c = f = 12$, $n = 60$.
(*b*) $I = i_f$, $c = 4$, $f = 12$, $n = 60$.

(c) $I = r/f, f = 12, n = 60$.

answers: (a) **L = 71.99**; (b) **L = 73.60**; (c) **L = 71.18**

8-44 Given PV = \$55,900, PMT = \$2400, BAL = \$25,000, and $r = 8.75\%$, find L for:
(a) $I = i_c, c = f = 4, n = 24$.
(b) $I = i_f, c = 6, f = 4, n = 24$.
(c) $I = r/f, f = 4, n = 24$.

8-45 Given $PV_d = \$40,669.98$, PMT = \$925.14, BAL = \$9500, and $r = 12.65\%$, find n for:
(a) $I = i_c, c = f = 6, L = 60$.
(b) $I = i_f, c = 2, f = 6, L = 60$.
(c) $I = r/f, f = 6, L = 60$.

answers: (a) **n = 90.00**; (b) **n = 86.29**; (c) **n = 92.14**

8-46 Given $PV_d = \$151,545.27$, PMT = \$1547, BAL = \$25,000, and $r = 11.13\%$, find n for:
(a) $I = i_c, c = f = 12, L = 300$.
(b) $I = i_f, c = 2, f = 12, L = 300$.
(c) $I = r/f, f = 12, L = 300$.

8-47 Given $PV_d = \$51,376.87$, PMT = \$455.65, BAL = \$6500, and $r = 7.35\%$, find L for:
(a) $I = i_c, c = f = 12, n = 168$.
(b) $I = i_f, c = 2, f = 12, n = 168$.
(c) $I = r/f, f = 12, n = 168$.

answers: (a) **L = 108**; (b) **L = 125.46**; (c) **L = 104.68**

8-48 Given $PV_d = \$101,436.28$, PMT = \$3750, BAL = \$25,000, and $r = 15.74\%$, find L for:
(a) $I = i_c, c = f = 4, n = 40$.
(b) $I = i_f, c = 12, f = 4, n = 40$.
(c) $I = r/f, f = 4, n = 40$.

8-49 Given PV = \$34,302.97, PMT = \$305.60, and BAL = \$10,000, find $r\%$ for:
(a) $I = i_c, c = f = 12, L = n, n = 360$.
(b) $I = i_f, c = 2, f = 12, L = n, n = 360$.
(c) $I = r/f, f = 12, L = n, n = 360$.

answers: (a) **r = 10.341%, i_c = .8617%**; (b) **r = 10.5664%, i_c = 5.2832%**; (c) **r = 10.2967%, j = .8581%**

8-50 Given PV = \$93,380.39, PMT = \$1549.16, and BAL = \$50,000, find $r\%$ for:
(a) $I = i_c, c = f = 6, L = n, n = 120$.
(b) $I = i_f, c = 12, f = 6, L = n, n = 120$.
(c) $I = r/f, f = 6, L = n, n = 120$.

8-51 Given $PV_d = \$59,093.63$, PMT = \$675.43, and BAL = \$29,000, find $r\%$ for:
(a) $I = i_c, c = f = 12, L = n, n = 98$.
(b) $I = i_f, c = 6, f = 12, L = n, n = 98$.
(c) $I = r/f, f = 12, L = n, n = 98$.

answers: (a) **r = 9.7176%, i_c = .8098%**; (b) **r = 9.7570%, i_c = 1.6262%**; (c) **r = 9.6785%, j = .8065%**

8-52 Given $PV_d = \$49,424.93$, PMT = \$1650, and BAL = \$20,000, find $r\%$ for:
(a) $I = i_c, c = f = 4, L = n, n = 23$.
(b) $I = i_f, c = 2, f = 4, L = n, n = 23$.
(c) $I = r/f, f = 2, L = n, n = 23$.

8-53 Given PV = \$156,515.70, PMT = \$1250, and BAL = \$50,000, find $r\%$ for:
(a) $I = i_c, c = f = 12, L = n + 1, n = 156$.
(b) $I = i_f, c = 2, f = 12, L = n + 1, n = 156$.
(c) $I = r/f, f = 12, L = n + 1, n = 156$.

answers: (a) **r = 6.1428%, i_c = .5119%**; (b) **r = 6.2219%, i_c = 3.1110%**; (c) **r = 6.1271%, j = .5106%**

8-54 Given PV = \$20,000, PMT = \$950, and BAL = \$12,000, find $r\%$ for:
(a) $I = i_c, c = f = 4, L = 57, n = 56$.

(b) $I = i_f$, $c = 6$, $f = 4$, $L = 57$, $n = 56$.

(c) $I = r/f$, $f = 4$, $L = 57$, $n = 56$.

8-55 Given $PV_d = \$119,500$, $PMT = \$3500$, and $BAL = \$50,000$, find $r\%$ for:

(a) $I = i_c$, $c = f = 6$, $L = n + 1$, $n = 65$.

(b) $I = i_f$, $c = 12$, $f = 6$, $L = n + 1$, $n = 65$.

(c) $I = r/f$, $f = 6$, $L = n + 1$, $n = 65$.

answers: (a) **$r = 15.9405\%$, $i_c = 2.6568\%$**; (b) **$r = 15.8360\%$, $i_c = 1.3197\%$**; (c) **$r = 15.7325\%$, $j = 2.6221\%$**

8-56 Given $PV_d = \$65,435.80$, $PMT = \$744.85$, and $BAL = \$9500$, find $r\%$ for:

(a) $I = i_c$, $c = f = 12$, $L = n + 1$, $n = 250$.

(b) $I = i_f$, $c = 2$, $f = 12$, $L = n + 1$, $n = 250$.

(c) $I = r/f$, $f = 12$, $L = n + 1$, $n = 250$.

8-57 Given $PV = \$49,849.46$, $PMT = \$395.47$, and $BAL = \$10,000$, find $r\%$ for:

(a) $I = i_c$, $c = f = 12$, $L = 108$, $n = 248$.

(b) $I = i_f$, $c = 4$, $f = 12$, $L = 108$, $n = 248$.

(c) $I = r/f$, $f = 12$, $L = 108$, $n = 248$.

answers: (a) **$r = 8.75\%$, $i_c = .7292\%$**; (b) **$r = 8.8140\%$, $i_c = 2.2035\%$**; (c) **$r = 8.7183\%$, $j = .7265\%$**

8-58 Given $PV = \$23,575.32$, $PMT = \$498.75$, and $BAL = \$7500$, find $r\%$ for:

(a) $I = i_c$, $c = f = 6$, $L = 112$, $n = 100$.

(b) $I = i_f$, $c = 12$, $f = 6$, $L = 112$, $n = 100$.

(c) $I = r/f$, $f = 6$, $L = 112$, $n = 100$.

8-59 Given $PV_d = \$66,451.03$, $PMT = \$487.65$, and $BAL = \$15,000$, find $r\%$ for:

(a) $I = i_c$, $c = f = 12$, $L = 60$, $n = 360$.

(b) $I = i_f$, $c = 6$, $f = 12$, $L = 60$, $n = 360$.

(c) $I = r/f$, $f = 12$, $L = 60$, $n = 360$.

answers: (a) **$r = 9.75\%$, $i_c = .8125\%$**; (b) **$r = 9.7896\%$, $i_c = 1.6316\%$**; (c) **$r = 9.7106\%$, $j = .8092\%$**

8-60 Given $PV_d = \$56,874.10$, $PMT = \$2700$, and $BAL = \$50,000$, find $r\%$ for:

(a) $I = i_c$, $c = f = 4$, $L = 48$, $n = 40$.

(b) $I = i_f$, $c = 12$, $f = 4$, $L = 48$, $n = 40$.

(c) $I = r/f$, $f = 4$, $L = 48$, $n = 40$.

8-61 Given $PMT = \$650.75$, $n = 240$, $BAL_1 = \$5000$, $L_1 = 60$, $BAL_2 = \$15,000$, $L_2 = 120$, $BAL_3 = \$20,000$ $L_3 = 180$, and $r = 8.35\%$, find PV for:

(a) $I = i_c$, $c = f = 12$.

(b) $I = i_f$, $c = 4$, $f = 12$.

(c) $I = r/f$, $f = 12$.

answers: (a) **$91,379.62$**; (b) **$91,796.25$**; (c) **$91,169.46$**

8-62 Given $PMT = \$2000$, $n = 40$, $BAL_1 = \$6000$, $L_1 = 8$, $BAL_2 = \$5000$, $L_2 = 16$, $BAL_3 = \$10,000$, $L_3 = 28$, and $r = 9.46\%$, find PV for:

(a) $I = i_c$, $c = f = 4$.

(b) $I = i_f$, $c = 6$, $f = 4$.

(c) $I = r/f$, $f = 4$.

8-63 Given $PMT = \$5000$, $n = 20$, $BAL_1 = \$15,000$ $L_1 = 4$, $BAL_2 = \$20,000$, $L_2 = 10$, and $r = 11.56\%$, find PV_d for:

(a) $I = i_c$, $c = f = 2$.

(b) $I = i_f$, $c = 12$, $f = 2$.

(c) $I = r/f$, $f = 2$.

answers: (a) **$85,145.80$**; (b) **$84,305.13$**; (c) **$84,132.06$**

8-64 Given $PMT = \$2800$, $n = 32$, $BAL_1 = \$5000$, $L_1 = 8$, $BAL_2 = \$10,000$, $L_2 = 16$, $BAL_3 = \$20,000$, $L_3 = 24$, and $r = 10.28\%$, find PV_d for:

(a) $I = i_c$, $c = f = 4$.

(b) $I = i_f$, $c = 52$, $f = 4$.

(c) $I = r/f$, $f = 4$.

8-65 Given PV = $140,900, $n = 185$, $BAL_1 = \$16,000$, $L_1 = 24$, $BAL_2 = \$30,000$, $L_2 = 60$, $BAL_3 = \$50,000$, $L_3 = 96$, and $r = 8.5\%$, find PMT for:

(a) $I = i_c$, $c = f = 12$.

(b) $I = i_f$, $c = 4$, $f = 12$.

(c) $I = r/f$, $f = 12$.

answers: (a) **$800.20**; (b) **$795.42**; (c) **$802.62**

8-66 Given PV = $26,800, $n = 48$, $BAL_1 = \$12,000$, $L_1 = 12$, $BAL_2 = \$14,000$, $L_2 = 24$, $BAL_3 = \$6000$, $L_3 = 36$, and $r = 9.49\%$, find PMT for:

(a) $I = i_c$, $c = f = 4$.

(b) $I = i_f$, $c = 52$, $f = 4$.

(c) $I = r/f$, $f = 4$.

8-67 Given $PV_d = \$78,500$, $n = 26$, $BAL_1 = \$25,000$, $L_1 = 4$, $BAL_2 = \$20,000$, $L_2 = 10$, $BAL_3 = \$15,000$, $L_3 = 15$, $BAL_4 = \$10,000$, $L_4 = 24$, and $r = 11.34\%$, find PMT for:

(a) $I = i_c$, $c = f = 2$.

(b) $I = i_f$, $c = 6$, $f = 2$.

(c) $I = r/f$, $f = 2$.

answers: (a) **$2656.52**; (b) **$2708.10**; (c) **$2734.97**

8-68 Given $PV_d = \$45,775$, $n = 240$, $BAL_1 = \$10,000$, $L_1 = 24$, $BAL_2 = \$8000$, $L_2 = 36$, $BAL_3 = \$5000$, $L_3 = 60$, and $r = 12.15\%$, find PMT for:

(a) $I = i_c$, $c = f = 12$.

(b) $I = i_f$, $c = 2$, $f = 12$.

(c) $I = r/f$, $f = 12$.

8-69 Given PV = $94,500, $n = 276$, PMT = $507.65, $BAL_1 = \$5000$, $L_1 = 24$, $BAL_2 = \$10,000$, $L_2 = 36$, and $r = 7.75\%$, find BAL_x when $L_x = 60$ for:

(a) $I = i_c$, $c = f = 12$.

(b) $I = i_f$, $c = 2$, $f = 12$.

(c) $I = r/f$, $f = 12$.

answers: (a) **$24,983.90**; (b) **$23,804.19**; (c) **$25,225.67**

8-70 Given PV = $239,400, $n = 44$, PMT = $6500, $BAL_1 = \$25,000$, $L_1 = 12$, $BAL_2 = \$20,000$, $L_2 = 36$, and $r = 8.44\%$, find BAL_x when $L_x = 8$ for:

(a) $I = i_c$, $c = f = 4$.

(b) $I = i_f$, $c = 52$, $f = 4$.

(c) $I = r/f$, $f = 4$.

8-71 Given $PV_d = \$94,800$, $n = 180$, PMT = $965.47, $BAL_1 = \$2500$, $L_1 = 36$, $BAL_2 = \$3500$, $L_2 = 60$, and $r = 11.78\%$, find BAL_x when $L_x = 12$ for:

(a) $I = i_c$, $c = f = 12$

(b) $I = i_f$, $c = 2$, $f = 12$

(c) $I = r/f$, $f = 12$

answers: (a) **$9998.35**; (b) **$8540.80**; (c) **$10,298.16**

8-72 Given $PV_d = \$244,281.32$, $n = 80$, PMT = $5000, $BAL_1 = \$25,000$, $L_1 = 12$, $BAL_2 = \$50,000$, $L_2 = 36$, and $r = 12.75\%$, find BAL_x when $L_x = 4$ for:

(a) $I = i_c$, $c = f = 4$.

(b) $I = i_f$, $c = 12$, $f = 4$.

(c) $I = r/f$, $f = 4$.

Mortgage and Loan Applications

For this group of mortgage and loan application problems, assume that all regular payments are made at the *end* of the payment period.

8-73 What is the monthly payment for a $65,000 mortgage with a balloon of $11,100.00 due with the last payment at the end of the twenty-fifth year? Interest is 8.3% annual, compounded monthly.

    answer: **$503.55**

8-74 What is the monthly payment for a $46,800 mortgage with a balloon of $8435.67 due with the last payment at the end of the seventeenth year? Interest is 7.25% annual compounded monthly.

8-75 A $54,000 mortgage has 300 regular monthly payments of $462.27. Interest is 9.65% annual compounded monthly. What is the amount of the balloon payment if it is made at the end of the:

    (*a*) 300th month?
    (*b*) 301st month?
    (*c*) 312th month?

    answers: (*a*) **$18,966.05**; (*b*) **$19,118.56**; (*c*) **$20,879.43**

8-76 An $80,000 mortgage has 200 regular monthly payments of $617.44. Interest is 6.5% compounded monthly. What is the amount of the balloon payment if it is made at the end of the:

    (*a*) 200th month?
    (*b*) 201st month?
    (*c*) 212th month?
    (*d*) 224th month?

8-77 A $68,500 loan has monthly payments of $569.68 with a balloon of $17,836.10 at the end of the twenty-sixth year. What is the annual interest rate, assuming monthly compounding?

    answer: $r = 9.3001\%, i_c = .7750\%$

8-78 A $185,000 loan has quarterly payments of $4,534.24 with a balloon of $74,771.14 at the end of the fifteenth year. What is the annual interest rate, assuming quarterly compounding?

8-79 A $78,000 loan has monthly payments of $614.99 with a balloon of $30,152.16 due with the last payment. Interest is 8.25% compounded monthly. What is the number of regular payments?

    answer: **240.00**

8-80 A $50,000 loan has monthly payments of $385.47 with a balloon of $19,170.53 due with the last payment. Interest is 7.65% compounded monthly. What is the number of regular payments?

8-81 Henrietta sold her coal mine for $1,750,000. The loan agreement calls for monthly payments and for balloon payments of $250,000 at the end of years 1, 3, and 5. The loan is to be paid off in 8 years. Interest is 9.2% annual compounded monthly. What is the amount of the monthly payment?

    answer: **$17,319.81**

8-82 Tex sold his oil well for $1,500,000. The loan agreement calls for monthly payments and for balloon payments of $200,000 at the end of years 1 and 2; $300,000 at the end of years 3 and 4. The loan is to be paid off in 6 years. Interest is 8.75% annual compounded monthly. What is the amount of the monthly payment?

8-83 (*a*) What is the monthly payment on a $155,000 mortgage at 9.3% annual for a term of 25 years assuming monthly compounding?

    (*b*) What balloon payment is required in addition to the regular payment to pay off the loan at the end of the fifteenth year?

    (*c*) Answer part (*a*) assuming semiannual compounding.

    (*d*) Answer part (*b*) assuming semiannual compounding.

    answers: (*a*) **$1332.74**; (*b*) **$103,873.03**; (*c*) **$1314.02**; (*d*) **$103,180.41**

8-84 (*a*) What is the monthly payment on a $95,000 mortgage at 8.75% annual for a term of 30 years, assuming monthly compounding?

    (*b*) What balloon payment is required in addition to the regular payment to pay off the loan at the end of the twentieth year?

    (*c*) Answer part (*a*) assuming quarterly compounding.

    (*d*) Answer part (*b*) assuming quarterly compounding.

8-85 A $78,000 mortgage at 8.5% for 25 years has monthly payments of $599.75. Assuming monthly compounding, what is the amount of the balloon payment if it is:

(*a*) Made at the end of the last regular payment period?
(*b*) Made one period after the last regular payment period?
(*c*) Made at the end of the tenth year?
(*d*) Made at the end of year 28?
(*e*) Repeat (*a*) through (*d*) assuming semiannual compounding.
   answers: (*a*) **$29,235.24**; (*b*) **$29,442.33**; (*c*) **$8206.03**; (*d*) **$37,693.06**. (*e*) **$20,787.93;**
$20,932.64; $5963.89; $26,685.02

8-86 A $210,000 mortgage at 9.45% for 15 years has quarterly payments of $5281.78. Assuming quarterly compounding, what is the amount of the balloon payment if it is:
(*a*) Made at the end of the last payment period?
(*b*) Made one period after the last regular payment period?
(*c*) Made at the end of the twentieth year?
(*d*) Made at the end of the fifth year?
(*e*) Repeat parts (*a*) through (*d*) assuming monthly compounding.

8-87 For a $75,000 mortgage at 8.9% compounding monthly with monthly payments of $598.08, what is the loan balance remaining after:
(*a*) 12 payments?
(*b*) 24 payments?
(*c*) 36 payments?
(*d*) 200 payments?
(*e*) 360 payments?
   answers: (*a*) **$74,477.05**; (*b*) **$73,905.61**; (*c*) **$73,281.19**; (*d*) **$55,916.76**; (*e*) **$-2.96**
Assuming semiannual compounding, what is the loan balance remaining after:
(*f*) 12 payments?
(*g*) 36 payments?
(*h*) 48 payments?
(*i*) 250 payments?
   answers: (*f*) **$74,351.99**; (*g*) **$72,873.74**; (*h*) **$72,032.28**; (*i*) **$38,421.99**
[*Hint:* The remaining balance is the same as the balloon necessary to pay off the mortgage at the end of the period ($L = n$).]

8-88 For a $94,000 mortgage at 9.8% compounded quarterly with quarterly payments of $2527.66, what is the loan balance remaining after:
(*a*) 4 payments?
(*b*) 8 payments?
(*c*) 13 payments?
(*d*) 72 payments?
(*e*) 100 payments?
Assuming monthly compounding, what is the loan balance remaining after:
(*f*) 4 payments?
(*g*) 8 payments?
(*h*) 20 payments?
(*i*) 90 payments?

8-89 A 25-year mortgage has monthly payments of $2775.95 and a balloon payment of $133,724.57 to be paid with the last regular payment. Interest is compounded monthly at 9% annual, and 24 payments have been made on the loan.
(*a*) What was the amount of the original loan?
(*b*) What is the current loan balance?
(*c*) If the mortgage is sold to yield 9.75%, what is the price?
(*d*) If the mortgage is sold to yield 8.65%, what is the price?
(*e*) If the mortgage is sold for $335,000, what is the annual yield?
(*f*) If the mortgage is sold for $347,000, what is the annual yield?
(*g*) Assuming semiannual compounding, answer questions (*a*) through (*f*).
   answers: (*a*) **$345,000**; (*b*) **$340,064.78**; (*c*) **$319,373.67**; (*d*) **$350,477.22**; (*e*) **9.1766%;**

(*f*) **8.7650%**. (*g*) **$350,073.42; $344.888.17; $324,479.84; $355,156.38; i_f = .7647%, i_c = 4.6769%, r = 9.3538%; i_f = .7304%, i_c = 4.4633%, r = 8.9266%**

8-90 A 15-year mortgage has quarterly payments of $3781.92 and a balloon payment of $79,195.06 to be paid with the last regular payment. Interest is compounded quarterly at 8.5% annual and 27 payments have been made.

    (*a*) What was the amount of the original loan?
    (*b*) What is the current loan balance?
    (*c*) If the mortgage is sold to yield 9.7%, what is the price?
    (*d*) What is the price if the mortgage is sold to yield 7.75%?
    (*e*) If the mortgage is sold for $125,000, what is the annual yield?
    (*f*) What is the annual yield, if the mortgage is sold for $132,500?
    (*g*) Assuming monthly compounding, answer questions (*a*) through (*f*).

8-91 A 10-year loan has monthly payments of $532.09 and a $20,000 balloon payment to be paid at the end of the tenth year. Interest is compounded monthly at 11.4% annual, and 21 payments have been made.

    (*a*) What was the amount of the original loan?
    (*b*) What is the current loan balance?
    (*c*) If the loan is sold to yield 12%, what is the price?
    (*d*) If the loan is sold to yield 10.7%, what is the price?
    (*e*) If the loan is sold for $50,000, what is the yield?
    (*f*) If the loan is sold for $51,800, what is the yield?
    (*g*) Assume semiannual compounding and answer questions (*a*) through (*f*).
    (*h*) Assume continuous compounding and answer questions (*a*) through (*f*).

    answers: (*a*) **$44,430.82**; (*b*) **$41,887.65**; (*c*) **$40,808.48**; (*d*) **$43,198.56**; (*e*) **7.4933%**; (*f*) **6.7439%**. (*g*) **$45,008.38; $42,371.04; $41,324.08; $43,643.88; i_f = .6244%, i_c = 3.8056%, r = 7.6112%; i_f = .5620%, i_c = 3.4197%, r = 6.8394%**. (*h*) **$44,312.29; $41,788.29; $40,702.40; $43,107.12; i_f = .6244%, j = .6225%, r = 7.4700%; i_f = .5620%, j = .5604%, r = 6.7250%**

8-92 A 5-year loan has quarterly payments of $1250 and a $9020.27 balloon payment to be paid at the end of the second year. Interest is compounded quarterly at 9.4% annual and two payments have been made.

    (*a*) What was the amount of the original loan?
    (*b*) What is the current loan balance?
    (*c*) If the loan is sold to yield 9.8%, what is the price?
    (*d*) What is the price if the loan is sold to yield 9%?
    (*e*) If the loan is sold for $23,950, what is the yield?
    (*f*) What is the yield if the loan is sold for $24,500?
    (*g*) Assume monthly compounding and answer questions (*a*) through (*f*).
    (*h*) Assume continuous compounding and answer questions, (*a*) through (*f*).

Other Applications

8-93 A machine is being leased for 5 years with quarterly payments being made. The machine has an expected market value of $15,000 at the end of the 5 years and a current market value of $120,000. The lessor wants to earn 14.25% on the lease. What is the amount of the quarterly payment assuming:

    (*a*) Beginning-of-period payments and quarterly compounding?
    (*b*) End-of-period payments and quarterly compounding?
    (*c*) Beginning-of-period payments and monthly compounding?
    (*d*) End-of-period payments and monthly compounding?
    answers: (*a*) **$7690.17**; (*b*) **$7964.13**; (*c*) **$7720.68**; (*d*) **$7999.01**

8-94 A machine is being leased for 7 years with monthly payments being made. The machine has a current market value of $95,000, and a residual value of $25,000 at the end of the 7 years. The lessor wants to earn 13.65% on the lease. What is the amount of the monthly payment assuming:

(*a*) Beginning-of-period payments and monthly compounding?
(*b*) End-of-period payments and monthly compounding?
(*c*) Beginning-of-period payments and quarterly compounding?
(*d*) End-of-period payments and quarterly compounding?

8-95 A lease had monthly payments of $2397.63 with a residual value of $96,133.95 at the end of 10 years. Interest is compounded monthly at 13.8% annual and 84 payments remain.

(*a*) What was the original present value of the lease assuming beginning-of-period payments and monthly compounding?

(*b*) What was the original present value of the lease assuming end-of-period payments and monthly compounding?

(*c*) Assuming monthly compounding and end-of-period payments, what is the current present value?

(*d*) Assuming monthly compounding and beginning of period payments, what is the current present value?

(*e*) Assuming quarterly compounding, what is the answer to (*a*) through (*d*)?

answers: (*a*) **$181,789.50**; (*b*) **$179,999.84**; (*c*) **$165,490.38**; (*d*) **$166,970.42**. (*e*) **$183,104.85; $181,324.61; $166,483.46; $167,953.56**

8-96 A 12-year lease originally has quarterly payments of $5501.29 and a residual value of $37,659.66. Interest is compounded quarterly at 11.75% annual and eight payments have been made.

(*a*) What was the original present value of the lease, assuming beginning-of-period payments and quarterly compounding?

(*b*) What was the original present value of the lease assuming end-of-period payments and quarterly compounding?

(*c*) What is the current present value assuming end-of-period payments and quarterly compounding?

(*d*) What is the current present value assuming beginning-of-period payments and quarterly compounding?

(*e*) Assuming monthly compounding, what is the answer to (*a*) through (*d*)?

8-97 A company is leasing a machine with the option to purchase at the end of 8 years. The quarterly payments are $3854 computed using an 11.75% discount rate. The current value of the machine is $90,000 and it can be purchased at the end of the lease for the unamortized balance of the market value. What is the purchase price assuming:

(*a*) Beginning-of-period payments and quarterly compounding?
(*b*) End-of-period payments and quarterly compounding?
(*c*) Beginning-of-period payments and monthly compounding?
(*d*) End-of-period payments and monthly compounding?

answers: (*a*) **$21,267.93**; (*b*) **$27,147.40**; (*c*) **$22,218.88**; (*d*) **$28,186.04**

8-98 A company is leasing a machine with the option to purchase at the end of 7 years. The $1100 monthly payments are computed using a 12.15% discount rate. The current value of the machine is $65,000, and it can be purchased at the end of the lease for the unamortized balance of the market value. What is the purchase price assuming:

(*a*) Beginning-of-period payments and monthly compounding?
(*b*) End-of-period payments and monthly compounding?
(*c*) Beginning-of-period payments and semiannual compounding?
(*d*) End-of-period payments and semiannual compounding?

8-99 What is the annual yield on a 3-year auto lease given a $15,000 current value, $260.24 monthly lease payment, and a residual value of $10,135.19:

(*a*) For beginning-of-period payments and monthly compounding?
(*b*) For end-of-period payments and monthly compounding?

(c) For beginning-of-period payments and semiannual compounding?

(d) For end-of-period payments and semiannual compounding?

answers: (a) i_c = .9993%; r = **11.9914%**; (b) i_c = .9792%, r = **11.7499%**; (c) i_c = **6.1475%**, r = **12.2950%**; (d) i_c = **6.0206%**, r = **12.0413%**

8-100 What is the annual yield on a 5-year lease given an $85,000 current value, $5,158.17 quarterly lease payments, and a residual value of $24,870.15:

(a) For beginning-of-period payments and quarterly compounding?

(b) For end-of-period payments and quarterly compounding?

(c) For beginning-of-period payments and monthly compounding?

(d) For end-of-period payments and monthly compounding?

8-101 A company is considering the purchase of a machine that costs $65,000 and has an estimated salvage value of $5000 at the end of 8 years. It is estimated that the machine will reduce labor costs by $3000 at the end of each quarter. The company requires a 12% return on such projects. Assume that all cash flows are after taxes and quarterly compounding.

(a) What is the present value of the savings and salvage value?

(b) What is the net present value (i.e., present value of savings and salvage less outlay cost)?

(c) What is the internal rate of return (i.e., interest rate)?

answers: (a) **$63,107.98**; (b) **$−1892.02**; (c) i_c = **2.7927%**, r = **$11.1706%**

8-102 A company is considering the purchase of an asset for $38,600 which will save $980 at the end of each month for 5 years and have a $2000 salvage value at the end of the 5 years. The company requires a return on similar projects of 16% annual. Assume that all cash flows are after taxes and use monthly compounding.

(a) What is the present value of the savings and salvage value?

(b) What is the net present value (i.e., present value of savings and salvage value less outlay cost)?

(c) What is the internal rate of return (i.e., interest rate) on the project?

Bonds Sold on Interest Date

8-103 A $1000, $8\frac{1}{2}$% bond with interest payable semiannually matures at par in 17 years. What is the purchase price for an annual yield rate of:

(a) 8%?

(b) 7.5%?

(c) 9%?

(d) 8.75%?

(e) 8.5%?

answers: (a) **$1046.03**; (b) **$1095.20**; (c) **$956.88**; (d) **$978.09**; (e) **$1000.00**

8-104 A $1000, $7\frac{3}{4}$% bond with interest payable semiannually matures in 9 years. What is the purchase price for an annual yield rate of:

(a) 7.5%?

(b) $7\frac{1}{4}$%?

(c) 8%?

(d) 9.28%?

(e) $7\frac{3}{4}$%?

8-105 A $1000, 7.25% bond with interest payable semiannually matures in 14 years. What is the annual yield if the bond is sold for:

(a) $985.25?

(b) $920.15?

(c) $1028.50?

(d) $1102.85?

(e) $1000?

answers: (a) **7.4212%**; (b) **8.2206%**; (c) **6.9287%**; (d) **6.1441%**; (e) **7.25%**

8-106 A $1000, 8.75% bond with interest payable semiannually matures in 9 years. What is the annual yield if the bond is sold for:
   (*a*) $990.25?
   (*b*) $909.09?
   (*c*) $1050.50?
   (*d*) $1125.80?
   (*e*) $1000?

Bonds Sold Between Interest Dates

8-107 A $1000 bond pays 10.2% annually and has coupons due on June 15 and December 15. The bond is due on December 15, 1995. The bond was sold on July 20, 1979 (settlement date). For your convenience the various day values are shown below. Assume semiannual compounding.

	Actual days	30/360 days
C	183	180
B	148	145
A	35	35
n	32	32

   (*a*) Using actual days, what is the selling price of the bond if the bond is sold to yield:
      (1) 10.8%?
      (2) 11%?
      (3) 9%?
      (4) 8.3%
   answers: (1) **$954.666023**; (2) **$940.308140**; (3) **$1100.284919**; (4) **$1165.956455**
   (*b*) Using actual days, what is the annual yield if the bond is sold for:
      (1) $1050?
      (2) $1100?
      (3) $975?
      (4) $950?
   answers: (1) **9.579089%**; (2) **9.003170%**; (3) **10.524489%**; (4) **10.864488%**
   (*c*) Using the 30/360-day count method, answer part (*a*).
   answers: (1) **$954.665148**; (2) **$940.307730**; (3) **$1100.278109**; (4) **$1165.946286**
   (*d*) Using the 30/360-day count method, answer part (*b*).
   answers: (1) **9.579035%**; (2) **9.003095%**; (3) **10.524468%**; (4) **10.864478%**

8-108 A $1000 bond pays 6.5% annually and has coupons due on March 1 and September 1. The bond is due on September 1, 1985. The bond was sold on August 3, 1979 (settlement date). The various day count values are shown below for your convenience. (Assume semiannual compounding.)

	Actual days	30/360 days
C	183	180
B	148	145
A	35	35
n	32	32

(a) Using actual days, what is the selling price of the bonds if the bond is sold to yield:
(1) 10.5%?
(2) 9.4%?
(3) 6.2%?
(4) 5.7%?

(b) Using actual days, what is the annual yield if the bond is sold for:
(1) $1100?
(2) $1050?
(3) $875?
(4) $920?

(c) Using the 30/360-day count method, answer part (a).
(d) Using the 30/360-day count method, answer part (b).

8-109 A 5.75% $1000 bond is due on November 1, 1981. The semiannual coupon dates are May 1 and November 1. The bond was sold on July 15, 1979. The various day count values are shown below for your convenience. Assume semiannual compounding.

	Actual days	30/360 days
C	184	180
B	109	106
A	75	74
n	4	4

(a) Using actual days, what is the selling price of the bond if the bond is sold to yield:
(1) 7%?
(2) 10%?
(3) 5.5%?
(4) 5%?

answers: (1) **$979.12143**; (2) **$931.502630**; (3) **$1004.126754**; (4) **$1012.647105**

(b) Using actual days, what is the annual yield if the bond is sold for:
(1) $1,075?
(2) $1,050?
(3) $745?
(4) $925?

answers: (1) **1.500857%**; (2) **2.871169%**; (3) **24.025911%**; (4) **10.425227%**

(c) Using the 30/360-day count method, answer part (a).
answers: (1) **$979.140122**; (2) **$931.563130**; (3) **$1004.122586**; (4) **$1012.635006**

(d) Using the 30/360-day count method, answer part (b).
answers: (1) **1.496954%**; (2) **2.868512%**; (3) **24.043373%**; (4) **10.429568%**

8-110 A 8.75%, $1000 bond is due on August 15, 1990. The semiannual coupon dates are February 15 and August 15. The bond was sold on June 25, 1979. The various day-count values are shown below for your convenience. Assume semiannual compounding.

	Actual days	30/360 days
C	181	180
B	51	50
A	130	130
n	22	22

(a) Using actual days, what is the selling price of the bonds if the bond is sold to yield:
   (1) 11.5%?
   (2) 9.75%?
   (3) 8.25%?
   (4) 7.65%?
(b) Using actual days, what is the annual yield if the bond is sold for:
   (1) $1065?
   (2) $1155?
   (3) $967?
   (4) $848?
(c) Using the 30/360-day count method, answer part (a).
(d) Using the 30/360-day count method, answer part (b).

SPECIAL APPLICATIONS

IN THIS CHAPTER

In this chapter a variety of advanced applications, not covered elsewhere, are described. These include:

Deferred annuities.
Constant-increment annuities and grouped cash flows.
Constant-ratio annuities (growth and decay models).
Perpetuities.
Loans with advanced, skipped, or equal principal payments.
Add-on interest.
Foreign interest calculations.

• • • • •

In this chapter, we will examine a variety of applications that build on the fundamental annuity and compound interest relationships. The topics discussed are (1) specialized annuities where payment is deferred, varies at a constant rate of change, or continues indefinitely; (2) converting annuities to new interest rates, payments, or periods; (3) useful applications involving mortgages and loans; and (4) grouped cash flows.

The approach is similar to that used in Chap. 8—breaking a problem into components that match fundamental concepts before solving it. We do not solve for all possible unknowns for each application, but concentrate on computing the primary unknown values. Remember that the variable-cash-flow equation will solve for the present value, future value, and interest rate for all of the applications in this book not covered elsewhere, even though it may be time-consuming.

9-1 SPECIALIZED ANNUITIES

This section will discuss a group of special annuity applications, in which the cash flows vary according to a specific pattern or continue indefinitely. These annuities will be classified as *deferred annuities, ratio annuities* (growth annuities), *increment annuities,* and *perpetual annuities.* These annuities are of value in practical business situations because they encompass a number of practical problems. Deferred annuities, for example, are used for "long or short odd-days" loan calculations. Ratio annuities can be used for investments where the periodic cash flow is expected to increase or decrease by a constant ratio each period, while increment annuities describe situations where the increase is a fixed dollar each period.

The formulas for these specialized annuities are developed using time diagrams to decompose the problem into components that can be solved using the concepts discussed in previous chapters.

9-1.1 Deferred Annuities

Loans and mortgages that have the first payment made at some future date are called *deferred annuities.* Figure 9-1 shows such a deferred annuity, where n represents the number of payments and t_Y the time location of the first payment. The method of analysis will be to decompose the original annuity problem into a simpler annuity problem where the solution formulas are known from the material presented in Chaps. 3 to 8. It is for this reason that the symbol Y is introduced. The problem can best be broken into two parts:

1. Solve an annuity situation where the first payment occurs at the end of period Y and the last payment occurs at the end of period n, as shown in part (a) of Fig. 9-1. We can compute the present value at the end of period Y, using Eq. (4-4) for PV_d, to get

$$PV_Y = (1 + i) \times PMT \times A(n,i) \tag{9-1}$$

where PV_Y is the present value at the end of period Y.

2. Solve for PV using compound interest by discounting PV_Y for Y periods, as indicated in part (b) of Fig. 9-1,

$$PV = PV_Y(1 + i)^{-Y} \tag{9-2}$$

Next, we can combine the two equations, to form

$$PV = (1 + i)^{1-Y} \times PMT \times A(n,i) \tag{9-3}$$

(a)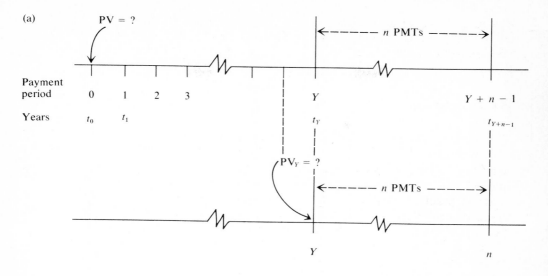

(b)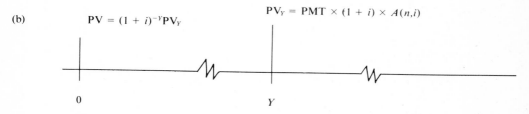

Figure 9-1 Deferred annuity.

Note that the final equation (9-3) is identical to the equation for an ordinary annuity except for the term $(1 + i)^{1-Y}$. By extending this approach, we can develop the equation for the present-value case, deferred annuities, with a balloon:

$$PV = PMT(1 + I)^{1-Y}A(n,I) + BAL(1 + I)^{-L-Y} \qquad (9\text{-}4)$$

where PV = present value at time t_0
Y = number of payment periods from the origination date to the first payment
n = number of regular payments
$Y + n - 1$ = number of payment periods from the origination date to the end of the period when the last regular payment occurs
L = number of periods *after* first payment when BAL occurs
$L + Y$ = number of payment periods from the time t_0 (origination date) to the end of the period when BAL occurs

BAL = balloon payment made L periods after the first payment
PMT = regular payment made n times
$I = i_f$ if $c = f$
$\quad = (1 + i_c)^{c/f} - 1$ if $c \neq f$
$\quad = e^{r/f} - 1$ for continuous compounding f times per year

The generalized equation for deferred annuities can be rearranged to solve for the terms PMT, BAL, n, or I, as indicated below.

Payment (PMT) can be written as follows:

$$PMT = \frac{PV - BAL(1 + I)^{-L-Y}}{(1 + I)^{1-Y}A(n,I)} \qquad (9\text{-}5)$$

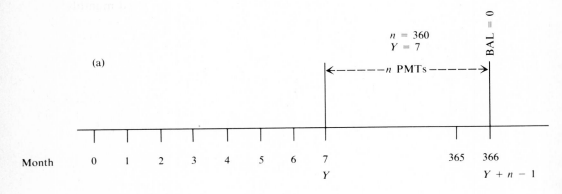

(a)

$n = 360$
$Y = 7$
$BAL = 0$

$\longleftarrow\!-\!-\!-\!-\!-n \ \text{PMTs} -\!-\!-\!-\!-\!\longrightarrow$

Month   0   1   2   3   4   5   6   7   365   366
                                              Y $Y + n - 1$

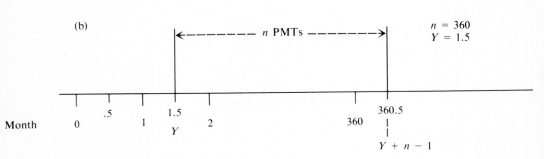

(b)

$\longleftarrow\!-\!-\!-\!-\!-\!- n \ \text{PMTs} -\!-\!-\!-\!-\!-\!\longrightarrow$

$n = 360$
$Y = 1.5$

Month   0   .5   1   1.5   2   360   360.5
                        Y $Y + n - 1$

(c)

$\longleftarrow\!-\!-\!-\!-\!-\!- n \ \text{PMTs} -\!-\!-\!-\!-\!-\!-\!\longrightarrow$

$n = 360$
$Y = \frac{1}{3}$

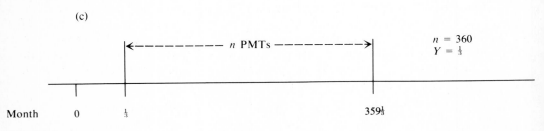

Month   0 $\frac{1}{3}$ $359\frac{1}{3}$

Time Diagram 9-1

Or, the *balloon* can be computed by

$$BAL = [PV - PMT \times (1 + I)^{1-Y}A(n,I)](1 + I)^{L+Y} \qquad (9\text{-}6)$$

The *interest rate* can be computed using either the variable-cash-flow iteration procedure (Chap. 7) or by trial-and-error approximation. The iteration equation (8-18) can also be used to solve for the interest rate if $1 - Y$ is substituted for K and $L + Y$ for L in the equation.

Let's consider a simple example involving deferred annuities.

Example 9-1 Suppose that you wish to borrow \$50,000 for 30 years, to be repaid monthly, but want the first payment to be 7 months after the origination of the loan. Assuming that interest is 8.4% annual compounded monthly:

(*a*) What is the payment amount PMT, assuming end-of-month payments?

(*b*) What is the payment amount if the first payment is made 45 days after the loan origination date?

(*c*) Solve part (*b*) but use 10 days instead of 45.

We proceed to solve these problems as follows.

(*a*) To solve this deferred-annuity PV case, we must first determine the values for n and the number of deferred periods (see Time Diagram 9-1). The other values are determined as follows and substituted into Eq. (9-5).

$$PV = \$50,000$$
$$Y = 7$$
$$Y + n - 1 = 366$$
$$n = 360$$
$$BAL = 0$$
$$I = \frac{.084}{12} = .007$$
$$PMT = \frac{50,000}{(1.007)^{1-7}A(360,.007)}$$
$$= \$397.2000223$$

The monthly payment is \$397.20 (as compared to \$380.92 per month if the initial payment is not deferred, or \$16.28 larger per month).

We can also use part (*a*) of this example to demonstrate the impact of small differences in regular payments on the balloon required. Suppose, for example, that the payments are rounded to \$397. Then the ending balance, or balloon necessary to pay off the loan at the end of period 366 ($L + Y = 366$), can be computed using Eq. (9-6):

$$BAL = [50,000 - 397(1.007)^{-6}A(360,.007)](1.007)^{366}$$
$$= \$323.4636267$$

Note that rounding the payment down by only 20 cents will require a balloon of $323.46 to pay off the loan.

(*b*) In this part of the example, dealing with *long odd-days interest,* the Y period is equal to 1.5 periods because the first payment is made 45 days after the loan originated. (Each month is assumed to have 30 days.) As shown in Time Diagram 9-1, the last payment occurs after $360\frac{1}{2}$ periods. The values for Eq. (9-5) are

$$PV = \$50,000$$

$$Y = 1.5$$

$$Y + n - 1 = 360.5$$

$$n = 360$$

$$BAL = 0$$

$$i_c = .007$$

$$PMT = \frac{50,000}{(1.007)^{1-1.5}A(360,.007)}$$

$$= \$382.2497202$$

The monthly payment due after 45 days is $382.25.

(*c*) In this part of the example, again dealing with long odd-days interest, the Y period is equal to one-third of a period, because the first payment is made 10 days after the loan originated. As shown in Time Diagram 9-1, part (c), the last payment occurs after $359\frac{1}{3}$ periods. The values for Eq. (9-5) are

$$PV = \$50,000$$

$$Y = \tfrac{1}{3}$$

$$n = 360$$

$$Y + n - 1 = 359\tfrac{1}{3}$$

$$PMT = \frac{50,000}{(1.007)^{1-(1/3)}A(360,.007)}$$

$$= \$379.1515134$$

The monthly payments are $379.15, starting after 10 days.

9-1.2 Constant-Ratio Payment Annuities

A constant-ratio annuity has payments which increase or decrease by a specified ratio or percentage each period. More specifically, the payment for any one period can be described as $PMT(1 + g)^n$, where g represents the constant growth or decline rate. This is a useful form of annuity to use when evaluating the impact of inflation on investments or for projects that have growth or an increasing return in prospect. Because the payments change at a constant rate, we can develop specific equations to solve this type of annuity.

We have constructed a situation in Fig. 9-2 where the payment occurs at the end of each period. The growth rate is g and the first payment is defined as $PMT(1 + g)^1$, with the nth cash flow as $PMT(1 + g)^n$. Assuming that the cash flows are discounted at $i\%$, the present value would then be

$$PV = \frac{PMT(1 + g)^1}{(1 + i)^1} + \frac{PMT(1 + g)^2}{(1 + i)^2} + \frac{PMT(1 + g)^3}{(1 + i)^3} + \cdots$$

$$+ \frac{PMT(1 + g)^n}{(1 + i)^n} \quad (9\text{-}7)$$

Note that the PMT term remains constant each period, while the terms $(1 + g)$ and $(1 + i)$ are both raised to the same power in any given period. We can then restate the relationship as

$$PV = \frac{PMT}{(1 + i)^1(1 + g)^{-1}} + \frac{PMT}{(1 + i)^2(1 + g)^{-2}} + \frac{PMT}{(1 + i)^3(1 + g)^{-3}} + \cdots$$

$$+ \frac{PMT}{(1 + i)^n(1 + g)^{-n}} \quad (9\text{-}8)$$

Next, we will determine an interest rate b, which is defined as follows:

$$1 + b = (1 + i)(1 + g)^{-1} \quad (9\text{-}9)$$

$$= \frac{1 + i}{1 + g}$$

$$b = \frac{1 + i}{1 + g} - 1 \quad (9\text{-}10)$$

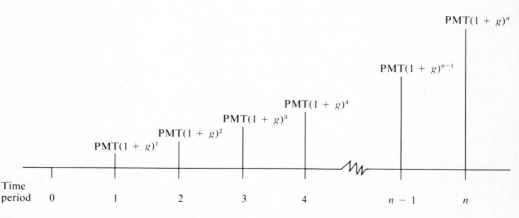

Figure 9-2 Constant-ratio payment annuities.

Now the series can be expressed as

$$PV = \frac{PMT}{1 + b} + \frac{PMT}{(1 + b)^2} + \frac{PMT}{(1 + b)^3} + \cdots + \frac{PMT}{(1 + b)^n} \qquad (9\text{-}11)$$

$$= PMT \times A(n,b) \qquad (9\text{-}12)$$

Some care must be taken when it comes to interpreting the meaning of Eq. (9-12) and how to use it. For instance, once the relationship for PV is determined from Eq. (9-12), it becomes possible to evaluate the future value FV. From Chap. 4,

$$FV = (1 + i)^n \times PV \qquad (9\text{-}13)$$

However, some additional analysis is required to determine the formula for the present value PV_d for the beginning-of-period payments. Following the approach used to develop Eqs. (9-12) and (9-13), we obtain, for the annuity-due case,

$$PV_d = (1 + b) \times PV \qquad (9\text{-}14)$$

Once PV_d is known in terms of PV, the formula for FV_d becomes

$$FV_d = (1 + i)^n \times PV_d \qquad (9\text{-}15)$$

or

$$FV_d = (1 + i)^n \times (1 + b) \times PV \qquad (9\text{-}16)$$

These relationships are similar to those presented in Chap. 4 for simple annuities, except for substitution of the term $A(n,b)$. The PV and PV_d equations use only the equivalent interest rate b, which means that all the formulas in Chap. 4 hold for the present-value cases. Thus any of the unknown values can be computed using the financial function routines on Level II and III machines for the PV and PV_d cases.

However, when solving for the interest rate for the PV and PV_d cases remember that b (not i) is computed from the iteration routine; the b must be converted to i using

$$i = (1 + b)(1 + g) - 1 \qquad (9\text{-}17)$$

Of course, this simplified procedure is *not* valid for the FV cases, since an additional term, $(1 + i)^n$, is involved in the formulas.

Now, let's demonstrate the procedures involved with an example.

Example 9-2 A company is purchasing a machine that initially incurs $5000 of annual operating costs. However, these operating costs are expected to increase 10% each year (starting at the end of the first year) over the 6-year life of the machine. Assuming that the company uses a 15% discount rate, we wish to determine:

(*a*) The *present value* of the costs, assuming that the costs occur at the end of each year.

(b) The *future value,* for the end-of-year costs.

(c) The *present value* of the operating costs, assuming that the costs are incurred at the *beginning* of each year.

(d) The *future value* for the beginning-of-year costs.

We proceed to solve these problems as follows.

(a) Time Diagram 9-2, part (a), shows the cash flow pattern for payments occurring at the end of the period. Notice that the first payment is $5500, not $5000, because the increase in payments occurs at the end of each period. Solving for part (a), the PV will first require computation of the equivalent interest rate b, using Eq. (9-10):

$$b = \frac{1 + i}{1 + g} - 1$$

$$= \frac{1.15}{1.10} - 1$$

$$= .0454545455$$

Next, we compute the present value using Eq. (9-12):

$$PV = PMT \times A(n,b)$$

$$= 5000A(6,.0454545455)$$

$$= \$25,751.5821$$

(a) End of Period

(b) Beginning of Period

Time Diagram 9-2

(*b*) Given this present value for end-of-period payments, the future value can be computed by simply moving the present value forward (at the 15% interest rate) using Eq. (9-13):

$$FV = (1 + i)^n \times PV$$

$$= 25{,}751.5821(1.15)^6$$

$$= \$59{,}564.97422$$

(*c*) Now let's assume that payments occur at the *beginning* of each period, as shown in part (b) of Time Diagram 9-2. Here the first payment in the diagram is only $5000, since the growth in payment is assumed to occur at the beginning of each period. As a result of the nature of the assumed growth in payments for each period, the actual dollar values of the various payments are different for the ordinary and annuity-due cases. To compute PV_d, we use Eq. (9-14):

$$PV_d = (1 + b) \times PV$$

$$= (1.045454546)25{,}751.5821$$

$$= \$26{,}922.10856$$

(*d*) Solving for FV_d, we use Eq. (9-15):

$$FV_d = (1 + i)^n \times PV_d$$

$$= (1.15)^6 \times 26{,}922.10856$$

$$= \$62{,}272.47304$$

In this example, the amount of the first payment varied depending on whether it was made at the beginning or the end of the period. Defining the initial operations cost, $5000, as PMT, the first payment for the ordinary annuity case was $PMT(1 + g)$. If we had wished the payment at the end of the first period to be the base amount PMT ($5000), we would have to modify the equations for PV or FV. This can be done using an equivalent payment, PMT*, defined as that amount which, compounded one period at the growth rate g, will be equal to PMT. This can be expressed as

$$PMT^* = \frac{PMT}{1 + g} \tag{9-18}$$

PMT* is simply inserted in place of PMT in Eqs. (9-12) and (9-13). Of course, this conversion is not necessary for the PV_d and FV_d cases, where the base payment *is* the first payment.

9-1.3 Constant-Increment Annuities

A constant-*increment* annuity has payments that change each period by a constant dollar *amount* (rather than a constant *ratio*). More specifically,

$$\text{payment for a given period } h = (h - 1) \times \Delta p + PMT \tag{9-19}$$

where PMT = first period's payment
Δp = dollar amount of constant increment
h = period number 1, 2, 3, . . . , n

The time diagram for an *ordinary annuity* with four constant-increment payments is shown in Fig. 9-3.

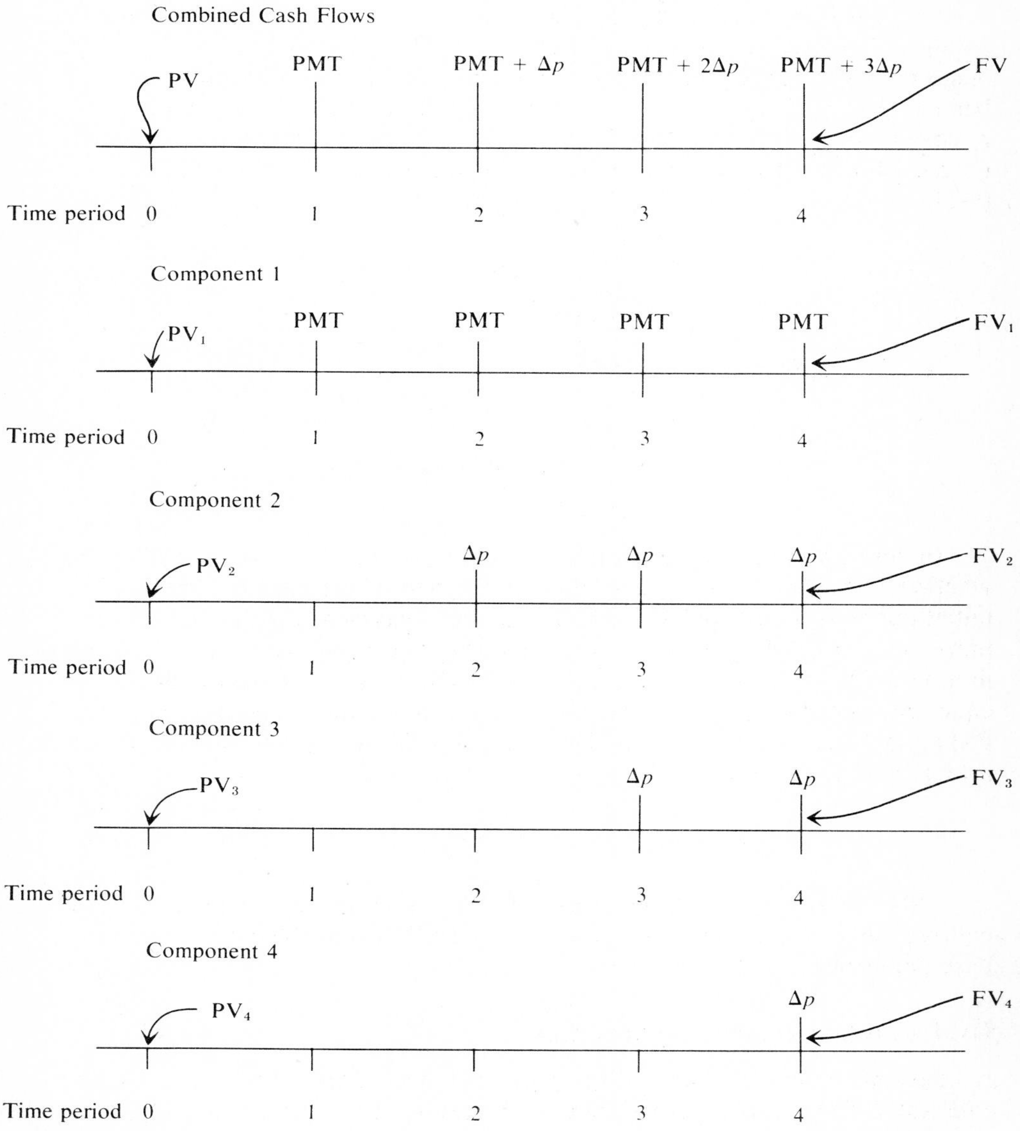

Combined Cash Flows

Component 1

Component 2

Component 3

Component 4

Figure 9-3 Constant-increment payments.

Note that the cash flows have been broken into four simple annuities. The future value of the constant-increment annuity is computed by summing the FV calculated for each of the four simple annuities, $FV_1 + FV_2 + FV_3 + FV_4$.

We can develop a special annuity equation to compute the present value, future value, and payment for a constant-increment annuity using this approach. For the example in Fig. 9-3, the *future* value is

$$FV = PMT \times S(4,i) + \Delta p\, S(3,i) + \Delta p\, S(2,i) + \Delta p\, S(1,i)$$

$$= PMT \times S(4,i) + \Delta p[S(3,i) + S(2,i) + S(1,i)]$$

$$= PMT \times S(4,i) + \frac{\Delta p}{i}[(1 + i)^3 - 1 + (1 + i)^2 - 1 + (1 + i)^1 - 1] \quad (9\text{-}20)$$

$$= PMT \times S(4,i) + \frac{\Delta p}{i}[(1 + i)^3 + (1 + i)^2 + (1 + i)^1 - 3] \quad (9\text{-}21)$$

Equation (9-21) can be simplified by rearranging to give

$$FV = PMT \times S(4,i) + \frac{\Delta p}{i} \times A \quad (9\text{-}22)$$

where A is expressed as

$$A = (i + i)^3 + (1 + i)^2 + (1 + i)^1 - 3 \quad (9\text{-}23)$$

or in the form

$$A = (1 + i)^3 + (1 + i)^2 + (1 + i)^1 + (1 + i)^0 - 4 \quad (9\text{-}24)$$

and finally

$$A + 4 = (1 + i)^3 + (1 + i)^2 + (1 + i)^1 + (1 + i)^0 \quad (9\text{-}25)$$

The right-hand side of Eq. (9-25) is simply the future value of an ordinary annuity with payments of $1.00. That is,

$$A + 4 = S(4,i) \quad (9\text{-}26)$$

or

$$A = [S(4,i) - 4] \quad (9\text{-}27)$$

Substituting the value for A back into Eq. (9-22), we have

$$FV = PMT \times S(4,i) + \frac{\Delta p}{i}[S(4,i) - 4] \quad (9\text{-}28)$$

By substituting n for the specific number of payments, we can develop a general equation for future value:

$$FV = PMT \times S(n,i) + \frac{\Delta p}{i}[S(n,i) - n] \qquad (9\text{-}29)$$

$$= \left(PMT + \frac{\Delta p}{i} \right) S(n,i) - n\frac{\Delta p}{i} \qquad (9\text{-}30)$$

Given the future value FV, we can generalize the equation (as in Chap. 4) to solve for the other three cases—PV, FV_d, and PV_d—and the increment Δp:

$$V_K = (1 + i)^{K-n}\left[\left(PMT + \frac{\Delta p}{i} \right) S(n,i) - n\frac{\Delta p}{i} \right] \qquad (9\text{-}31)$$

$$PMT = \left[\frac{V_K}{(1 + i)^{K-n}} - \frac{\Delta p}{i} S(n,i) + n\frac{\Delta p}{i} \right] \bigg/ S(n,i) \qquad (9\text{-}32)$$

$$\Delta p = \left[\frac{i V_K}{(1 + i)^{K-n}} - i \times PMT \times S(n,i) \right] \bigg/ [S(n,i) - n] \qquad (9\text{-}33)$$

where V_K = case FV, PV, FV_d, and PV_d

K = n for FV

= 0 for PV

= $n + 1$ for FV_d

= 1 for PV_d

The interest rate can be found using Eq. (7-18).

Use of Eq. (9-32) can be illustrated by an example.

Example 9-3 The manager of a small business has borrowed $50,000 from a bank. She has agreed to repay the loan in seven end-of-year payments with interest at 13.5% annually. Because she expects the business to grow during the period, she wants the smallest possible payment the first year. She is willing to increase the payment to the bank by $4000 a year starting with the second payment (see Time Diagram 9-3). What is the amount of the first payment?

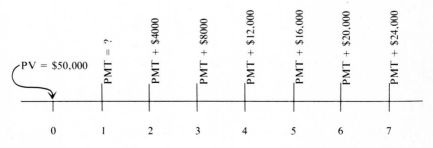

Time Diagram 9-3

The variables are identified as follows:

$$\Delta p = \$4000$$

$$PV = \$50,000$$

$$i_c = 13.5\%$$

$$n = 7$$

Because the payments occur at the end of each period, this represents an ordinary annuity with $K = 0$. Substituting the appropriate values into Eq. (9-32):

$$PMT = \left[\frac{50,000}{(1.135)^{-7}} - \frac{4000}{.135}S(7,.135) + 7\left(\frac{4000}{.135} \right) \right] \Big/ S(7,.135)$$

$$= \$1481.576857$$

The initial payment is $1481.58, with the remaining payments as follows:

Year	Payment
2	$ 5,481.58
3	9,481.58
4	13,481.58
5	17,481.58
6	21,481.58
7	25,481.58

In a situation where the payments decline, the generalized equations can be applied, but the Δp value is negative.

9-1.4 Present Value of a Perpetuity

A *perpetuity* is defined as a situation in which annuity payments go on indefinitely; that is, there are an infinite number of payments. Consider the formula to compute the present value of an ordinary annuity with n payments:

$$PV = PMT(1 + i)^{-n}S(n,i)$$

$$= PMT(1 + i)^{-n} \frac{(1 + i)^n - 1}{i}$$

$$= PMT\left[\frac{1 - (1 + i)^{-n}}{i} \right]$$

As the value of n increases without limit, the value $(1 + i)^{-n}$ approaches zero. As a result, the present value of an ordinary annuity paid indefinitely is

$$PV = \frac{PMT}{i} \tag{9-34}$$

For a general annuity the present value is

$$PV = \frac{PMT}{i_f} = \frac{PMT}{(1 + i_c)^{c/f} - 1} \qquad (9\text{-}35)$$

Using the same logic, we develop the equation for the present value of an annuity due in perpetuity. Because the first payment is received at the beginning of the period and n is infinite, we add the payment to the amount computed in Eq. (9-34) or (9-35).

$$PV_d = PMT + \frac{PMT}{i_c} \qquad (9\text{-}36)$$

$$= PMT + \frac{PMT}{(1 + i_c)^{c/f} - 1} \qquad (9\text{-}37)$$

Example 9-4 A state highway department has made a permanent agreement to pay a county $50,000 at the end of each 6-month period, forever, for road maintenance. If the department can count on earning 6% annual, what amount should be invested to fund this agreement?

Since the payments continue to infinity, this situation represents a perpetuity. The interest rate per 6-month period is .06/2, or .03. Solving for the present value, we find that

$$PV = \frac{\$50,000}{.03} = \$1,666,666.67$$

$1,666,666.67 must be invested to fund this project.

9-2 CONVERTING ANNUITIES

At this point it's appropriate to summarize what is involved in converting an annuity to a new payment, life, or interest rate. Many of the applications considered, including refinancing of loans or mortgages or rescheduling payments, require the conversion of one or more terms. In general, when one annuity and its values are known, we can set it equal to a new annuity as follows and solve for the new values:

known annuity(PV or FV) = revised annuity(FV or PV)

Once the present value or future value of the old annuity at the conversion date is determined, the new values can be computed using the equations in Chap. 4 for computing PMT, n, or i_f. Recall that the basic annuity equation (4-35) is

$$V_K = PMT(1 + i)^{K-n} S(n, i_f) \qquad (9\text{-}38)$$

9-3 SPECIALIZED LENDING, MORTGAGE, AND LOAN APPLICATIONS

This section will describe a number of common applications requiring the use of compound interest and annuities. Because the applications are relatively specialized, we will not develop a general relationship for all possible variations of the present-value and future-value cases. Instead, the illustrations will focus on solving for values that are generally required in practical applications.

9-3.1 Loans or Leases with Advanced Payments

Occasionally, a situation arises where advance payments are required at the time a loan or lease is signed. If we assume that the advance payments replace the same number of regular payments at the end of the agreement's life, we can develop a diagram of the cash flows as shown in Fig. 9-4.

In the illustration we assume that three advance payments are made at time zero, which replace payments at periods $n - 2$, $n - 1$, and n. Note that this is really the reverse of a deferred annuity, where payments are postponed for a number of periods. The solution is straightforward. Letting Y stand for the number of advance payments,

$$PV = Y(PMT) + PMT \times A(n - Y, i) + BAL(1 + i)^{-n} \qquad (9\text{-}39)$$

$$PV - Y(PMT) = PMT \times A(n - Y, i) + BAL(1 + i)^{-n} \qquad (9\text{-}40)$$

The right-hand side of Eq. (9-40) is now in the form of a balloon annuity [Eq. (8-5)], and by substituting $PV - Y(PMT)$ for V_K in the balloon equation, the interest rate, $n - Y$ periods, BAL, or L can be computed using the balloon equations for an ordinary annuity, where $L \neq n$. Present value is computed using Eq. (9-39). Computing the payment requires

$$PMT = \frac{PV - BAL(1 + i)^{-n}}{A(n - Y, i) + Y} \qquad (9\text{-}41)$$

For situations without a balloon, Eq. (9-40) reduces to

$$PV = Y(PMT) + (PMT)A(n - Y, i) \qquad (9\text{-}42)$$

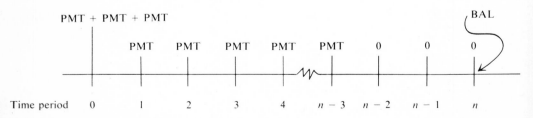

Time period   0   1   2   3   4 $n - 3$ $n - 2$ $n - 1$ n

Figure 9-4 Advance-payment annuity.

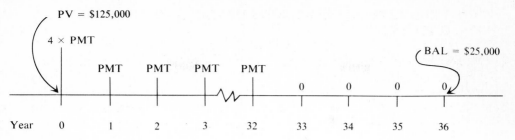

Time Diagram 9-5

Again by subtracting $Y(PMT)$ from PV, the right-hand side can be shown as an ordinary annuity PV case:

$$PV - Y(PMT) = (PMT)A(n - Y, i) \tag{9-43}$$

In this form the Level II and III calculator routines can solve for the *yield* or $n - Y$ payments using the following equivalent values for entry with the financial keys:

$$\mathbf{PV} = PV - Y(PMT)$$

$$\mathbf{n} = n - Y$$

$$\mathbf{PMT} = PMT$$

$$\mathbf{i} = i$$

Computing the interest rate or yield with a balloon requires Eq. (8-18), where the PV is $PV - Y(PMT)$ and n is $n - Y$.

Example 9-5 A machine leased for 3 years has a residual value of $25,000 and a current value of $125,000. Assuming that the lessee agrees to make four advance payments and the lessor earns 15% compounded monthly, what is the monthly payment? See Time Diagram 9-5.

Using Eq. (9-41) with Y equal to 4:

$$PMT = \frac{125,000 - 25,000(1 + .15/12)^{-36}}{A(36 - 4, .15/12) + 4}$$

$$= \$3,604.833924$$

The monthly lease payment is $3604.83.

9-3.2 Loans or Leases with Skipped Payments

An equivalency approach can be used to compute the payment for a loan or lease which has certain payments omitted or skipped, as long as the omitted payments are the same each year. Part (a) of Fig. 9-5 shows the first year of a yearly payment schedule for a loan with a life of T years, where payments are omitted in the sixth through ninth months of every year. A key point is that the same pattern is repeated each year for 7 years. It then becomes possible to take advantage of this seasonal pattern.

It is possible to express all the monthly payments, within a year, in terms of an equivalent end-of-year payment. A shortcut method is used to obtain the equivalent yearly payment, PMT_{EY}.

We first compute the future value at the end of the first year by assuming that all 12 payments were made:

$$\text{future value of 12 payments} = PMT \times S(12, i_c) \qquad (9\text{-}44)$$

Next, we compute the future value at the end of month 9 of the payments that were omitted (in periods 6, 7, 8, and 9) and compound the FV forward to the end of the year, as follows:

$$\text{end-of-year future value of omitted payments} = PMT \times S(4, i)(1 + i)^3 \qquad (9\text{-}45)$$

Netting the two values together, we have the equivalent yearly payment made at the end of the first year:

$$PMT_{EY} = PMT \times S(12, i_c) - PMT \times S(4, i)(1 + i_c)^3 \qquad (9\text{-}46)$$

(a) First Year Only

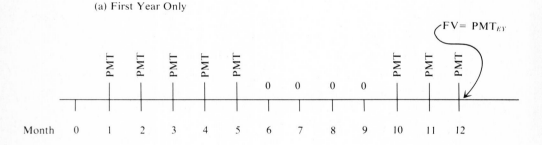

(b) Annual Equivalent Payments

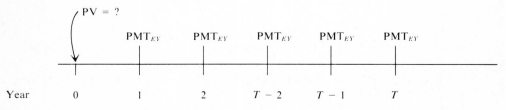

Figure 9-5 Repeated skipped payments.

The reason for developing an expression for PMT_{EY} is to express the monthly payment schedule of the annuity into an equivalent yearly payment schedule. However, it is useful to generalize Eq. (9-46) as follows:

$$PMT_{EY} = PMT[S(f,i_c) - S(Y,i_c)(1 + i_c)^{f-Y-e}] \qquad (9\text{-}47)$$

where f = number of payments per year if none are skipped
$\quad c$ = number of compounding periods per year
$\quad i_c$ = interest rate per regular payment period
$\quad T$ = number of years for loan or lease
PMT = regular periodic payment made f times per year
$\quad Y$ = number of skipped payments
$\quad e$ = last payment made before first payment skipped

To simplify the analysis, Eq. (9-47) is restricted to simple annuity cases where $f = c$.

Now that the equivalent yearly payments are known for the general case, the next step is to transform the annuity into annual payments, as shown in part (b) of Fig. 9-5. Since we want the present value for the annuity, we obtain

$$PV = PMT_{EY} \times A(T,r) \qquad (9\text{-}48)$$

where T = number of years for the loan
$\quad r$ = equivalent annual interest rate

A value for r can be obtained from

$$r = (1 + i_c)^c - 1 \qquad (9\text{-}49)$$

Substituting the relationship for PMT_{EY} and r into (9-48), we obtain

$$PV = PMT[S(f,i_c) - S(Y,i_c)(1 + i_c)^{f-Y-e}]A(T,r) \qquad (9\text{-}50)$$

Equation (9-50) reduces to

$$PV = PMT\left[1 - \frac{(1 + i_c)^{f-e}A(Y,i_c)}{S(f,i_c)}\right]A(n,i_c) \qquad (9\text{-}51)$$

Payment for the PV case is

$$PMT = PV \Big/ \left\{\left[1 - \frac{(1 + i_c)^{f-e}A(Y,i_c)}{S(f,i_c)}\right]A(n,i_c)\right\} \qquad (9\text{-}52)$$

The simplification of Eq. (9-50) removes the term r from the formula, thus simplifying the relationship for computation purposes to Eq. (9-52).

Of course, once the present value for end-of-period payments is known, the annuity due, PV_d, is

$$PV_d = PV(1 + i_c)$$

The payment for an end-of-period payment loan or lease is

$$\text{equivalent PMT for } PV_d \text{ case} = \frac{\text{PMT for } PV \text{ case}}{1 + i_c} \qquad (9\text{-}53)$$

Now, let's solve an example involving skipped payments.

Example 9-6 Because a company has a seasonal business, the bank allows it to skip the sixth through ninth monthly payments on its loan each year. If the loan is $50,000 for 6 years and interest is 11.8% annual compounded monthly, what is the monthly payment? See Time Diagram 9-6.

First, we identify the variables necessary to compute the payment.

$$PV = 50,000$$

$$f = 12$$

$$i_c = \frac{.118}{12}$$

$$T = 6$$

$$Y = 4$$

$$e = 5$$

$$n = 12 \times 6 = 72$$

Inserting these values into Eq. (9-52):

$$PMT = 50,000 \Big/ \left\{ \left[1 - \frac{(1 + .118/12)^{12-5}A(4,.118/12)}{S(12,.118/12)} \right] A(72,.118/12) \right\}$$

$$= \$1451.044173$$

We find that a payment of $1451.04 is required. If made at the *beginning* of the period, the payment using Eq. (9-53) would be

$$PMT = \frac{1451.044173}{1 + .118/12}$$

$$= \$1436.914513$$

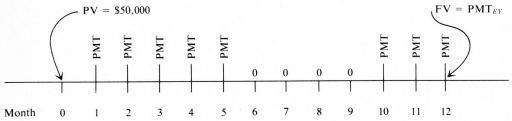

Time Diagram 9-6

9-3.3 Loans with Equal Principal Payments

When an equal or constant amount is paid on the principal of a loan each period (in addition to the interest for the period), the periodic payments are unequal. Since the interest on the remaining principal will decline over time, the total payment declines each period, with the first payment being the largest. This is in contrast to the level payments computed for ordinary annuities, where the amount of principal paid each period increases while the amount of interest declines.

With the principal payment equal, the equations for computing the unknowns are not complex.

$$PV = n(PP) \tag{9-54}$$

$$PP = \frac{PV}{n} \tag{9-55}$$

$$n = \frac{PV}{PP} \tag{9-56}$$

$$IP_h = BAL_h \times i \tag{9-57}$$

$$TP_h = BAL_h(i) + PP \tag{9-58}$$

$$TP_h = IP_h + PP \tag{9-59}$$

$$BAL_h = PV - (h - 1)PP \tag{9-60}$$

$$BAL_j = PV - (j - 1)PP$$

$$\begin{array}{l}\text{accumulated interest} \\ \text{periods } j \text{ through } h\end{array} = i(h + 1 - j)BAL_j - PP\left[\frac{(h - j)(h + 1 - j)}{2}\right] \tag{9-61}$$

where TP_h = total payment for period h
$\quad IP_n$ = interest for period h
$\quad PP$ = equal principal payment
$\quad n$ = number of payments
$\quad i$ = interest rate per payment period
$\quad PV$ = original amount of loan
$\quad BAL_h$ = beginning balance for period h, where $h = 1, 2, 3, \ldots , n$
$\quad BAL_j$ = beginning balance for period j, where $j = 1, 2, 3, \ldots , h - 1$

A constant-principal example follows.

Example 9-7 An $85,000, 8-year loan is repaid with equal monthly principal payments and 10.8% annual interest. What are the monthly payment and the interest paid the first year? See Time Diagram 9-7.

Because each total payment has an equal payment to principal, the total

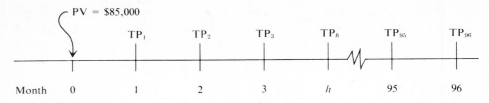

Month   0   1   2   3 h 95   96

Time Diagram 9-7

payment per month will vary. Using Eq. (9-55), the principal payment is

$$PP = \frac{85,000}{96}$$

$$= \$885.4166667$$

The first monthly payment is then the sum of the principal payment, $885.41,†$ and the interest payment, computed as follows:

$$IP_1 = 85,000 \times \frac{.108}{12}$$

$$= \$765$$

The total payment is

$$TP_1 = 885.41 + 765$$

$$= \$1650.41$$

The second-period payment is computed as follows:

$$IP_2 = [85,000 - (2 - 1)885.42] \times \frac{.108}{12}$$

$$= (84,114.58)\frac{.108}{12}$$

$$PP_2 = 757.03122$$

$$TP_2 = 885.41 + 757.03$$

$$= \$1642.44$$

†Because the constant monthly principal payment was rounded, the balance after the last payment should be checked as follows:
$$TP_{96} = [85,000 - (96 - 1)885.41](.108/12) + 885.41$$
$$= 7.97445 + 885.41$$
$$= \$893.38445$$
The balance after the 96th payment is $.64:
$$85,000 - (97 - 1)885.41 = \$.64$$
The final payment, which reduces the balance of the loan to zero, is
$$\text{final payment} = 893.38 + .64$$
$$= \$894.02$$

The total interest paid for the first year can be computed using Eq. (9-61). Remember that BAL_h and BAL_j represent balances at the beginning of periods h and j, respectively, in using this equation.

$$BAL_1 = 85,000 - (1 - 1)885.41 = 85,000$$

$$\begin{array}{l} \text{accumulated} \\ \text{interest for} \\ \text{months 1 through 12} \end{array} = \left[(12 + 1 - 1)85,000 - 885.41\frac{(12 - 1)(12 + 1 - 1)}{2} \right]\frac{.108}{12}$$

$$= \$8654.06646$$

For the second year, the accumulated interest for months 13 through 24 is

$$BAL_{13} = 85,000 - (13 - 1)885.41$$

$$= \$74,375.08$$

$$\begin{array}{l} \text{accumulated} \\ \text{interest} \\ \text{second year} \end{array} = \left[(24 + 1 - 13)(74,375.08) - 885.41\frac{(24 - 13)(24 + 1 - 13)}{2} \right]\frac{.108}{12}$$

$$= \$7506.5751$$

9-3.4 Loans with Level Monthly Payments and a Yearly Balloon

Loans or mortgages sometimes involve level monthly payments and a yearly balloon payment. By assuming that the balloon occurs each year at the end of the last monthly payment (in addition to the regular payment), the ordinary annuity formulas (with $n = 12$) can be used to compute the equivalent end-of-year payment, PMT_{EY}, to which the balloon is added. The expression for the equivalent yearly payments, PMT_{EY}, is similar to that developed in Sec. 9-3.2.

The value for PMT_{EY} is determined by evaluating the future value of the monthly payment, plus the balloon, at the end of the first year. For the ordinary annuity case,

$$PMT_{EY} = PMT \times S(12,i_c) + BAL \tag{9-62}$$

and for the annuity-due case,

$$PMT_{EY} = PMT(1 + i_c)S(12,i_c) + BAL \tag{9-63}$$

These amounts are the future value of the respective annuity at the end of the twelfth month.

We can compute the present value for T equivalent yearly payments (PMT_{EY}) using the equivalent annual compounding rate r:

$$PV = PMT_{EY}A(T,r) \tag{9-64}$$

where

$$r = (1 + i_c)^{12/1} - 1 \tag{9-65}$$

Once we have the equation to compute the present value, we can solve for the monthly payment for the end-of-month case as follows:

End-of-month regular payments:

$$PMT = \left[\frac{PV}{A(T,r)} - BAL \right] \Big/ S(12,i_c) \tag{9-66}$$

$$= \frac{PV}{A(n,i_c)} - \frac{BAL}{S(12,i_c)} \tag{9-67}$$

Beginning-of-month regular payments:

$$PMT = \left[\frac{PV}{A(T,r)} - BAL \right] \Big/ S(12,i_c)(1 + i_c) \tag{9-68}$$

$$= \left[\frac{PV}{A(n,i_c)} - \frac{BAL}{S(12,i_c)} \right] \frac{1}{1 + i_c} \tag{9-69}$$

$$= \frac{\text{end-of-month regular payment}}{1 + i_c} \tag{9-70}$$

As shown in Eq. (9-67), the conversion of i_c to r is unnecessary after the equation is reduced. Furthermore, solving for the beginning-of-month regular payment is also simplified because, as shown by Eq. (9-70), it is computed by dividing the end-of-month payment by $(1 + i_c)$.

The next example demonstrates the use of Eqs. (9-67) and (9-70).

Example 9-8 Suppose that you wished to borrow $65,000 to purchase a new house at 9.75% annual for 30 years, but are able to make an $800 balloon payment at the end of each year. What is your required monthly payment

(*a*) For end-of-month payments?

(*b*) For beginning-of-month payments?

See Time Diagram 9-8.

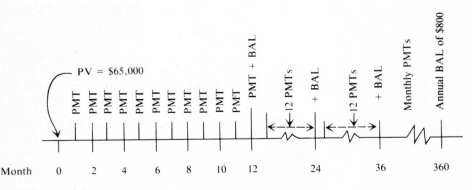

Time Diagram 9-8

(*a*) We solve for the regular monthly payment using Eq. (9-67).

$$\frac{\text{regular end-of}}{\text{month payment}} = \frac{65{,}000}{A(360,.0975/12)} - \frac{800}{S(12,.0975/12)}$$

$$= \$494.7106422$$

The $800 balloon payment each year reduces the monthly payment to $494.71, as compared to $558.45 without the yearly balloons.

(*b*) The regular beginning-of-month payment is determined using Eq. (9-70).

$$\frac{\text{regular beginning-}}{\text{of-month payment}} = \frac{494.7106422}{1 + .0975/12}$$

$$= \$490.7235137$$

9-3.5 Add-on Interest Loans and the Rule of 78

Add-on interest loans are common, especially in consumer lending.† In these loans, the total amount repaid is the amount borrowed plus an interest charge (also called the *finance charge*), which is equal to the annual simple interest times the number of years for the loan. The periodic payment is simply the total of the amount borrowed plus the finance charge divided by the number of payments:

$$\text{finance charge} = PV \times AR \times T \qquad (9\text{-}71)$$

$$PMT = \frac{PV + \text{finance charge}}{n} \qquad (9\text{-}72)$$

where PMT = periodic payment
  PV = amount borrowed
  AR = annual add-on interest rate as a decimal
  n = total number of payments
  T = life of loan in years

The nominal annual interest rate is determined for an add-on loan by solving for the unknown interest rate of an ordinary annuity and multiplying by

†Federal Regulation Z requires that a lender disclose the annual percentage rate (APR) on a loan. APR is normally the same as the nominal annual interest rate used in this book. Any difference is due to charges included or excluded by Regulation Z from the present value used to solve for the interest rate, or rounding allowed in quoted rates. While many lenders prefer using add-on interest to calculate the amount of monthly payments, the APR must still be calculated. Because monthly payments are often calculated using add-on interest, the APR rate changes as the number of payments increases.

the number of payments per year, using the techniques discussed in Chap. 4. Normally, the nominal interest rate is much larger than the add-on rate:

$$PV = PMT \times A(n,i_c) \tag{9-73}$$

where i_c is unknown and

$$\text{nominal annual interest rate} = i_c \times f$$

with $\qquad\qquad f = \text{number of payments per year}$

The interest in dollars for each periodic payment is often computed using the *rule of 78*. It is so named because the sum of the numbers 1 through 12 is 78, although the method is used for loans with terms other than 1 year. This method allocates interest differently than the annuity or compound interest method that is used in mortgages.

For example, a 1-year loan would have the first payment's interest equal to $\frac{12}{78}$ of the finance charge, while the second payment's interest is $\frac{11}{78}$ of the finance charge. The numerator declines by 1 for each period until the twelfth and last period's interest is $\frac{1}{78}$ of the finance charge. The amount of interest for a specific payment is

$$\text{period } k \text{ interest} = \frac{2(n - k + 1)}{n(n + 1)} \times (\text{finance charge}) \tag{9-74}$$

where k is the payment for period k, where $k = 1, 2, 3, \ldots, n$. The term $n(n + 1)/2$ is equal to the sum of digits for n, and the $(n - k + 1)$ term converts the payment-period number to the correct numerator value. The interest allocated to payments for k periods is derived from formula (9-74):

$$\begin{array}{l}\text{interest allocated} \\ \text{to payments} \\ \text{for } k \text{ periods}\end{array} = \left[1 - \frac{(n - k)(n - k + 1)}{n(n + 1)} \right] \times \text{finance charge} \tag{9-75}$$

Using Eq. (9-75), we can determine the amount required to pay off an add-on interest loan *after* the kth payment is made. First:

$$\begin{array}{l}\text{balance, including} \\ \text{finance charge} \\ \textit{after } k\text{th payment}\end{array} = (PV + \text{finance charge}) - k(PMT) \tag{9-76}$$

But if the loan is paid off early, the finance charge not allocated to payments must be removed from the total computed with Eq. (9-76). This unallocated finance charge is commonly called the *unearned interest rebate* or *interest rebate* and represents the amount saved by paying the loan off early. Because the rule-of-78 method allocates most of the finance charge to early payments, very little is saved by paying off the loan near the end of its life. The interest rebate is computed using Eq. (9-77) and the payoff amount using Eq. (9-78).

$$\begin{array}{l}\text{unearned interest}\\\text{rebate after}\\k\text{th payment}\end{array} = \frac{(n - k)(n - k + 1)}{n(n + 1)} \times \text{finance charge} \qquad (9\text{-}77)$$

$$\begin{array}{l}\text{amount required}\\\text{to pay off loan}\\\text{after }k\text{th payment}\end{array} = \begin{array}{l}\text{current balance}\\\text{with financial}\\\text{charge}\end{array} - \begin{array}{l}\text{unearned}\\\text{interest}\\\text{rebate}\end{array} \qquad (9\text{-}78)$$

$$= [(PV + \text{finance charge}) - k \times PMT]$$

$$- \frac{(n - k)(n - k + 1)}{n(n + 1)} \times \text{finance charge} \qquad (9\text{-}79)$$

These concepts can be demonstrated by an example.

Example 9-9 Suppose that you finance the purchase of a car with a loan of $8450 for 48 months using 7% add-on interest. Compute:

(*a*) The monthly payment.

(*b*) The nominal annual interest rate.

(*c*) The amount of interest that can be deducted on your tax return for years 1, 2, and 4 (assuming that the first payment is on January 31).

(*d*) The amount necessary to pay off the loan after the thirty-fifth payment.

We proceed to solve these problems as follows:

(*a*) We must first compute the total finance charge using Eq. (9-71) and then the payment amount using Eq. (9-72).

$$\text{finance charge} = 8450(.07)4$$

$$= \$2366$$

$$PMT = \frac{8450 + 2366}{48}$$

$$= \$225.3333333$$

Rounding to the nearest cent, the payment is $225.33.

(*b*) We compute the annual nominal interest rate by solving for the monthly interest rate of an ordinary annuity—PV case and multiplying by 12.

$$8450 = 225.33 \times A(48, i_c)$$

$$i_c = 1.056216448\%$$

$$\begin{array}{l}\text{annual nominal}\\\text{interest rate}\end{array} = 12(1.056216448)$$

$$= 12.67459738\%$$

The annual nominal interest rate is 12.67%, quite different from the 7% add-on rate used to compute the payment.

(*c*) To compute the interest allocated to the first year, we use Eq. (9-75).

$$\begin{matrix} \text{interest for} \\ \text{periods 1 through 12} \end{matrix} = \left[1 - \frac{(48 - 12)(48 - 12 + 1)}{48(48 + 1)} \right] (2366)$$

$$= \$1026.071429$$

Note that almost half of the total finance charge can be deducted (for tax purposes) in the first year. For the second year we compute the amount by subtracting the total interest through month 12 from the total interest through month 24.

$$\begin{matrix} \text{interest} \\ \text{for periods} \\ \text{1 through 24} \end{matrix} = \left[1 - \frac{(48 - 24)(48 - 24 + 1)}{48(48 + 1)} \right] (2366)$$

$$= \$1762.428571$$

$$\begin{matrix} \text{interest} \\ \text{for periods} \\ \text{13 through 24} \end{matrix} = 1762.428571 - 1026.071429$$

$$= \$736.357142$$

For the final year, we use the total finance charge, $2366 less the interest through period 36.

$$\begin{matrix} \text{interest for periods} \\ \text{1 through 36} \end{matrix} = \left[1 - \frac{(48 - 36)(48 - 36 + 1)}{48(48 + 1)} \right] (2366)$$

$$= \$2209.071429$$

$$\begin{matrix} \text{interest for periods} \\ \text{37 through 48} \end{matrix} = 2366 - 2209.071429$$

$$= \$156.9285714$$

(*d*) The amount required to pay off the loan after the thirty-fifth payment is determined in three steps. First, we compute the balance of the loan, including the unallocated finance charge after period 35, using Eq. (9-76):

$$\begin{matrix} \text{balance with} \\ \text{finance charge} \\ \text{after period 35} \end{matrix} = (8450 + 2366) - 35(225.33)$$

$$= \$2929.45$$

Second, we compute the unearned interest rebate or unallocated finance charge, using Eq. (9-77):

$$\begin{matrix} \text{unearned} \\ \text{interest} \\ \text{rebate} \end{matrix} = \frac{(48 - 35)(48 - 35 + 1)}{48(48 + 1)}(2366)$$

$$= \$183.0833333$$

Third, we compute the amount required to pay off the loan, using Eq. (9-78):

$$\text{payoff amount} = 2929.45 - 183.083$$

$$= \$2746.367$$

Paying off the loan after the thirty-fifth payment requires $2746.37, saving $183.08 in interest charges.

9-3.6 Grouped Cash Flows

Loans, mortgages, and leases occasionally have "grouped" payments. A grouped cash flow is one that remains constant for one or more periods and then changes to a new amount, which again remains constant for one or more periods. This pattern repeats until all payments are made. Of course, the variable-cash-flow equations described in Chap. 7 can solve this type of problem, but the solution is very cumbersome. For a normal mortgage, 200 to 300 payments (most of which are equal) would have to be entered and stored in memory, exceeding the capacity of most calculators. Therefore, we will develop an alternative method which allows Level II and III calculators to solve a grouped-cash-flow problem with numerous cash flows.

Consider the series of cash flows in Fig. 9-6 for a mortgage. One hundred payments of PMT_1 are made at the end of each month until period 101, when the payment changes to PMT_2, which continues for 200 periods, followed by PMT_3 for 60 periods.

The procedure developed here is to compute the equivalent payments at the *end* of periods 100, 300, and 360, which are then discounted back to time period 0. Thus the problem is changed from one of 360 payments to three end-of-period equivalent payments. The total present value is

$$PV_E = PMT_1 \times S(100,i)(1 + i)^{-100} + PMT_2 \times S(200,i)(1 + i)^{-300}$$

$$+ PMT_3 \times S(60,i)(1 + i)^{-360} \quad (9\text{-}80)$$

This approach is also used to compute the interest rate, although a number of iterations may be necessary. The equation used is the basic variable-cash-flow relationship, slightly modified. The following key equations for grouped cash flows are presented in summary form without further development.

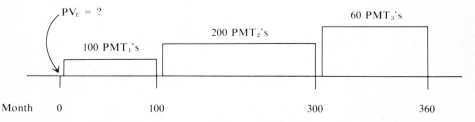

Figure 9-6 Grouped cash flows

Solve for V_K:

$$V_K = \sum_{Y=1}^{X} \text{PMT}_Y \times S(n_Y,i)(1 + i)^{K-(A_Y+n_Y-1)} \tag{9-81}$$

Solve for the interest rate by determining j, which is converted to i by $e^j - 1 = i$:

$$j_{k+1} = j_k + \Delta j_k \tag{9-82}$$

$$\Delta i_k = \frac{V_K - \sum_{Y=1}^{X} \text{PMT} \times \dfrac{e^{jn} - 1}{e^j - 1} e^{(K-A-n+1)j}}{\sum_{Y=1}^{X}\left[K - (A - n + 1)\dfrac{e^{jn} - 1}{e^j - 1} \right] \times \text{PMT} \times e^{(K-A-n+1)j}} \tag{9-83}$$

Although not shown in Eq. (9-83), the symbols PMT, A, and n should have subscript Y, which is indexed with the summation term Σ. The symbols used are:

$V_K = \text{PV}_E, \text{FV}_E, \text{FV}_B, \text{ or } \text{PV}_B \text{ case}$
$N = \text{total number of payments}$
$K = 0 \text{ for } \text{PV}_E \text{ case}$
$\quad = N \text{ for } \text{FV}_E \text{ case}$
$\quad = 1 \text{ for } \text{PV}_B \text{ case}$
$\quad = N + 1 \text{ for } \text{FV}_B$
$Y = \text{index, where } Y = 1, 2, 3, \ldots, X \text{ for groups of payments}$
$X = \text{total number of groups of payments}$
$\text{PMT}_Y = \text{payment received in group period } Y$
$A_Y = \text{first period } \text{PMT}_Y \text{ is received}$
$n_Y = \text{number of times } \text{PMT}_Y \text{ is made}$
$i = e^j - 1$

The initial guess for j_0 should be an estimated value thought to be close to the actual interest rate, provided that the initial estimate is a nonzero value. After determining j, i is computed using the conversion $i = e^j - 1$.

We'll demonstrate the solving of grouped payment annuities with two examples, solving first for the present value and then for the interest rate.

Example 9-10 Suppose that you are purchasing a mortgage which has the following remaining end-of-month payments over the next 10 years:

Months	Number of payments	Amount of payments
1–72	72	$425.36
73–108	36	475.45
109–228	120	510.54

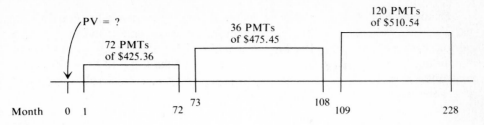

Time Diagram 9-10

The mortgage has a current balance of $54,573.29. You are seeking an 8.75% annual compounded monthly return on the investment. How much should you pay for this mortgage?

As Time Diagram 9-10 shows, this problem represents a grouped-cash-flow situation. The following values can be substituted in Eq. (9-81) to compute the present value:

$$i = \frac{.0875}{12}$$

$$K = 0$$

$$X = 3$$

Y	PMT$_Y$	n_Y	A_Y
1	$425.36	72	1
2	475.45	36	73
3	510.54	120	109

$$PV = (425.36)\,S\left(72,\frac{.0875}{12}\right)\left(1 + \frac{.0875}{12}\right)^{-(1+72-1)}$$

$$+ (475.45)\,S\left(36,\frac{.0875}{12}\right)\left(1 + \frac{.0875}{12}\right)^{-(73+36-1)}$$

$$+ (510.54)\,S\left(120,\frac{.0875}{12}\right)\left(1 + \frac{.0875}{12}\right)^{-(109+120-1)}$$

$$= \$51,242.255$$

So unless you can buy the mortgage at a discount below the balance of $54,573.29 balance, specifically $51,242.26 or less, the yield will be less than 8.75%.

Now, let's apply this approach to solve for the yield of a variable-rate mortgage.

Example 9-11 A homeowner is selling a house purchased using a $55,000 variable-rate mortgage. To pay off the mortgage at the end of the ninety-sixth period with no penalties, the required payment is $50,051.19, which is the remaining balance at that time. The homeowner would like to know the nominal interest rate that was paid over the past 8 years. Payments over the 8 years the mortgage was held were as follows:

Yearly interest rate (%)	Period first stepped payment made	Number of payments	Amount of payment
$7\frac{1}{2}$	1	12	$384.57
$7\frac{3}{4}$	13	24	393.85
8	37	24	402.85
$8\frac{1}{4}$	61	35	411.53
$8\frac{1}{2}$	96	1	$411.53 + 50,051.19

Note that the payments increased according to changing interest rates, as specified in the variable mortgage agreement. Assuming that the mortgage is paid off as described, find the nominal interest rate paid by the homeowner.

The grouped-cash-flow situation, described in Time Diagram 9-11, will require Eq. (9-82) to solve for i. First, let's identify the variables:

$$K = 0$$

$$PV = \$55,000$$

Y	PMT_Y	A_Y	n_Y
1	$ 384.57	1	12
2	393.85	13	24
3	402.85	37	24
4	411.53	61	35
5	50,462.72	96	1

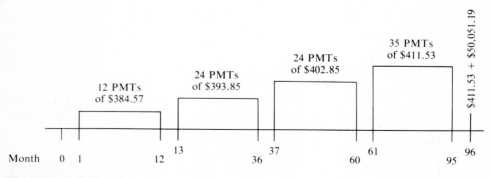

Time Diagram 9-11

For this example we will select $\ln(1 + .08/12) = .0066445427$ as our initial guess for j because the answer should be somewhere near 8% annual.

A table for the first iteration follows.

Y	PMT_Y	n_Y	A_Y	$\dfrac{e^{jn}-1}{e^j-1}PMT_Y e^{(K-A-n+1)j}$	$(K-A-n+1)\dfrac{e^{jn}-1}{e^j-1}PMT_Y e^{(K-A-n+1)j}$
1	$ 384.57	12	1	$ 4,420.932808	$-$ 53,051.1937
2	393.85	24	13	8,040.850939	$-$ 289,470.6338
3	402.85	24	37	7,012.260021	$-$ 420,735.6012
4	411.53	35	61	8,597.324107	$-$ 816,745.7903
5	50,462.72	15	96	26,665.18401	$-$ 2,559,857.664
				$54,736.55188	$-$4,199,860.882

Note that the subscripts for PMT, A, and n were omitted from the last two column headings.

With these values for the summation terms, the value for j_1 can be computed as

$$j_1 = .0066445427 + \frac{55,000 - 54,736.55188}{-4,139,860.882}$$

$$= .0066445427 + (-.0000636369)$$

$$= .0065809058$$

After seven iterations,

$$j = .0065751493$$

The discrete interest is determined from $e^j - 1$ and, using the calculated value for j above, we compute the interest rate i_c to be .0065968131 (an annual rate of 7.91617572%). An effective interest rate of 7.92% was paid for the loan.†

9-3.7 Graduated-Payment Mortgages

A special case of grouped-payment loans or mortgages is the situation where payments increase by a fixed percent z at the end of each year for m years after the first year. After the $(m + 1)$th year, the payment remains constant at the value of $PMT(1 + z)^m$ for the remaining life of $n - (m + 1)$ years, as shown in Fig. 9-7. While the grouped-cash-flow equations (9-82) and (9-81) can be used to solve for the yield and present value of the mortgage, an extension of the grouped cash flow approach is used to determine either the present-

---

†Because of the number of keystrokes and iterations necessary to arrive at an answer with a reasonable degree of accuracy, this application should be programmed for efficient solution. However, the calculation burden is reduced somewhat if a Level II machine with two memories is used for the manual solution. A program for grouped cash flows is found at the end of the chapter.

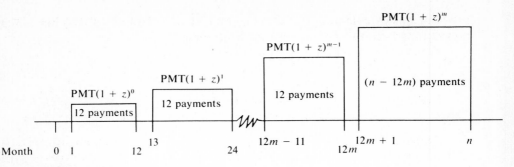

Figure 9-7 Graduated-payment mortgages.

value or the variable-payment amounts. Finding the variable payments reduces to the problem of finding the first year's payments. By using the approaches developed for ratio annuities and grouped cash flows, we can compute the present value for a loan where 12 monthly payments are made each year, with a $z\%$ increase in payments at the end of each year for m years with n total payments.

The PV equation can be expressed as

$$PV = \frac{PMT(1+z)^0 A(12,i)}{(1+i)^0} + \frac{PMT(1+z)^1 A(12,i)}{(1+i)^{12}} + \cdots$$

$$+ \frac{PMT(1+z)^{m-1} A(12,i)}{(1+i)^{(12)(m-1)}} + \frac{PMT(1+z)^m A(n-m\times 12,i)}{(1+i)^{12(m)}} \quad (9\text{-}84)$$

By using an equivalence relationship for the term $(1+z)/(1+i)^{12}$, we can develop the equivalent interest rate μ written in the form

$$1 + \mu = \frac{1+z}{(1+i)^{12}} \quad (9\text{-}85)$$

Eliminating the term $(1+z)/(1+i)^{12}$ from Eq. (9-84) by using (9-85), we get

$$PV = PMT \times A(12,i)[(1+\mu)^0 + (1+\mu)^1 r + (1+\mu)^{m-1}]$$

$$+ PMT \times A(n-12m,i)\frac{(1+z)^m}{(1-i)^{12m}} \quad (9\text{-}86)$$

Equation (9-86) reduces to

$$PV = PMT\left[A(12,i)S(m,\mu) + \frac{(1+z)^m A(n-12m,i)}{(1+i)^{12m}} \right] \quad (9\text{-}87)$$

where m = number of years where payment is increased by $z\%$ at the end of the period

z = percent increase in the monthly payment at the end of a year for m years

Equation (9-87) is in a usable form when solving for PV. However, if the objective is to compute the variable payments, the key is determining the payment for the first year, or PMT. The equation is

$$PMT = PV \bigg/ \left[A(12,i)\, S(m,\mu) + \frac{(1 + z)^m A(n - m \times 12,i)}{(1 + i)^{m \times 12}} \right] \qquad (9\text{-}88)$$

Let's use this equation to solve for the first 12 months' payments in a "section 245" mortgage as described in the following example.

Example 9-12 A \$40,000, 30-year, "section 245" mortgage at 8.4% annual, compounded monthly, has payments increasing 5% each year for 5 years after the first year and then remaining constant from the end of the sixth year to the end of the thirtieth year. That is, if the first year's payment is PMT, the second year's payment is $PMT(1 + .05)^1$, and so on until the sixth year's payment of $PMT(1.05)^5$. This timing of payments is shown in Time Diagram 9-12. What is the amount of the payments?

In order to solve for the payment, we must first determine the equivalent interest rate μ, using Eq. (9-85):

$$\mu = \frac{1.05}{(1 + .084/12)^{12}} - 1 = -.034314629$$

Next, the following values are substituted in Eq. (9-88) along with the μ rate.

$$i = \frac{.084}{12} = .007$$

$$m = 5$$

$$n = 360$$

$$z = .05$$

$$PV = \$40,000$$

$$PMT = 40,000 \bigg/ \left[A(12,.007)\, S(5, -.034314629) + \frac{(1.05)^5 A(300,.007)}{(1.007)^{60}} \right]$$

$$= \$252.0063418$$

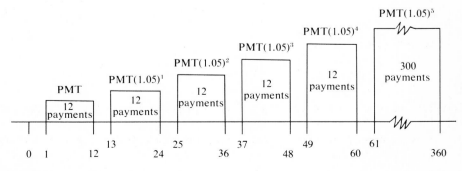

Time Diagram 9-12

Now that the payment of \$252.01 is known for the first year, the remaining payments can be computed without difficulty by repeated use of $(1 + z)$. The monthly payment for the first year is \$252.01, and the complete payment schedule is as follows:

Year	Payment	Explanation
1	\$252.01	$(1.05)^0 \times 252.01$
2	264.61	$(1.05)^1 \times 252.01$
3	277.84	$(1.05)^2 \times 252.01$
4	291.73	$(1.05)^3 \times 252.01$
5	306.32	$(1.05)^4 \times 252.01$
Remaining 25 years	321.64	

This grouped-payment approach provides the flexibility to compute the present value and interest rate for many mortgage and loan situations. In fact, the only variable-cash-flow problems that cannot conveniently be solved on a Level III machine are those requiring storage exceeding the calculator's memory capacity.

9-4 COMMENTS ON FOREIGN INTEREST CALCULATIONS

So far, this book has used the U.S. practice of determining the periodic interest rate, wherein a nominal annual rate is stated and divided by the number of compounding periods per year to determine the interest rate per compounding period. In some countries (especially in Europe) the annual rate specified *is* the effective annual rate, so that the periodic compounding rate cannot be determined using the U.S. method. The effective annual rate is the equivalent yearly rate for nominal annual interest compounded for periods other than 1 year. Table 9-1 compares the two methods for computing the periodic interest rate.

The European or effective-interest-method compounding rate is computed using the equivalent formula of Eq. (5-1).

$$(1 + r^*)^1 = (1 + i_c)^c$$

$$r^* = (1 + i_c)^{c/1} - 1 \tag{9-89}$$

$$i_c = (1 + r^*)^{1/c} - 1 \tag{9-90}$$

We have used this relationship often in this book, especially in Chap. 5 and in this chapter, to compute the equivalent annual interest rate. When the

Table 9-1

	U.S. method	European method
Number of compounding periods/year	c	c
Annual rate	r	r^*
Periodic compounding rate	$i_c = r/c$	$i_c = (1 + r^*)^{1/c} - 1$

effective annual interest rate is given, remember to compute the periodic compounding interest rate i_c, using Eq. (9-90) rather than r/c. When you want to express the period compounding rate as the annual effective rate, use Eq. (9-89). The methods developed in this book allow either the nominal annual interest or the effective annual interest to be used.

To illustrate the difference between the two methods of determining the periodic compounding rate, the monthly payments for a mortgage are computed in Example 9-13. This example indicates the importance of computing the i_c correctly.

Example 9-13 For a 30-year, $50,000 mortgage, compute the monthly end-of-period payments assuming:

(*a*) A 9% annual effective interest rate compounded monthly.

(*b*) A 9% nominal annual interest rate compounded monthly.

We proceed to solve these problems as follows.

(*a*) First, we compute the monthly compounding rate using Eq. (9-89).

$$r^* = .09$$

$$c = 12$$

$$i_c = (1 + .09)^{1/12} - 1 = .0072073233$$

Second, using the monthly compounding rate i_c, the payment is computed using Eq. (4-4).

$$PMT = \frac{PV}{A(n,i_c)}$$

$$= \frac{50,000}{A(360,.0072073233)}$$

$$= \$389.74141$$

The monthly payment using a 9% effective annual interest rate is $389.74.

(b) Now compare it to the payment computed using a 9% nominal annual rate.

$$r = .09$$

$$c = 12$$

$$i_c = \frac{.09}{12} = .0075$$

$$\text{PMT} = \frac{50,000}{A(360,.0075)}$$

$$= 402.3113085$$

$$= \$402.31$$

The payment computed using the nominal annual rate is $12.57 larger than the amount computed using an effective annual rate.

Example 9-14 illustrates solving for the effective annual interest rate.

Example 9-14 What is the effective annual interest rate for a $60,000, 30-year mortgage with monthly payments of $526.54?

First, solve for i_c using Eq. (4-16) and the procedures in Chap. 4, which gives

$$i_c = .008333278037$$

Second, the monthly compounding rate is converted to the effective annual rate using Eq. (9-89).

$$r^* = 1.008333278037^{12} - 1$$

$$= .1047123405$$

The resulting effective annual interest rate is 10.47%, as compared to the nominal annual rate of 9.99% (.008333278037 × 12).

In summary, after identifying the method of compounding interest and number of payments and compounding periods per year and determining the correct interest rate per compounding period, most foreign interest situations can be solved using our equations.

9-5 CALCULATING ACCUMULATED INTEREST, REMAINING BALANCE, AND AMORTIZATION SCHEDULES

For financial reporting and income tax returns, it is often necessary to determine the accumulated interest included in a series of payments and the loan balance (remaining principal) at the end of the last payment period. Interest procedures for the rule of 78 were discussed in Sec. 9-3.5; this section will assume the *compound interest method* of amortization (*actuarial method*), which is used to amortize bond premium and discount and for various types of loans and mortgages.

Two methods for determining the remaining balance and accumulated interest will be described. The first method assumes that equal periodic payments are made, while the second method is valid for equal or unequal payments.

9-5.1 Level (Equal) Payments

The key to computing accumulated interest is first to determine the balance after the last payment period. As discussed in Chap. 8, the ending balance can conveniently be determined using the balloon equation (8-6):

$$\text{BAL} = [V_K - (1 + i)^K \times \text{PMT} \times A(n,i)](1 + i)^L \qquad (9\text{-}91)$$

To solve for the remaining balance, L is always set equal to n, where n represents the number of periods for which interest is accumulated and V_K represents the balance at the beginning of the first period for which accumulated interest is determined. The K is 0 for end-of-period payments and 1 for beginning-of-period payments. Remember, you must enter the payment amount rounded to two decimal places to represent the expenditure of funds to the nearest penny. This means that when a Level II or III calculator routine is used to find the payment amount, it must be reentered in rounded form before using the remaining balance routine.

After determining the remaining balance, the amount paid toward principal is

$$\frac{\text{total}}{\text{principal}} = \frac{\text{beginning}}{\text{balance}} - \frac{\text{ending}}{\text{balance}} \qquad (9\text{-}92)$$

The accumulated interest is determined by

$$\text{accumulated interest} = n\text{PMT} - \text{total principal} \qquad (9\text{-}93)$$

Now, let's demonstrate this procedure with an example.

Example 9-15 Tom is borrowing $50,000 for 30 years at 9% annual compounded monthly, with an end-of-month payment of $402.31. What is the accumulated interest, the principal paid during the first 2 years, and the remaining balance at the end of each year?

Step 1: Calculate the balance at the end of year 1, using Eq. (8-6) as follows:

$$\text{BAL} = [50,000 - (1 + .09/12)^{-12}402.31 \times S(12,.09/12)](1 + .09/12)^{12}$$

$$= \$49,658.41781$$

Rounding to two places gives a balance at the end of year 1 equal to $49,658.42.

Step 2: Calculate the principal paid and accumulated interest.

$$\text{principal paid} = 50,000 - 49,658.42$$

$$= \$341.58$$

$$\text{accumulated interest} = 12(402.31) - 341.58$$

$$= \$4486.14$$

During the first year, with 12 payments of $402.31, Tom pays $341.58 toward principal, $4486.14 in interest, and has a loan or principal balance of $49,658.42 at the end of the year.

Repeat the process for the second year.

Step 1:

$$\text{BAL} = [49,658.42 - (1 + .09/12)^{-12}402.31 \ S(12,.09/12)]$$

$$\times (1 + .09/12)^{12}$$

$$= 49,284.79525$$

rounded loan balance = $49,284.80

Step 2:

$$\text{principal paid} = 49,658.42 - 49,284.80$$

$$= \$373.62$$

$$\text{accumulated interest} = 12 \times 402.31 - 373.62$$

$$= \$4454.10$$

Please notice where we rounded for our calculations in this example. The decision on rounding often depends on arbitrary rules employed by various companies, and a difference of a penny may occur in the answer. For example, rounding the remaining balance down gives a customer the benefit of any differences because it slightly increases the principal payment. Repeating Example 9-15 with the remaining balance rounded down:

	Year 1	Year 2
Remaining balance	$49,658.41	$49,284.78
Principal paid	341.59	373.63
Accumulated interest	4,486.13	4,454.09

As you see by comparing these values, where we rounded down to the nearest penny, we have a penny difference in the remaining balances. This difference might be considered immaterial in many situations, but it could be important if large amounts were involved. As a result, when determining accumulated interest, principal paid, and the remaining balance where legal or regulatory agencies are involved, check on the rounding procedure they recommend or require.

This procedure is also adequate for stepped payments where the payment amount changes once or twice, but for situations where payments vary each period, an unequal-payment method is required.

9-5.2 Unequal Payments

When payments vary, a simple but repetitive procedure is used to calculate the interest and principal portion for each payment and the remaining balance.

$$\text{interest} = \text{beginning balance} \times i$$

$$\text{principal} = \text{payment} - \text{interest}$$

$$\text{ending balance} = \text{beginning balance} - \text{principal}$$

Because each period's payment requires a calculation series, a programmable Level II or III machine saves many keystrokes.

Example 9-16 Use the loan values given in Example 9-15, but assume that the following six monthly payments are made:

Month	Payment	Month	Payment
1	$403	4	$415
2	420	5	420
3	450	6	410

What is the accumulated interest, principal paid, and remaining balance? The unequal-payment procedure works best using a table approach as follows, where a Level I machine is used:

(1) Period	(2) Beginning balance	(3) Payment	(4) Interest: (2) × (.09/12)	(5) Principal: (3) − (4)	(6) Ending balance: (2) − (5)
1	$50,000	$ 403	$ 375	$ 28	$49,972
2	49,972	420	374.79	45.21	49,926.79
3	49,926.79	450	374.45	75.55	49,851.24
4	49,851.24	415	373.88	41.12	49,810.12
5	49,810.12	420	373.57	46.43	49,763.69
6	49,763.69	410	373.22	36.78	49,726.91
		$2518	$2244.91	$273.09	

In this example we rounded the interest payment down to give the borrower the rounding advantage, which results in $2244.91 of interest and $273.09 of principal being paid during the 6-month time period. The numbers could be slightly different if interest is rounded to the nearest cent or rounded up.

This example assumed end-of-period payments, but for beginning-of-period payments, omit the interest calculation for period 1. The ending balance then represents the beginning balance for period 1, which is PV − PMT. But the remaining periods are computed as above.

9-5.3 Amortization Schedules

The second method shown is the easiest method to keystroke or program using a calculator when computing a monthly amortization schedule, but, as noted above, some differences can occur due to rounding if the schedule totals are compared to the yearly totals computed using the formula approach described first. But if you are interested in yearly totals for loans with equal payments, the first method is fast and accurate keeping the rounding assumptions in mind.

9-6 GROUPED-CASH-FLOW PROGRAM FOR THE TI-58/59

This program, which is written for the TI-58 or 59, computes V_K, i, and j using Eqs. (9-81) and (9-82). For programming simplification, all interest rate calculations use the continuous compounding form, where the program automatically makes the necessary transformations for discrete compounding. The number of grouped cash flows stored are as follows:

	TI-58	TI-59
Without memory partitioning	10	25
With memory partitioning	N/A	40

The memory partitioning command for the TI-59 is **9, Op, 17**.

Data entry and subsequent calculations are executed by the use of "user-defined label keys." The functional use of these label keys (**A, B, C, D, E, D′,** and **E′**) is indicated in Fig. 9-8, which can be used as a convenient reminder of the location and use of each label key in the program. The label keys' inputs and functions are described next in the order of execution. Note that inputs for **E′, A, B,** and **C** must be entered before pressing **D** or **E**. Their use is discussed below.

9-6.1 Execution of Program

9-6.1.1 Phase one—data entry

Step 1: Press **E′**. Initialize the program. This step also initializes the interest rate with .0001.

A′	B′	C′	D′	E′
A	B	C	D	E

			i guess	Init.
PMT_y	n_y	K	Enter i; solve for V_k	Enter V_k; solve for i

Figure 9-8 Use of user-defined label keys.

Step 2a: Enter PMT_Y and press **A**.

Enter the value PMT_Y beginning with the first grouped PMT.

Step 2b: Enter N_Y and press **B**.

Enter the value N_Y that corresponds to the PMT_Y value entered in step 2a.

Step 3:

Repeat step 2 until all grouped cash flows are entered.

Step 4: Enter K value and press **C**.

The K factor for FV_E, PV_E, FV_B, or PV_B is entered.

Step 5: Enter decimal guess for i and press **D**.

If solving for i and an initial guess other than .0001 is necessary, the alternative guess is entered in this step.

9-6.1.2 Phase two—solve for unknown

Step 6a: Enter decimal value for i_c and press **D′**.
or

Solve for V_K where the value entered is i_c in decimal form.

Step 6b: Enter V_K and press **E**.

Solve for i_c and j. The answer in the display is i_c. Press **R/S** for j, the continuous rate.

Lbl sin	)	+/−	Lbl A
RCL Ind 01	=	x ⇄ t	Op 20
STO 06	SUM 09	RCL 08	STO Ind 00
×	RCL 06	|x|	Prt
RCL 04	INV SUM 03	x ≥ t	R/S
=	Op 31	tan	
INV Ln x	0	RCL 04	Lbl B
−	x ⇄ t	INV Ln x	Op 20
1	RCL 03	−	STO Ind 00
=	INV	1	SUM 07
÷	x = t	=	Prt
(	sin	INV EE	R/S
RCL 04	INV SBR	Prt	
INV Ln x		R/S	Lbl C
−	Lbl E	RCL 04	STO 02
1	STO 05	Prt	Prt
)	Lbl tan	R/S	R/S
×	RCL 00		
Op 31	STO 01	Lbl D	Lbl D′
RCL Ind 01	RCL 07	+	+
×	STO 03	1	1
(	0	=	=
(	STO 08	Ln x	Ln x
RCL 02	STO 09	STO 04	STO 04
−	SBR sin	RCL 00	R/S
RCL 03	RCL 05	STO 01	
)	−	0	Lbl E′
×	RCL 08	STO 08	CMs
RCL 04	=	STO 09	9
)	÷	RCL 07	STO 00
INV Ln x	RCL 09	STO 03	.0001
=	=	SBR sin	STO 04
SUM 08	Pause	RCL 08	CLR
×	SUM 04	STO 05	R/S
(	STO 08	INV EE	
RCL 02	1	Prt	
−	EE	R/S	
RCL 03	10		

KEYSTROKE SOLUTIONS

This section contains keystroke solutions for selected examples from this chapter. These solutions are organized by *type* of calculator (Type A or R) and within each type by *level* (Level I, II, or III).

Type	Level	Example number	Page
A	II	9-1, 9-2, 9-3, 9-5, 9-6, 9-8, 9-10, 9-12	389, 392, 397, 401, 404, 408, 414, 419
	III	9-1, 9-2, 9-3, 9-5, 9-6, 9-8, 9-10, 9-11, 9-12	389, 392, 397, 401, 404, 408, 414, 416, 419
R	II	9-1, 9-2, 9-3, 9-5, 9-6, 9-8, 9-10, 9-11, 9-12	389, 392, 397, 401, 404, 408, 414, 416, 419
	III	9-1, 9-2, 9-3, 9-5, 9-6, 9-8, 9-10, 9-11, 9-12	389, 392, 397, 401, 404, 408, 414, 416, 419

Type A, Level II keystrokes for Example 9-1

TI-MBA/BA-II keystrokes	Display	Comments
CLR	0	Clear
FIX 2	0.00	Set display
.7	0.7	$i_c\%$
%i	0.70	
360	360	n
N	360.00	
1.007	1.007	$1 + i_c$
y^x	1.01	
6	6	$-(1-Y)$
×	1.04	
50000	50000	PV
=	52137.09	$PV(1+i_c)^h$
PV	52137.09	
CPT	52137.09	
PMT	397.20	PMT, part (a)
1.007	1.007	$1 + i_c$
y^x	1.01	
6	6	h
+/-	-6	
×	0.96	
397	397	PMT
=	380.73	$PMT(1+i_c)^6$
PMT	380.73	
CPT	380.73	

TI-MBA/BA-II keystrokes	Display	Comments
PV	49974.82	
+/-	-49974.82	
+	-49974.82	
50000	50000	
=	25.18	
PV	25.18	
366	366	$L + Y$
N	366.00	
0	0	
PMT	0.00	
CPT	0.00	
FV	323.46	BAL, part (a)
360	360	n
N	360.00	
1.007	1.007	$1 + i_c$
y^x	1.01	
.5	0.5	$-(1 - Y)$
×	1.00	
50000	50000	PV
=	50174.69	$PV(1 + i_c)^{.5}$
PV	50174.69	
CPT	50174.69	
PMT	382.25	PMT, part (b)

Type A, Level II keystrokes for Example 9-2

TI-MBA/BA-II keystrokes	Display	Comments
CLR	0	Clear
FIX 2	0.00	Set display
1.15	1.15	$1 + i_c$
÷	1.15	
1.1	1.1	$1 + 9$
−	1.05	$1 + b$
1	1	
=	0.05	b
×	0.05	
100	100	
=	4.55	$b\%$
%i	4.55	
6	6	n
N	6.00	
5000	5000	PMT
PMT	5000.00	
CPT PV	25751.58	PV
DUE PV	26922.11	PV_d
15	15	$i_c\%$
%i	15.00	
0	0	
PMT	0.00	
25751.58	25751.58	PV
PV	25751.58	
CPT	25751.58	
FV	59564.97	FV
26922.11	26922.11	PV_d
PV	26922.11	
CPT	26922.11	
FV	62272.48	FV_d

Type A, Level II keystrokes for Example 9-3

TI-BA-II keystrokes	Display	Comments
CMR	0.00	Clear memory
C	0	Clear display
FIX 2	0.00	Set display
1.135	1.135	$1 + i_c$
y^x	1.14	
7	7	n
+/-	-7	
=	0.41	
1/x	2.43	
×	2.43	
50000	50000	PV
=	121322.41	
STO	121322.41	
13.5	13.5	$i_c\%$
%i	13.50	
7	7.00	n
N	1	
1	1.00	
PMT		
CPT FV	10.57	$S(7,.135)$

TI-BA-II keystrokes	Display	Comments
×	10.57	
4000	4000	Δp
÷	42265.13	
.135	0.135	i_c
=	313075.06	
+/-	-313075.06	
SUM	-313075.06	
7	7	n
×	7.00	
4000	4000	Δp
÷	28000.00	
.135	0.135	i_c
=	207407.41	
SUM	207407.41	
CPT FV	10.57	$S(7,.135)$
1/x	0.09	
×	0.09	
RCL	15654.76	
=	1481.58	PMT

432

Type A, Level II keystrokes for Example 9-3

TI-MBA keystrokes	Display	Comments
CA	0	Clear
FIX 2	0.00	Set display
13.5	13.5	$i_c\%$
%i	13.50	
7	7	n
N	7.00	
1	1	
PMT	1.00	
50000	50000	PV
÷	50000.00	
1.135	1.135	$1 + i_c$
y^x	1.14	
7	7	n
+/-	-7	$-n$
-	121322.41	
4000	4000	Δp
÷	4000.00	
.135	.135	i_c
×	29629.63	
CPT	29629.63	
FV	-191752.65	$S(7, .135)$
+	7	n
7	7.00	
×	4000	Δp
4000	28000.00	
÷	0.135	i_c
.135	15654.76	
=	15654.76	
÷	15654.76	
CPT	10.57	$S(7, .135)$
FV	1481.58	PMT
=		

Type A, Level II keystrokes for Example 9-5

TI-MBA/BA-II keystrokes	Display	Comments
CLR	0	
FIX 2	0.00	
32	32	
N	32.00	n
15	15	$r\%$
÷	15.00	
12	12	c
=	1.25	$i_c\%$
%i	1.25	
1	1	
PMT	1.00	
CPT PV	26.24	$A(32,.15/12)$
+	26.24	
4	4	
=	30.24	$A(32,.15/12) + 4$
STO 0	30.24	
.15	0.15	r
÷	0.15	

TI-MBA/BA-II keystrokes	Display	Comments
12	12	c
+	0.01	i_c
1	1	
=	1.01	$1 + i_c$
y^x	1.01	
36	36	n
+/-	−36	
=	0.64	
×	0.64	
25000	25000	
=	15985.23	BAL
+/-	−15985.23	
+	−15985.23	
125000	125000	
=	109014.77	PV
÷	109014.77	
RCL 0	30.24	
=	3604.83	PMT

Type A, Level II keystrokes for Example 9-6

TI-MBA/BA-II keystrokes	Display	Comments
CLR	0.00	Clear
FIX 2	0.00	Set display
.118	0.118	r
÷		
12	12	c
+	0.01	i_c
1	1	
=	1.01	$1 + i_c$
y^x	1.01	
7	7	$f - e$
=	1.07	
PMT	1.07	
4	4	Y
N	4.00	
11.8	11.8	$r\%$
÷	11.80	
12	12	c
=	0.98	
%i	0.98	
CPT PV	4.18	$(1 + i_c)^{f-e} A(Y, i_c)$
STO 0	4.18	
1	1	

TI-MBA/BA-II keystrokes	Display	Comments
PMT	1.00	
12	12	f
N	12.00	
CPT FV	12.67	$S(f, i_c)$
1/x	0.08	
×	0.08	
RCL 0	4.18	
+/-	-4.18	
+	-0.33	
1	1	
=	0.67	
STO 0	0.67	
72	72	n
N	72.00	
CPT PV	51.42	$A(n, i_c)$
×	51.42	
RCL 0	0.67	
=	34.46	
1/x	0.03	
×	0.03	
50000	50000	PV
=	1451.04	PMT

Type A, Level II keystrokes for Example 9-8

TI-MBA/BA-II keystrokes	Display	Comments
CLR	0	Clear
FIX 2	0.00	Set display
9.75	9.75	$r\%$
÷	9.75	
12	12	c
=	0.81	
%i	0.81	$i_c\%$
360	360	n
N	360.00	
1	1	
PMT	1.00	
CPT PV	116.39	$A(n,i_c)$
1/x	0.01	
×	0.01	
65000	65000	
=	558.45	PV
STO 0	558.45	
12	12	
N	12.00	
CPT FV	12.55	$S(12,i_c)$
1/x	0.08	
×	0.08	
800	800	
+/−	−800	
+	−63.74	BAL
RCL 0	558.45	
=	494.71	PMT

436

Type A, Level II keystrokes for Example 9-10

TI-MBA/BA-II keystrokes	Display	Comments	TI-MBA/BA-II keystrokes	Display	Comments
CLR	0	Clear	CPT FV	19492.17	
FIX 2	0.00	Set display	108	108	
8.75	8.75	$r\%$	N	108.00	
÷	8.75		0	0	
12	12		PMT	0.00	
=	0.73	$i_c\%$	CPT PV	8893.94	
%i	0.73		SUM 0	8893.94	
72	72	n_1	120	120	n_3
N	72.00		N	120.00	
425.36	425.36	PMT_1	510.54	510.54	PMT_3
PMT	425.36		PMT	510.54	
CPT FV	40090.32		CPT FV	97412.55	
0	0		228	228	
PMT	0.00		N	228.00	
CPT PV	23760.86		0	0	
STO 0	23760.86		PMT	0.00	
36	36	n_2	CPT PV	18587.46	
N	36.00		SUM 0	18587.46	
475.45	475.45	PMT_2	RCL 0	51242.26	PV
PMT	475.45				

Type A, Level II keystrokes for Example 9-12

TI-MBA keystrokes	Display	Comments
FIX 2		Set display
CLR	0	Clear
300	300	$n - 5m$
N	300.	
.7	0.7	$i_c\%$
%i	0.7	
1	1	
PMT	1.	
CPT PV	125.23	$A(n - 5m, i_c)$
×	125.23	
1.05	1.05	
y^x	1.05	
5	5	
÷	159.84	
1.007	1.007	
y^x	1.01	
60	60	
=	105.17	
STO 0	105.17	
12	12	
N	12.00	
CPT PV	11.47	$A((12, i_c)$

TI-MBA keystrokes	Display	Comments
STO 1	11.47	m
5	5	
N	5.00	
1.05	1.05	
÷	1.05	
1.007	1.007	
y^x	1.01	
12	12	
−	0.97	
1	1	
=	−0.03	μ
STO %i	−0.03	
CPT FV	4.67	$S(m, \mu)$
×	4.67	
RCL 1	11.47	
+	53.55	
RCL 0	105.17	
=	158.73	
1/x	0.01	
×	0.01	
40000	40000	PV
=	252.01	PMT

Type A, Level III keystrokes for Example 9-1

TI-58/59 keystrokes	Display	Comments
CLR	0.	Clear
Pgm 19	0.	Call Pgm 19
E'	0.	Initialize
C'	0.	PV case
.7	0.7	$i_c\%$
B	0.7000	
360	360.	n
A	360.	
1.007	1.007	$1 + i_c$
y^x	1.007	
6	6	$-(1 - Y)$
×	1.042741896	
50000	50000	PV
=	52137.09481	
D	52137.09	
0	0	
C	397.20	PMT, part (a)
1.007	1.007	$1 + i_c$
y^x	1.01	
6	6	
+/−	−6	$1 - Y$
×	0.96	
397	397	PMT

TI-58/59 keystrokes	Display	Comments
=	380.73	$PMT(1 + i_c)^{-h}$
C	380.73	
0	0	
D	49974.82	
+/−	−49974.82	
+	−49974.82	
50000	50000	
=	25.18	
×	25.18	
1.007	1.007	
y^x	1.01	
366	366	$L + Y$
=	323.46	BAL, part (a)
1.007	1.007	$1 + i_c$
y^x	1.01	
.5	0.5	h
×	1.00	
50000	50000	
=	50174.68	PV
D	50174.68	$PV(1 + i_c)^{.5}$
0	0	
C	382.25	PMT, part (b)

Type A, Level III keystrokes for Example 9-2

TI-58/59 keystrokes.	Display	Comments
CLR	0	Clear
Pgm 19	0.	Call Pgm 19
E'	0.	Initialize
C'	0.	PV case
1.15	1.15	$1 + i_c$
÷	1.15	
1.1	1.1	$1 + g$
−	1.045454545	
1	1	
=	.045454545	u
×	.045454545	
100	100	
=	4.545454545	$u\%$
B	4.5455	
6	6	n
A	6.	
5000	5000	PMT

TI-58/59 keystrokes	Display	Comments
C	5000.00	
0	0	
D	25751.58	PV
×	25751.58	
1.15	1.15	$1 + i_c$
y^x	1.15	
6	6	n
=	59564.97	FV
E'	0.	
D'	0.	
0	0	
D	26922.11	PV_d
×	26922.11	
1.15	1.15	$1 + i_c$
y^x	1.15	
6	6	n
=	62272.47	FV_d

Type A, Level III keystrokes for Example 9-3

TI-58/59 keystrokes	Display	Comments
CLR	0	Clear
Pgm 19	0.	Call Pgm 19
E'	0.	Initialize
A'	0.	FV case
7	7	
A	7.	n
13.5	13.5	
B	13.5000	$i_c\%$
1	1	
C	1.00	
50000	50000	PV
÷	50000.00	
1.135	1.135	
y^x	1.14	
7	7	
+/−	−7	
−	121322.41	
4000	4000	Δp
÷	4000.00	

TI-58/59 keystrokes	Display	Comments
.135	0.135	
×	29629.63	
(	29629.63	
0	0	
D	10.57	$S(n,i_c)$
)	10.57	
+	−191752.65	
7	7	n
×	7.00	
4000	4000	Δp
÷	28000.00	
.135	0.135	i_c
=	15654.76	
÷	15654.76	
(	15654.76	
0	0	
D	10.57	$S(n,i_c)$
)	10.57	
=	1481.58	PMT

Type A, Level III keystrokes for Example 9-5

TI-58/59 keystrokes	Display	Comments		TI-58/59 keystrokes	Display	Comments
CLR	0.	Clear		**1/x**	0.03	
Pgm 19	0.	Call Pgm 19		×	0.03	
E'	0.	Initialize		(	0.03	
C'	0.	PV case		**125000**	125000	PV
32	32	$n - Y$		–	125000.00	
A	32.			**25000**	25000	BAL
15	15			×	25000.00	
÷	15.			(	25000.00	
12	12			**1**	1	
=	1.25	$i_c\%$		+	1.00	
B	1.2500			**.15**	0.15	
1	1			÷	0.15	
C	1.00			**12**	12	
0	0			)	1.01	
D	26.24			**y^x**	1.01	
+	26.24			**36**	36	n
4	4			**+/-**	-36	
=	30.24	$A(n - Y, i_c) + 4$		=	3604.83	PMT

Type A, Level III keystrokes for Example 9-6

TI-58/59 keystrokes	Display	Comments	TI-58/59 keystrokes	Display	Comments
CLR	0	Clear	×	0.08	
Pgm 19	0.	Call Pgm 19	(	0.08	
E'	0.	Initialize	**E'**	0.	Initialize
A'	0.	FV case	**C'**	0.	PV case
12	12	f	**4**	4	Y
A	12.	r	**A**	4.	
11.8	11.8	$r\%$	**0**	0	
÷	11.8		**D**	3.90	$A(Y, i_c)$
12	12	c	**)**	3.90	
=	.983333333		**+/−**	−3.90	
B	0.9833	i_c	**+**	−0.33	
1	1		**1**	1	
C	1.00		**=**	0.67	
0	0		**×**	0.67	
D	12.67	$S(f, i_c)$	**(**	0.67	
1/x	0.08		**72**	72	n
×	0.08		**A**	72.	
(	0.08		**0**	0	
1	1		**D**	51.42	$A(n, i_c)$
+	1.00		**)**	51.42	
.118	0.118		**=**	34.46	
÷	0.12		**1/x**	0.03	
12	12		**×**	0.03	
)	1.01	$1 + i_c$	**50000**	50000	PV
y^x	1.01	$f - e$	**=**	1451.04	PMT
7	7				

Type A, Level III keystrokes for Example 9-8

TI-58/59 keystrokes	Display	Comments
CLR	0	Clear
Pgm 19	0.	Call Pgm 19
E'	0.	Initialize
C'	0.	PV case
360	360.	n
A	360.	
9.75	9.75	$r\%$
÷	9.75	
12	12	c
=	0.8125	i_c
B	0.8125	
1	1	
C	1.00	
0	0	
D	116.39	$A(n,i_c)$
1/x	0.01	
×	0.01	
65000	65000	PV
−	558.45	
(	558.45	
E'	0.	Initialize
A'	0.	FV case
12	12	
A	12.	
0	0	
D	12.55	$S(12,i_c)$
)	12.55	
1/x	0.08	
×	0.08	
800	800	BAL
=	494.71	PMT

Type A, Level III keystrokes for Example 9-10

TI-58/59 keystrokes	Display	Comments
E'	0	Load grouped cash flow program / Initialize
425.36	425.36	PMT$_1$
A	425.36	
72	72	n_1
B	72.	
475.45	475.45	PMT$_2$
A	475.45	
36	36	n_2
B	36.	
510.54	510.54	PMT$_3$
A	510.54	
120	120	n_3
B	120.	
0	0	$K = 0$
C	0.	
.0875	0.0875	r
÷	0.0875	
12	12	c
=	.0072916667	i_c
D	51242.25566	PV

Type A, Level III keystrokes for Example 9-11

TI-58/59 keystrokes	Display	Comments
E'	0	Load grouped Cash flow program
384.57	384.57	PMT$_1$
A	384.57	
12	12	n_1
B	12.	
393.85	393.85	PMT$_2$
A	393.85	
24	24	n_2
B	24.	
402.85	402.85	PMT$_3$
A	402.85	
24	24	n_3
B	24.	
411.53	411.53	PMT$_4$
A	411.53	
35	35	n_4
B	35.	
50462.72	50462.72	PMT$_5$
A	50462.72	
1	1	n_1
B	1.	
0	0	$K = 0$
C	0.	
55000	55000	PV
E	.0065968131	i_c
×	.0065968131	
12	12	c
×	.0791617567	r
100	100	
=	7.91617567	$r\%$

Type A, Level III keystrokes for Example 9-12

TI-58/59 keystrokes	Display	Comments	TI-58/59 keystrokes	Display	Comments
CLR	0	Clear	1.05	1.05	
Pgm 19	0.	Call Pgm 19	÷	1.05	
E'	0.	Initialize	1.007	1.007	
C'	0.	PV	y^x	1.01	
300	300	$n - 5m$	12	12	
A	300.		−	0.97	
.7	0.7	$i_c\%$	1	1	
B	0.7000		=	−0.03	
1	1		×	−0.03	
C	1.00		100	100	
0	0		=	−3.43	$u\%$
D	125.23	$A(n - 5m,i_c)$	B	−3.4315	
×	125.23		5	5	m
1.05	1.05		A	5.	
y^x	1.05		E'	0.	Initialize
5	5		A'	0.	FV case
÷	159.84		0	0	
1.007	1.007		D	4.67	$S(m,u)$
y^x	1.01		×	4.67	
60	60		RCL 26	11.47	
=	105.17		+	53.55	
STO 25	105.17		RCL 25	105.17	
12	12		=	158.73	
A	12.		1/x	0.01	
0	0		×	0.01	
D	11.47		40000	40000	PV
STO 26	11.47		=	252.01	PMT

Type R, Level II keystrokes for Example 9-1

HP-37E/38E keystrokes	Display	Comments	HP-37E/38E keystrokes	Display	Comments
END	0.00		CHS	-6.	
ALL	0.00	Clear	y^x	0.96	
50000	50,000.		×	380.73	
ENTER↑	50,000.00	PV	PMT	380.73	
1.007	1.007		PV	-49,974.82	
ENTER↑	1.01		50000	50,000.	
6	6.	$-(1 - Y)$	+	25.18	
y^x	1.04	$PV(1 + i_c)^h$	1.007	1.007	
×	52,137.09		ENTER↑	1.01	$L + Y$
PV	52,137.09		366	366.	BAL, part (a)
360	360.	n	y^x	12.85	
n	360.00		×	323.46	$1 + i_c$
.7	0.7	$i_c\%$	1.007	1.007	
i	0.70		ENTER↑	1.01	$-(1 - Y)$
PMT	-397.20	Payment, part (a)	.5	0.5	
397	397		y^x	1.00	PV
ENTER↑	397.00		50000	50,000	
1.007	1.007	$1 + i_c$	×	50,174.69	$PV(1 + i_c)^{.5}$
ENTER↑	1.01		PV	50,174.69	
6	6.	n	PMT	-382.25	PMT, part (b)

Type R, Level II keystrokes for Example 9-2

HP-37E/38E keystrokes	Display	Comments
END	0.00	
ALL	0.00	Clear
1.15	1.15	$1 + i_c$
ENTER↑	1.15	
1.1	1.1	$1 + g$
÷	1.05	
1	1	
−	0.05	
100	100	
×	4.55	$u\%$
i	4.55	
6	6	
n	6.00	n
5000	5,000	PMT
PMT	5,000.00	
PV	−25,751.58	PV
BEGIN	−25,751.58	
PV	−26,922.11	PV_d
0	0.	
PMT	0.00	
15	15.	$i_c\%$
i	15.00	
FV	62,272.47	FV_d
25751.58	25,751.58	PV
PV	25,751.58	
FV	−59,564.97	FV

Type R, Level II keystrokes for Example 9-3

HP-37E/38E keystrokes	Display	Comments
END	0.00	
ALL	0.00	Clear
7	7.	n
n	7.00	
13.5	13.5	$i_c\%$
i	13.50	
1	1.	
PMT	1.00	
FV	−10.57	$S(7,.135)$
4000	4,000	Δp
×	−42,265.13	
.135	.135	i_c
÷	−313,075.06	
50000	50,000.	PV
ENTER↑	50,000.00	
1.135	1.135	$1 + i_c$
ENTER↑	1.14	
7	7.	
CHS	−7.	n
y^x	0.41	
÷	121,322.41	
+	−191,752.65	
7	7	n
ENTER↑	7.00	
4000	4,000	Δp
×	28000	
.135	0.135	
÷	207,407.41	
+	15,654.76	
ENTER↑	15,654.76	
FV	−10.57	$S(7,.135)$
÷	−1481.58	PMT

Type R, Level II keystrokes for Example 9-5

HP-37E/38E keystrokes	Display	Comments
END	0.00	
ALL	0.00	Clear
15	15.	$r\%$
(g) 12 ÷	1.25	$i_c\%$
36	36.	
n	36.00	
25000	25,000.	
FV	25,000.00	BAL
PV	−15,985.23	
125000	125,000.	PV
+	109,014.77	
STO 1	109,014.77	
1	1.	
PMT	1.00	
0	0.	
FV	0.00	
32	32.	
n	32.00	n
PV	−26.24	$A(32,.15/12)$
CHS	26.24	
4	4.	
+	30.24	$A(32,.15/12) + 4$
1/x	0.03	
RCL 1	109,014.77	
×	3,604.83	PMT

Type R, Level II keystrokes for Example 9-6

HP-37E/38E keystrokes	Display	Comments
END	0.00	Clear
ALL	0.00	
11.8	11.8	$r\%$
(g) 12 ÷	0.98	$i_c\%$
7	7.	$f - e$
n	7.00	
1	1.	
PV	1.00	
FV	-1.07	$(1 + i_c)^{f-e}$
ENTER↑	-1.07	
4	4.00	Y
n	4.00	
1	1.	
PMT	1.00	
0	0.	
FV	0.00	
PV	-3.90	
×	4.18	$(1 + i_c)^{f-e} A(Y,i_c)$
ENTER↑	4.18	

HP-37E/38E keystrokes	Display	Comments
12	12.	f
n	12.00	
0	0.	
PV	0.00	
FV	-12.67	$S(f,i_c)$
÷	-0.33	
1	1.	
+	0.67	
ENTER↑	0.67	
72	72.	n
n	72.00	
0	0.	
FV	0.00	
PV	-51.42	$A(n,i_c)$
×	-34.46	
1/x	-0.03	
50000	50,000	PV
×	-1,451.04	PMT

Type R, Level II keystrokes for Example 9-8

HP-37E/38E keystrokes	Display	Comments
END	0.00	
ALL	0.00	Clear
9.75	9.75	$r\%$
(g) 12 ÷	0.81	$i_c\%$
360	360	n
n	360.00	
1	1	
PMT	1.00	$A(n,i_c)$
PV	−116.39	
1/x	−0.01	
65000	65,000.	PV
×	−558.45	
CHS	558.45	
ENTER↑	558.45	
12	12.	
n	12.00	
0	0.	
PV	0.00	
FV	−12.55	$S(12,i_c)$
1/x	−0.08	
800	800.	BAL
×	−63.74	
CHS	63.74	
−	494.71	PMT

Type R, Level II keystrokes for Example 9-10

HP-38E keystrokes	Display	Comments
ALL	0.00	Clear
8.75	8.75	$r\%$
(g) 12 ÷	0.73	$i_c\%$
425.36	425.36	PMT_1
CFj	425.36	
72	72	
Nj	72.00	n_1
475.45	475.45	PMT_2
CFj	475.45	
36	36.	
Nj	36.00	n_2
510.54	510.54	PMT_3
CFj	510.54	
99	99.	
Nj	99.00	n_3
510.54	510.54	PMT_4
CFj	510.54	
21	21.	
Nj	21.00	n_4
NPV	51,242.26	PV

Type R, Level II keystrokes for Example 9-11

HP-38E keystrokes	Display	Comments
ALL	0.00	
55000	55,000.	PV
CHS	−55,000.	
CFo	−55,000.00	
384.57	384.57	PMT_1
CFj	384.57	
12	12.	n_1
Nj	12.00	
393.85	393.85	PMT_2
CFj	393.85	
24	24.	n_2
Nj	24.00	
402.85	402.85	PMT_3
CFj	402.85	
24	24.	n_3
Nj	24.00	
411.53	411.53	PMT_4
CFj	411.53	
35	35.	n_4
Nj	35.00	
50462.72	50,462.72	PMT_5
CFj	50,462.72	
1	1.	n_5
Nj	1.00	
IRR	0.66	$i_c\%$
(f)9	0.659681306	$i_c\%$
12	12.	f
×	7.916175668	$r\%$

Type R, Level II keystrokes for Example 9-12

HP-37E/38E keystrokes	Display	Comments	HP-37E/38E keystrokes	Display	Comments
END	0.00		**1.05**	1.05	
ALL	0.00	Clear	**ENTER↑**	1.05	
300	300.	$n - 5m$	**1.007**	1.007	
n	300.00		**ENTER↑**	1.01	
.7	.7	$i_c\%$	**12**	12.	
i	0.70		**y^x**	1.09	
1	1.		**÷**	0.97	
PMT	1.00		**1**	1.	
PV	−125.23	$A(n - 5m,i_c)$	**−**	−0.03	
ENTER↑	−125.23		**100**	100.	
1.05	1.05		**×**	−3.43	
ENTER↑	1.05		**i**	−3.43	$u\%$
5	5.		**5**	5.	
y^x	1.28		**n**	5.00	
×	−159.84		**0**	0.	
1.007	1.007		**PV**	0.00	
ENTER↑	1.01		**FV**	−4.67	$S(m,u)$
60	60.		**RCL 1**	−11.47	
y^x	1.52		**×**	53.55	
÷	−105.17		**RCL 0**	−105.17	
STO 0	−105.17		**CHS**	105.17	
12	12.		**+**	158.73	
n	12.00		**1/x**	0.01	
PV	−11.47	$A(12,i_c)$	**40000**	40,000.	PV
STO 1	−11.47		**×**	252.01	PMT

Type R, Level III keystrokes for Example 9-1

HP-97/67 keystrokes	Display	Comments	HP-97/67 keystrokes	Display	Comments
(f)A	0.00	Program SD-05A	D	49974.82	
1.007	1.007	$1 + i_c$	CHS	-49974.82	
ENTER↑	1.01		50000	50000	
6	6.	$-(1 - Y)$	+	25.18	
y^x	1.04		STO D	25.18	$L + Y$
50000	50000	PV	366	366.	
x	52137.09		STO A	366.00	
STO D	52137.09	$PV(1 + i_c)^6$	0	0	
360	360.	n	STO C	0.00	Balance, part (a)
STO A	360.00		E	323.46	
.7	.7	$i_c\%$	360	360.	
STO B	0.70		STO A	360.00	
C	397.20	Payment, part (a)	1.007	1.007	$1 + i_c$
1.007	1.007	$1 + i_c$	ENTER↑	1.01	
ENTER↑	1.01		.5	.5	$-(1 - Y)$
6	6.		y^x	1.00	
CHS	-6.	$1 - Y$	50000	50000	PV
y^x	0.96		x	50174.69	$PV(1 + i_c)^{.5}$
397	397		STO D	50174.69	
x	380.73		0	0	
STO C	380.73		STO E	0.00	
			C	382.25	Payment, part (b)

Type R, Level III keystrokes for Example 9-2

HP-97/67 keystrokes	Display	Comments
(f)A	0.00	Program SD-05A
1.15	1.15	
ENTER↑	1.15	$1 + i_c$
1.1	1.1	
÷	1.05	$1 + 9$
1	1.	
−	0.05	
100	100.	
×	4.55	$u\%$
STO B	4.55	
6	6.	
STO A	6.00	n
5000	5000.	
STO C	5000.00	PMT
D	25751.58	PV
(f)B	1.00	
D	26922.11	PV_d
0	0.	
STO C	0.00	
15	15.	
STO B	15.00	$i_c\%$
E	62272.47	FV_d
25751.58	25751.58	PV
STO D	25751.58	
E	59564.97	FV

Type R, Level II keystrokes for Example 9-3

HP-97/67 keystrokes	Display	Comments
(f)A	0.00	Program SD-05A
7	7.	n
STO A	7.00	
13.5	13.5	$i_c\%$
STO B	13.50	
1	1.	
STO C	1.00	$S(7,.135)$
E	10.57	Δp
4000	4000.	
×	42265.13	
.135	.135	i_c
÷	313075.06	
CHS	−313075.06	
50000	50000.	PV
ENTER↑	50000.00	
1.135	1.135	$1 + i_c$
ENTER↑	1.14	

HP-97/67 keystrokes	Display	Comments
7	7.	n
CHS	−7.	
y^x	0.41	
÷	121322.41	
+	−191752.65	
7	7.	n
ENTER↑	7.00	
4000	4000.	Δp
×	28000.	
.135	.135	
÷	207407.41	
+	15654.76	
STO 1	15654.76	
E	10.57	$S(7,.135)$
1/x	0.09	
RCL 1	15654.76	
×	1481.58	PMT

Type R, Level III keystrokes for Example 9-5

HP-97/67 keystrokes	Display	Comments
(f)A	0.00	Program SD-05A
15	15.	
ENTER↑	15.00	$r\%$
12	12.	
÷	1.25	
STO B	1.25	$i_c\%$
36	36.	
STO A	36.00	
25000	25000.	
STO E	25000.00	BAL
D	15985.23	
CHS	−15985.23	
125000	125000	
+	109014.77	PV
STO 1	109014.77	
1	1.	
STO C	1.00	
0	0.	
STO E	0.00	
32	32.	
STO A	32.00	n
D	26.24	
4	4.	$A(32,.15/12)$
+	30.24	
1/x	0.03	$A(32,.15/12) + 4$
RCL 1	109014.77	
×	3604.83	PMT

Type R, Level III keystrokes for Example 9-6

HP-97/67 keystrokes	Display	Comments	HP-97/67 keystrokes	Display	Comments
(f)A	0.00	Program SD-05A	12	12.	f
11.8	11.8	$r\%$	STO A	12.00	
ENTER↑	11.80		0	0.	
12	12.		STO D	0.00	
÷	0.98	$i_c\%$	E	12.67	$S(f,i_c)$
STO B	0.98		1/x	0.08	
7	7.		RCL 1	4.18	
STO A	7.00	$f - e$	×	0.33	
1	1.		CHS	−0.33	
STO D	1.00		1	1.	
E	1.07	$(1 + i_c)^{f-e}$	+	0.67	
STO 1	1.07		STO 1	0.67	
4	4.	Y	72	72.	n
STO A	4.00		STO A	72.00	
1	1.		0	0.	
STO C	1.00		STO E	0.00	
0	0.		D	51.42	$A(n,i_c)$
STO E	0.00		RCL 1	0.67	
D	3.90		×	34.46	
RCL 1	1.07	$(1 + i)^{f-e}A(Y,i_c)$	1/x	0.03	
×	4.18		50000	50000	PV
STO 1	4.18		×	1451.04	PMT

Type R, Level III keystrokes for Example 9-8

HP-97/67 keystrokes	Display	Comments
(f)A	0.00	Program SD-05A
9.75	9.75	$r\%$
ENTER↑	9.75	
12	12.	
÷	0.81	$i_c\%$
STO B	0.81	
360	360.	
STO A	360.00	n
1	1.	
STO C	1.00	
D	116.39	$A(n,i_c)$
1/x	0.01	
65000	65000.	PV
×	558.45	
STO 1	558.45	
0	0.	
STO D	0.00	
12	12.	
STO A	12.00	
E	12.55	$S(12,i_c)$
1/x	0.08	
800	800	BAL
×	63.74	
CHS	−63.74	
RCL 1	558.45	
+	494.71	PMT

Type R, Level III keystrokes for Example 9-10

HP-97/67 keystrokes	Display	Comments
8.75	8.75	BD1-03A
ENTER↑	8.75	$r\%$
12	12.	
÷	0.73	$i_c\%$
B	0.73	
72	72.	
C	72.00	n_1
425.36	425.36	PMT_1
D	23760.86	
36	36.	n_2
C	36.00	
475.45	475.45	PMT_2
D	32654.80	
120	120.	n_3
C	120.00	
510.54	510.54	PMT_4
D	51242.26	PV

Type R, Level III keystrokes for Example 9-11

HP-97/67 keystrokes	Display	Comments
55000	55000	Load program BD1-02B
A	55000.0000	PV
384.57	384.57	PMT_1
ENTER↑	384.5700	
12	12.	n_1
C	1.0000	
393.85	393.85	PMT_2
ENTER↑	393.8500	
24	24.	n_2
C	2.0000	
402.85	402.85	PMT_3
ENTER↑	402.8500	
24	24.	n_3
C	3.0000	
411.53	411.53	PMT_4
ENTER↑	411.5300	
35	35.	n_4
C	4.0000	
50462.72	50462.72	PMT_5
ENTER↑	50462.7200	
1	1.	n_5
C	5.0000	
D	0.6584	$i_c\%$
DSP 9	0.6583509	

Note: The i_c value is different from the text answer because BD1-02B drops off the cents in calculating IRR. It uses only even-dollar cash flows.

460

Type R, Level III keystrokes for Example 9-12

HP-97/67 keystrokes	Display	Comments
(f)A	0.00	Program SD-05A
.7	.7	$i_c\%$
STO B	0.70	
300	300.	$n - 5m$
STO A	300.00	
1	1.	
STO C	1.00	
D	125.23	$A(n - 5m, i_c)$
1.05	1.05	
ENTER↑	1.05	
5	5.	
y^x	1.28	
×	159.84	
1.007	1.007	
ENTER↑	1.01	
60	60.	
y^x	1.52	
÷	105.17	
STO 1	105.17	
12	12.	
STO A	12.00	
D	11.47	$A(12, i_c)$
STO 2	11.47	

HP-97/67 keystrokes	Display	Comments
1.05	1.05	
ENTER↑	1.05	
1.007	1.007	
ENTER↑	1.01	
12	12.	
y^x	1.09	
÷	0.97	
1	1.	
−	−0.03	
100	100.	
×	−3.43	$u\%$
STO B	−3.43	
5	5.	
STO A	5.00	
0	0.	
STO D	0.00	
E	4.67	$S(m,u)$
RCL 2	11.47	
×	53.55	
RCL 1	105.17	
+	158.73	
1/x	0.01	
40000	40000	PV
×	252.01	PMT

EXERCISES

Deferred Annuity Problems

9-1 You purchase a share in a real estate venture on 1/1/78 which will return $5000 a year for 7 years starting in 1982. You want to earn 11.5% annual on the investment. What is the amount you should pay assuming that:

(*a*) The $5000 payments occur at the end of each year?
(*b*) The $5000 payments occur at the beginning of each year?

answers: (*a*) **$15,000.68**; (*b*) **$16,725.76**

9-2 You are purchasing an annuity on 1/1/80 which pays $250 each month for 10 years starting in 2000. You want to earn 9% annual compounded monthly on the annuity. What is the price of the annuity assuming that:

(*a*) The monthly payments occur at the end of each month?
(*b*) The monthly payments occur at the beginning of each month?

For Exercises **9-3** through **9-10** assume 30-day months.

9-3 For a $750, 12-month loan at 12.5% annual compounded monthly, what is the monthly payment assuming that:

(*a*) The first payment is made 10 days after the loan origination date?
(*b*) The first payment is made 45 days after the loan origination date?

answers: (*a*) **$66.35**; (*b*) **$67.16**

9-4 For a $4500, 36-month loan at 12% annual, compounded monthly, what is the monthly payment assuming that:

(*a*) The first payment is made 7 days after the loan origination date?
(*b*) The first payment is made 75 days after the loan origination date?

9-5 For a $1500, 18-month loan at 13% annual compounded monthly, with a $500 balloon payment made with the last regular payment, what is the monthly payment assuming that:

(*a*) The first payment is made 38 days after the loan origination date?
(*b*) The first payment is made 12 days after the loan origination date?

answers: (*a*) **$67.13**; (*b*) **$66.27**

9-6 For a $2500, 12-month loan at 11.75% annual compounded monthly, with an $800 balloon payment made at the end of the last regular payment, what is the monthly payment assuming that:

(*a*) The first payment is made 20 days after the loan origination date?
(*b*) The first payment is made 54 days after the loan origination date?

9-7 A $4804.29 car loan has 48 end-of-month payments of $124.50. What is the annual interest rate if the first payment is made 48 days after the loan origination date, assuming monthly compounding?

answer: **10.8541%**

9-8 A $5923 consumer loan has 60 monthly payments of $106.23, with the first payment made 21 days after the loan origination date. What is the annual interest rate, assuming monthly compounding?

9-9 A company borrowed $115,000 to be repaid over 72 months with $2000 monthly payments and a balloon payment of $2154.86 with the last payment. The first payment is made 60 days after the loan origination date. What is the annual interest rate, assuming monthly compounding?

answer: **7.8922%**

9-10 A $10,000 loan has 60 monthly payments of $170.76 and a $3000 balloon due with the last payment. The first payment is due 22 days after the loan origination date. What is the annual interest rate, assuming monthly compounding?

Constant-Ratio Annuity Problems

9-11 Given PMT = $10, $n = 15$, $i = 11\%$, and $g = 2\%$, find FV, PV, FV_d, and PV_d.

answers: **$389.72, $81.45, $424.11, $88.64**

9-12 Given PMT = $1250, $n = 25$, $i = 6\%$, and $g = .5\%$, find FV, PV, FV_d, and PV_d.

9-13 Given $i = 8.5\%$, $g = 1.2\%$, and $n = 15$, find PMT for:
(a) PV = $15,000.
(b) PV_d = $19,000.
answers: (a) **$1748.19**; (b) **$2051.10**

9-14 Given $i = 11.5\%$, $g = .75\%$, and $n = 20$, find PMT for:
(a) PV = $90,000.
(b) PV_d = $110,000.

9-15 Given PMT = $1950, $g = 2\%$, and $n = 18$, find i for:
(a) PV = $15,695.70.
(b) PV_d = $16,900.00.
answers: (a) **12.5%**; (b) **12.9562%**

9-16 Given PMT = $2150, $g = 5\%$, and $n = 12$, find i for:
(a) PV = $20,981.45.
(b) PV_d = $18,500.

9-17 A machine used in a plant is leased under terms where the monthly lease payment is increased ½% each month. The lease has a 5-year life and the first payment is $350. Using a 13% annual, compounded monthly interest rate, solve for:
(a) PV.
(b) PV_d.
answers: (a) **$17,690.37**; (b) **$17,793.05**

Constant-Increment Annuities

9-18 Given $n = 72$, PMT = $500, $\Delta p = 10$, and $i = .84\%$, find:
(a) FV.
(b) PV.
(c) FV_d.
(d) PV_d.

9-19 Given $n = 104$, PMT = $275, $\Delta p = 5$, and $i = .72\%$, find:
(a) FV.
(b) PV.
(c) FV_d.
(d) PV_d.
answers: (a) **$77,071.69**; (b) **$36,547.72**; (c) **$77,626.61**; (d) **$36,810.86**

9-20 Given $n = 14$, $\Delta p = 150$, and $i = 8.7\%$, find PMT for:
(a) PV = $14,000.
(b) FV = $45,300.
(c) PV_d = $13,800.
(d) FV_d = $46,000.

9-21 Given $n = 48$, $\Delta p = 10$, and $i = .95\%$, find PMT for:
(a) PV = $14,000.
(b) FV = $25,000.
(c) PV_d = $14,500.
(d) FV_d = $26,500.
answers: (a) **$147.65**; (b) **$196.59**; (c) **$157.11**; (d) **$217.27**

9-22 You borrow $60,000 from a bank, and the loan is to be repaid in 36 years at an annual interest rate of 12.75% compounded monthly. The monthly payments are made at the end of each month and, starting with the second payment, increase by $1 each payment thereafter. What is the amount of the first payment?

9-23 You borrow $70,000 from a bank, and the loan is to be repaid in 10 years. The first payment occurs 1 year after the loan origination date. Starting with the second payment and the succeeding payments, each payment is increased by $1500. Interest is compounded at 14% annually. What is the amount of the first payment?

 answer: **$8246.40**

Perpetuities

9-24 Given $n = \infty$, PMT = $100, and $i = 5\%$, find:
 (a) PV.
 (b) PV$_d$.

9-25 Given $n = \infty$, PMT = $1000, and $i = 15\%$, find:
 (a) PV.
 (b) PV$_d$.
 answers: (a) **$6666.67**; (b) **$7666.67**

9-26 You have just received a gift from a rich uncle. You and your heirs will receive $10,000 a year forever. Your uncle can invest money at 7% annual. How much did your uncle invest:
 (a) Assuming end-of-year payments?
 (b) Assuming beginning-of-year payments?

Converting Annuities

9-27 A loan has 143 payments of $349.53 remaining and interest is 6% annual compounded monthly. Convert this loan to one with 240 payments using an 11% annual, compounded monthly, interest rate. What is the current balance and the new monthly payment, assuming:
 (a) End-of-month payments?
 (b) Beginning-of-month payments?
 answers: (a) **$35,647.56, $367.95**; (b) **$35,825.79, $366.43**

9-28 A loan has 250 payments of $498.15 remaining and interest is 10.5% annual compounded monthly. Convert this loan to one with 236 payments using a 9.2% annual, compounded monthly, interest rate. What is the current balance and the new monthly payment, assuming:
 (a) End-of-month payments?
 (b) Beginning-of-month payments?

Advance Payments

9-29 Given $Y = 2$, PMT = $5000, $n = 7$, and $i = 9\%$, find PV.
 answer: **$29,448.26**

9-30 Given $Y = 3$, PMT = $250, $n = 48$, and $i = 1\%$, find PV.

9-31 Given $Y = 3$, $n = 60$, $i = .9\%$, and PV = $8301.37, find PMT.
 answer: **$175.00**

9-32 Given $Y = 4$, $n = 72$, $i = 1.1\%$, and PV = $12,926.15, find PMT.

9-33 Given $Y = 3$, PMT = $2500, $n = 20$, and PV = $38,905.63, find $i\%$.
 answer: **3.5896%**

9-34 Given $Y = 2$, PMT = $2600, $n = 19$, and PV = $38,159.89, find $i\%$.

9-35 A lessor is leasing a machine currently worth $58,000. They want to earn 11.8% annual compounded monthly on the lease. The lease has a term of 3 years, at which time the machine will have a residual value of $5800. Assuming that three advance payments are made, what is the monthly payment?
 answer: **$1735.83**

9-36 A lessor is leasing a machine currently worth $75,000. They want to earn 12% annual compounded monthly on the lease. The lease has a term of 4 years, at which time the machine will have a residual value of $7500. Assuming that four advance payments are made, what is the monthly payment?

Loans or Leases with Skipped Payments

9-37 A 10-year, $72,000 loan is made where the third, fourth, or fifth monthly payments are skipped each year. Assuming a 10.72% annual interest rate compounded monthly, what is the amount of the monthly payment?

answer: **$1316.90**

9-38 A 9-year, $50,000 loan is made where the eighth and ninth monthly payments are skipped each year. Assuming a 12.4% annual interest rate compounded monthly, what is the amount of the payment?

Loans with Equal Principal Payments

9-39 A $75,000, 6-year loan is repaid with equal monthly principal payments and 11.5% annual interest compounded monthly.

(*a*) What is the monthly principal payment?
(*b*) What is the total payment, including interest and principal, for the second month?
(*c*) What is the total interest paid for the first year?

answers: (*a*) **$1041.67**; (*b*) **$1750.44**; (*c*) **$7966.14**

9-40 A $40,000, 10-year loan is repaid with equal monthly principal payments and 9.7% annual interest compounded monthly.

(*a*) What is the monthly principal payment?
(*b*) What is the total payment including interest and principal for the third month?
(*c*) What is the total interest paid for the second year?

Level Monthly Payments and Yearly Balloons

9-41 A $41,000, 30-year mortgage is made where 12 end-of-month payments are made each year and in addition a $600 balloon payment is made at the end of each year. Interest is 10% annual compounded monthly. What is the amount of the regular monthly payment?

answer: **$312.05**

9-42 A $65,000, 25-year mortgage is made where 12 end-of-month payments are made each year, and in addition a $1000 balloon payment is made at the end of each year. Interest is 9.7% annual compounded monthly. What is the amount of the regular monthly payment?

Add-on Interest and the Rule of 78

9-43 A bank makes a $9455 car loan with 48 monthly payments using $7\frac{1}{2}$% add-on interest to compute the payment. They use the rule of 78 to amortize interest.

(*a*) What is the monthly payment?
(*b*) What is the nominal annual interest rate?
(*c*) What is the amount of interest charged for year 1?
(*d*) What is the amount necessary to pay off the loan after the twenty-eighth payment?

answers: (*a*) **$256.07**; (*b*) **$13.5134%**; (*c*) **$1230.11**; (*d*) **$4615.02**

9-44 A consumer loan of $2750 with 36 monthly payments is made by a bank. The interest is $6\frac{3}{4}$% add-on with the rule of 78 used to amortize interest.

(*a*) What is the monthly payment?
(*b*) What is the nominal annual interest rate?
(*c*) What is the amount of interest charged for years 1, 2, and 3?
(*d*) What is the amount necessary to pay off the loan after the nineteenth payment?

Stepped Cash Flows

9-45 A company is evaluating a capital budgeting project that has the after-tax cash flows shown in the table. They require all projects to earn at least 20% compounded annually. The project requires an after-tax cash outlay of $275,000.

Years	End-of-year cash flows
1	$50,000
2	50,000
3	50,000
4	70,000
5	70,000
6	80,000
7	80,000
8	80,000
9	95,000
10	95,000
11	80,000
12	70,000
13	60,000
14	50,000

(*a*) What is the present value of the cash flows using a discount rate of 20%?
(*b*) What is the net present value?
(*c*) What is the internal rate of return?
answers: (*a*) **$296,811.87**; (*b*) **$21,811.87**; (*c*) **21.73991%**

9-46 You are buying a mortgage as an investment on which you want to earn 10.4% annual compounded monthly. The mortgage has a current balance of $42,660.87, with the following schedule of end-of-month payments remaining.

Months	Monthly payments
1–12	$290
13–24	304.50
25–36	319.73
37–408	335.72

(*a*) How much should be offered to purchase the mortgage?
(*b*) What was the original interest rate for the mortgage?

9-47 A modified-payment mortgage for $45,000 is made for 30 years with interest at 8.75% annual compounded monthly. At the end of the first year the monthly payment will increase by 5%, at the end of the second year the payment again increases by 5%, and the same increase in payments occurs at the end of the third, fourth and fifth. After the increase at the end of the fifth year, the amount of the payment remains constant for 25 years. What is the amount of the payment?
answer: **$293.19**

9-48 Answer Exercise **9-47**, but assume that the loan amount is $59,000, the increase in payments is 7.5%, and the interest rate is 9.75% annual, compounded monthly.

9-49 You are developing a personal savings plan where the following amounts will be placed in a savings account *monthly* during the next 10 years.

Year	Monthly deposit
1	$100
2	150
3	200
4	225
5	250
6	275
7	300
8	325
9	350
10	375

You assume that interest is 6% annual, compounded monthly.
What is the future value of the monthly payments at the end of 10 years, assuming:
(*a*) Beginning-of-month deposits?
(*b*) End-of-month payments?
answers: (*a*) **$39,649.98**; (*b*) **$39,452.71**

Foreign Interest Calculations

9-50 A $65,000 mortgage has a term of 30 years. The effective annual rate for interest is 9.5%.
(*a*) What is the monthly payment assuming end-of-period payments?
(*b*) What is the monthly payment assuming beginning-of-period payments?

9-51 A $20,000 loan has a term of 5 years. The effective annual interest rate is 9.8%.
(*a*) What is the monthly payment assuming end-of-period payments?
(*b*) What is the monthly payment assuming beginning-of-period payments?
answers: (*a*) **$418.92**; (*b*) **$415.67**

9-52 A mortgage with 250 end-of-month payments of $355.53 remaining is being purchased. The purchaser wants to earn an effective annual interest rate of 10% on his investment.
(*a*) How much should he pay?
(*b*) If he pays $39,000, what is the effective annual interest rate?

9-53 A company is evaluating a project that returns $6000 after taxes each month for 4 years. They require an effective annual return of 18%. The project requires an investment of $201,000.
(*a*) What is the net present value?
(*b*) What is the internal rate of return expressed as an effective annual rate?
answers: (*a*) **$8186.11**; (*b*) **20.6339%**

Amortization

9-54 A $65,000, 30-year mortgage has monthly payments of $495.19. Interest is 8.4% annual compounded monthly.

What is the amount of principal paid, interest paid, and the remaining balance at the end of the first year if:

(a) The interest portion of each month's payment is *rounded down* to the nearest penny?

(b) The interest portion of each month's payment is *rounded up* to the nearest penny?

(c) The interest portion of each month's payment is rounded to the nearest penny (.554 rounds to .55; .555 rounds to .56)?

INDEX

Date Due